Fred Powell   Tech
Eastgate Dorm
Box 34795
876-9813

SO-BZY-571

$8 \cdot \frac{25}{gw}$

$627 - 4960$

2	3	H.O.
2-	2	
3-	5	
7-	8-	
	20	

ELECTROMECHANICAL DYNAMICS

Part I: Discrete Systems

ELECTROMECHANICAL DYNAMICS

Part I: Discrete Systems

HERBERT H. WOODSON

Philip Sporn Professor of Energy Processing
Departments of Electrical and Mechanical Engineering

JAMES R. MELCHER

Associate Professor of Electrical Engineering
Department of Electrical Engineering

both of Massachusetts Institute of Technology

JOHN WILEY & SONS, INC., NEW YORK · LONDON · SYDNEY

To our parents

PREFACE

Part I: Discrete Systems

In the early 1950's the option structure was abandoned and a common core curriculum was instituted for all electrical engineering students at M.I.T. The objective of the core curriculum was then, and is now, to provide a foundation in mathematics and science on which a student can build in his professional growth, regardless of the many opportunities in electrical engineering from which he may choose. In meeting this objective, core curriculum subjects cannot serve the needs of any professional area with respect to nomenclature, techniques, and problems unique to that area. Specialization comes in elective subjects, graduate study, and professional activities.

To be effective a core curriculum subject must be broad enough to be germane to the many directions an electrical engineer may go professionally, yet it must have adequate depth to be of lasting value. At the same time, the subject must be related to the real world by examples of application. This is true because students learn by seeing material in a familiar context, and engineering students are motivated largely by the relevance of the material to the realities of the world around them.

In the organization of the core curriculum in electrical engineering at M.I.T. electromechanics is one major component. As our core curriculum has evolved, there have been changes in emphasis and a broadening of the topic. The basic text in electromechanics until 1954, when a new departure was made, was *Electric Machinery* by Fitzgerald and Kingsley. This change produced *Electromechanical Energy Conversion* by White and Woodson, which was used until 1961. At that time we started the revision that resulted in the present book. During this period we went through many versions of notes while teaching the material three semesters a year.

Our objective has always been to teach a subject that combines classical mechanics with the fundamentals of electricity and magnetism. Thus the subject offers the opportunity to teach both mechanics and electromagnetic theory in a context vital to much of the electrical engineering community.

Our choice of material was to some extent determined by a desire to give the student a breadth of background sufficient for further study of almost any type of electromechanical interaction, whether in rotating machinery, plasma dynamics, the electromechanics of biological systems, or magneto-elasticity. It was also chosen to achieve adequate depth while maintaining suitable unity, but, most important, examples were chosen that could be enlivened for the engineering student interested in the interplay of physical reality and the analytical model. There were many examples from which to choose, but only a few satisfied the requirement of being both mathematically lucid *and* physically demonstrable, so that the student could "push it or see it" and directly associate his observations with symbolic models. Among the areas of electrical engineering, electromechanics excels in offering the opportunity to establish that all-important "feel" for a physical phenomenon. Properly selected electromechanical examples can be the basis for discerning phenomena that are remote from human abilities to observe.

Before discussing how the material can be used to achieve these ends, a review of the contents is in order. The student who uses this book is assumed to have a background in electrostatics and magnetostatics. Consequently, Chapter 1 and Appendix B are essentially a review to define our starting point.

Chapter 2 is a generalization of the concepts of inductance and capacitance that are necessary to the treatment of electromechanical systems; it also provides a brief introduction to rigid-body mechanics. This treatment is included because many curricula no longer cover mechanics, other than particle mechanics in freshman physics. The basic ideas of Chapter 2 are repeated in Chapter 3 to establish some properties of electromechanical coupling in lumped-parameter systems and to obtain differential equations that describe the dynamics of lumped-parameter systems.

Next, the techniques of Chapters 2 and 3 are used to study rotating machines in Chapter 4. Physical models are defined, differential equations are written, machine types are classified, and steady-state characteristics are obtained and discussed. A separate chapter on rotating machines has been included not only because of the technological importance of machines but also because rotating machines are rich in examples of the kinds of phenomena that can be found in lumped-parameter electromechanical systems.

Chapter 5 is devoted to the study, with examples, of the dynamic behavior of lumped-parameter systems. Virtually all electromechanical systems are mathematically nonlinear; nonetheless, linear incremental models are useful for studying the stability of equilibria and the nature of the dynamical behavior in the vicinity of an equilibrium. The second half of this chapter develops the classic potential-well motions and loss-dominated dynamics in the context of electromechanics. These studies of nonlinear dynamics afford an opportunity to place linear models in perspective while forming further insights on the physical significance of, for example, flux conservation and state functions.

Chapter 6 represents our first departure from lumped-parameter systems into continuum systems with a discussion of how observers in relative motion will define and measure field quantities and the related effects of material motion on electromagnetic fields. It is our belief that dc rotating machines are most easily understood in this context. Certainly they are a good demonstration of field transformations at work.

As part of any continuum electromechanics problem, one must know how the electric and magnetic fields are influenced by excitations and motion. In quasi-static systems the distribution of charge and current are controlled by magnetic diffusion and charge relaxation, the subjects of Chapter 7. In Chapter 7 simple examples isolate significant cases of magnetic diffusion or charge relaxation, so that the physical processes involved can be better understood.

Chapters 6 and 7 describe the electrical side of a continuum electromechanical system with the material motion predetermined. The mechanical side of the subject is undertaken in Chapter 8 in a study of force densities of electric and magnetic origin. Because it is a useful concept in the analysis of many systems, we introduce the Maxwell stress tensor. The study of useful properties of tensors sets the stage for later use of mechanical stress tensors in elastic and fluid media.

At this point the additional ingredient necessary to the study of continuum electromechanics is the mechanical medium. In Chapter 9 we introduce simple elastic continua—longitudinal motion of a thin rod and transverse motion of wires and membranes. These models are used to study simple continuum mechanical motions (nondispersive waves) as excited electromechanically at boundaries.

Next, in Chapter 10 a string or membrane is coupled on a continuum basis to electric and magnetic fields and the variety of resulting dynamic behavior is studied. The unifying thread of this treatment is the dispersion equation that relates complex frequency ω with complex wavenumber k. Without material convection there can be simple nondispersive waves, cut off or evanescent waves, absolute instabilities, and diffusion waves. The effect of material convection on evanescent waves and oscillations and on wave amplification are topics that make a strong connection with electron beam and plasma dynamics. The method of characteristics is introduced as a convenient tool in the study of wave propagation.

In Chapter 11 the concepts and techniques of Chapters 9 and 10 are extended to three-dimensional systems. Strain displacement and stress-strain relations are introduced, with tensor concepts, and simple electromechanical examples of three-dimensional elasticity are given.

In Chapter 12 we turn to a different mechanical medium, a fluid. We first study electromechanical interactions with inviscid, incompressible fluids to establish essential phenomena in the simplest context. It is here that we introduce the basic notions of MHD energy conversion that can result when a conducting fluid flows through a transverse magnetic field. We also bring in electric-field interactions with fluids, in which ion drag phenomena are used as an example. In addition to these basically conducting processes, we treat the electromechanical consequences of polarization and magnetization in fluids. We demonstrate how highly conducting fluids immersed in magnetic fields can propagate Alfvén waves.

In Chapter 13 we introduce compressibility to the fluid model. This can have a marked effect on electromechanical behavior, as demonstrated with the MHD conduction machine. With compressibility, a fluid will propagate longitudinal disturbances (acoustic waves). A transverse magnetic field and high electrical conductivity modify these disturbances to magnetoacoustic waves.

Finally, in Chapter 14 we add viscosity to the fluid model and study the consequences in electromechanical interactions with steady flow. Hartmann flow demonstrates the effect of viscosity on the dc magnetohydrodynamic machine.

To be successful a text must have a theme; the material must be inter-related. Our philosophy has been to get into the subject where the student is most comfortable, with lumped-parameter (circuit) concepts. Thus many of the subtle approximations associated with quasi-statics are made naturally, and the student is faced with the implications of what he has assumed only after having become thoroughly familiar with the physical significance and usefulness of his approximations. By the time he reaches Chapter 4 he will have drawn a circle around at least a class of problems in which electromagnetic fields interact usefully with media in motion.

In dealing with physical and mathematical subjects, as we are here, in which the job is incomplete unless the student sees the physical laws put to work in some kind of physical embodiment, it is necessary for the thread of continuity to be woven into the material in diverse and subtle ways. A number of attempts have been made, to which we can add our early versions of notes, to write texts with one obvious, pedagogically logical basis for evolving the material; for example, it can be recognized that classes of physical phenomena could be grouped according to the differential equation that describes the pertinent dynamics. Thus we could treat magnetic diffusion, diffusion waves on elastic continua, and viscous diffusion waves in one chapter, even though the physical embodiments are entirely different. Alternatively, we could devise a subject limited to certain technological applications or cover superficially a wide range of basically unrelated topics such as "energy conversion" under one heading. This was the prevalent approach in engineering education a decade or so ago, even at the undergraduate level. It seems clear to us that organizing material in a teachable and meaningful fashion is far more demanding than this. To confess our own mistakes, our material went originally from the general to the specific; it began with the relativistic form of Maxwell's equations, including the effects of motion, and ended with lumped-parameter devices as special cases. Even if this were a pedagogically tenable approach, which we found it was not, what a bad example to set for students who should be learning to distinguish between the essential and the superfluous! Ideas connected with the propagation of electromagnetic waves (relativistic ideas) must be included in the curriculum, but their connection with media in motion should be made after the student is aware of the first-order issues.

A meaningful presentation to *engineers* must interweave and interrelate mathematical concepts, physical characteristics, the modeling process, and the establishment of a physical "feel" for the world of reality. Our approach is to come to grips with each of these goals as quickly as possible (let the student "get wet" within the first two weeks) and then, while reinforcing what he has learned, continually add something new. Thus, if one looks, he will see the same ideas coming into the flow of material over and over again.

For the organization of this book one should look for many threads of different types. We can list here only a few, in the hope that the subtle reinforcing interplay of mathematical and physical threads will be made evident. Probably the essential theme is Maxwell's equations and the ideas of quasi-statics. The material introduced in Chapter 1 is completely abstract, but it is reinforced in the first few chapters with material that is close to home for the student. By the time he reaches Chapter 10 he will have learned that waves exist which intimately involve electric and magnetic fields that are altogether quasistatic. (This is something that comes as a surprise to many late in life.) Lumped-parameter ideas are based on the integral forms of Maxwell's equations, so that the dynamical effects found with lumped-parameter time constants L/R and RC in Chapter 5 are easily associated with the subjects of magnetic diffusion and charge relaxation. A close tie is made between the "speed voltage" of Chapter 5 and the effects of motion on magnetic fields, as described by field transformations in Chapters 6 to 14. Constant flux dynamics of a lumped coil in Chapter 5 are strongly associated with the dynamics of perfectly conducting continuous media; for example, Alfvén waves in Chapter 12.

Consider another thread of continuity. The book begins with the mathematics of circuit theory. The machines of Chapter 4 are essentially circuits in the sinusoidal steady state. In Chapter 5 we linearize to pursue lumped-parameter ideas of stability and other transient responses and then proceed to nonlinear dynamics, potential-well theory, and other approaches that should form a part of any engineer's mathematical background. By the time the end of Chapter 10 is reached these ideas will have been carried into the continuum with the addition of tensor concepts, simple cases of the method of characteristics, and eigenvalue theory. The ω-k plot and its implication for all sorts of subjects in modern electrical engineering can be considered as a mathematical or a physical objective. The ideas of stability introduced with ordinary differential equations (exp st) in Chapter 5 evolve into the continuum stability studies of Chapter 10 [exp $j(\omega t - kx)$] and can be regarded as a mathematical or a physical thread in our treatment. We could list many other threads: witness the evolution of energy and thermodynamic notions from Chapters 3 to 5, 5 to 8, and 8 to 13.

We hope that this book is not just one more in the mathematics of electrical engineering or the technical aspects of rotating machines, transducers, delay lines, MHD converters, and so on, but rather that it is the mathematics, the physics, and, most of all, the engineering combined into one.

The material brought together here can be used in a variety of ways. It has been used by Professors C. N. Weygandt and F. D. Ketterer at the University of Pennsylvania for two subjects. The first restricts attention to Chapters 1 to 6 and Appendix B for a course in lumped-parameter electromechanics that both supplants the traditional one on rotating machines in the electrical engineering curriculum and gives the background required for further study in a second term (elective) covering Chapter 7 and beyond. Professors C. D. Hendricks and J. M. Crowley at the University of Illinois have used the material to follow a format that covers up through Chapter 10 in one term but omits much of the material in Chapter 7. Professor W. D. Getty at the University of Michigan has used the material to follow a one-term subject in lumped-parameter electromechanics taught from a different set of notes. Thus he has been able to use the early chapters as a review and to get well into the later chapters in a one-term subject.

At M.I.T. our curriculum seems always to be in a state of change. It is clear that much of the material, Chapters 1 to 10, will be part of our required (core) curriculum for the forseeable future, but the manner in which it is packaged is continually changing. During the fall term, 1967, we covered Chapters 1 to 10 in a one-semester subject taught to juniors and seniors. The material from Chapters 4 and 6 on rotating machines was used selectively, so that students had "a foot solidly in the door" on this important subject but also that the coverage could retain an orientation toward the needs of all the diverse areas found in electrical engineering today. We have found the material useful as the basis for early graduate work and as a starting point in several courses related to electromechanics.

Finally, to those who open this book and then close it with the benediction, "good material but unteachable," we apologize because to them we have not made our point. Perhaps not as presented here, but certainly as it is represented here, this material is rich in teaching possibilities. The demands on the teacher to see the subject in its total context, especially the related problems that lie between the lines, are significant. We have taught this subject many times to undergraduates, yet each term has been more enjoyable than the last. There are so many ways in which drama can be added to the material, and we do not need to ask the students (bless them) when we have been successful in doing so.

In developing this material we have found lecture demonstrations and demonstration films to be most helpful, both for motivation and for developing understanding. We have learned that when we want a student to see a particular phenomenon it is far better for us to do the experiment and let the student focus his attention on what he should see rather than on the wrong connections and blown fuses that result when he tries to do the experiment himself. The most successful experiments are often the simplest—those that give the student an opportunity to handle the apparatus himself. Every student should "chop up some magnetic field lines" with a copper "axe" or he will never really appreciate the subject. We have also found that some of the more complex demonstrations that are difficult and expensive to store and resurrect each semester come through very well in films. In addition to our own short films, three films have been produced professionally in connection with this material for the National Committee on Electrical Engineering Films, under a grant from the National Science Foundation, by the Education Development Center, Newton, Mass.

Synchronous Machines: Electromechanical Dynamics by H. H. Woodson
Complex Waves I: Propagation, Evanescence and Instability by J. R. Melcher
Complex Waves II: Instability, Convection and Amplification by J. R. Melcher

An additional film is in the early stages of production. Other films that are useful have been produced by the Education Development Center for the National Committee on Fluid Mechanics Films and for the College Physics Film Program. Of particular interest, from the former series, is *Magnetohydrodynamics* by Arthur Shercliff.

A book like this can be produced only with plenty of assistance. We gratefully acknowledge the help we received from many directions and hope we have forgotten no one after seven years of work. First of all we want to acknowledge our students with whom we worked as the material developed. They are the one most essential ingredient in an effort of this sort. Next we want to thank Dr. S. I. Freedman, Professor H. H. Richardson, and Dr. C. V. Smith, Jr., for their assistance in framing worthwhile approaches to several of our key topics. In seven years we have had the help of many able teachers in presenting this material to students. Their discussions and advice have been most useful. In this category we want particularly to mention Professors H. A. Haus, P. L. Penfield, D. C. White, G. L. Wilson, R. Gallager, and E. Pierson and Doctors J. Reynolds, W. H. Heiser, and A. Kusko. Professor Ketterer, who has taught this material at M.I.T. and the University of Pennsylvania, Professors C. D. Hendricks and J. M. Crowley, who have taught it at M.I.T. and the University of Illinois, and Professor W. D. Getty, who has taught it at M.I.T. and the University of Michigan, have been most generous with their comments. Messrs. Edmund Devitt, John Dressler, and Dr. Kent Edwards have checked the correctness of many of the mathematical treatments. Such a task as typing a manuscript repeatedly is enough to try the patience of anyone. Our young ladies of the keyboard, Miss M. A. Daly, Mrs. D. S. Figgins, Mrs. B. S. Morton, Mrs. E. M. Holmes, and Mrs. M. Mazroff, have been gentle and kind with us.

A lengthy undertaking of this sort can be successful only when it has the backing of a sympathetic administration. This work was started with the helpful support of Professor P. Elias, who was then head of the Department of Electrical Engineering at M.I.T. It was finished with the active encouragement of Professor L. D. Smullin, who is presently head of the Department.

Finally, and most sincerely, we want to acknowledge the perseverance of our families during this effort. Our wives, Blanche S. Woodson and Janet D. Melcher, have been particularly tolerant of the demands of this work.

This book appears in three separately bound, consecutively paged parts that can be used individually or in any combination. Flexibility is ensured by including with each part a complete Table of Contents and Index. In addition, for convenient reference, Parts II and III are supplemented by brief appendices which summarize the relevant material from the preceding chapters. Part I includes Chapters 1 to 6, hence emphasizes lumped-parameter models while developing background in field concepts for further studies.

H. H. Woodson
J. R. Melcher

Cambridge, Massachusetts
January 1968

CONTENTS

Part I: Discrete Systems

Part II: Fields, Forces, and Motion

Part III: Elastic and Fluid Media

Chapter 1

INTRODUCTION

1.0 INTRODUCTION

The human is first of all a mechanical entity who exists in a mechanical environment. The day-by-day habits of man are dictated largely by such considerations as how rapidly he can transport or feed himself. Communication with his environment is geared to such mechanical operations as the time required for his eye to scan a page or the speed with which he can speak or typewrite. Furthermore, his standard of living is very much a function of his ability to augment human muscle for better transportation and for the diverse industrial processes needed in an advanced society.

There are two major conclusions to be drawn from these thoughts. First, the unaided human faculties operate on limited time and size scales. Thus the mechanical effects of electric and magnetic forces on ponderable bodies were observed and recorded by the Greeks as early as 500 B.C., and electricity and magnetism were developed largely as classical sciences in the nineteenth century, on the basis of unaided human observations. Coulomb enunciated his inverse square law from measurements taken with an electrical torsion balance; magnetic forces, as they influenced ponderable objects such as magnetized needles, were the basis of experiments conducted by Oersted and Ampère. These electromechanical experiments constituted the origins of the modern theories of electricity and magnetism. Faraday and Maxwell unified the subjects of electrostatics and magnetostatics into a dynamical theory that predicted phenomena largely beyond the powers of direct human observation. Thus today we recognize that electromagnetic theory encompasses not only the electromechanical effects that first suggested the existence of electric and magnetic fields but also numerous radiation effects, whether they involve radio frequency waves or x-rays. Nonetheless, when man controls these phenomena, detects their existence, and puts them to good use, he most often does so by some type of electromechanical interaction—from the simple act of turning a switch to the remote operation of a computer with a teletypewriter.

The second major conclusion to be drawn from our opening remarks is that man's need for motive power for transportation and industrial processes is satisfied largely by conversion of electric energy to mechanical energy. Energy in electric form is virtually useless, yet the largest and fastest growing segment of our economy is the electric utility industry, whose source of income is the sale of electric energy. This is eloquent testimony to the fact that electric energy can be converted easily into a variety of forms to aid man in his mechanical environment. It is remarkable that the same 60-Hz power line can supply the energy requirements of a rolling mill, a television station, a digital computer, a subway train, and many other systems and devices that provide a fuller and more comfortable life. In the vast majority of these examples electromechanical energy conversion is required because of man's basic need for mechanical assistance.

As long as engineers are concerned with making the electrical sciences serve human needs, they will be involved with electromechanical phenomena.

1.0.1   Scope of Application

Because they serve so many useful functions in everyday situations, *transducers* are the most familiar illustration of applied electromechanical dynamics. These devices are essential to the operation of such diverse equipment as automatic washing machines, electric typewriters, and power circuit breakers in which they translate electrical signals into such useful functions as opening a switch. The switch can be conventional or it can open a circuit carrying 30,000 A while withstanding 400,000 V 2 msec later. The telephone receiver and high-fidelity speaker are familiar transducers; less familiar relatives are the high-power sonar antenna for underwater communication or the high-fidelity shake tables capable of vibrating an entire space vehicle in accordance with a recording of rocket noise.

Electromechanical transducers play an essential role in the automatic control of industrial processes and transportation systems, where the ultimate goal is to control a mechanical variable such as the thickness of a steel sheet or the speed of a train. Of course, a transducer can also be made to translate mechanical motion into an electrical signal. The cartridge of a phonograph pickup is an example in this category, as are such devices as telephone transmitters, microphones, accelerometers, tachometers and dynamic pressure gages.

Not all transducers are constructed to provide mechanical input or output. The (electro)mechanical filter is an example of a signal-processing device that takes advantage of the extremely high Q of mechanical circuits at relatively low frequencies. Filters, delay lines, and logic devices capable of performing even above 30 MHz are currently the object of research on electromechanical effects found in piezoelectric and piezomagnetic materials.

Primary sources of energy are often found in mechanical form in the kinetic energy of an expanding heated gas and in the potential energy of water at an elevation. Electromechanics has always played a vital role in obtaining large amounts of electric power from primary sources. This is accomplished by using large magnetic field-type devices called *rotating machines*. Today a single generator can produce 1000 MW (at a retail price of 2 cents/kWh this unit produces an income of $20,000/h), and as electric utility systems grow larger generating units (with attendant problems of an unprecedented nature) will be needed. This need is illustrated by the fact that in 1960 the national peak load in the United States was 138,000 MW, whereas it is expected that in 1980 it will be 493,000 MW, an increase of more than 250 per cent in 20 years.

A large part of this electric power will be used to drive electric motors of immense variety to do a multitude of useful tasks, from moving the hands of an electric clock at a fraction of a watt to operating a steel rolling mill at 20 MW.

Because of our need for great amounts of energy, it is in the national interest to seek ways of producing it more efficiently (to conserve natural resources) and with less costly equipment (to conserve capital). The *magnetohydrodynamic* generator, which employs an expanding heated gas as the moving conductor, shows some promise of meeting one or both of these objectives. Another possibility is the use of the interaction between charged particles and a flowing, nonconducting gas to achieve *electrohydrodynamic* power generation. Versions of this machine are similar in principle to the *Van de Graaff* generator which is currently producing extremely high voltages (20 million volts) for a variety of purposes, including medical treatment, physical research, and irradiation of various substances.

The efficient and economical conversion of mechanical energy to electrical form is not only of great interest to the rapidly expanding utility industry but is also of extreme importance to the space program, in which sources of electric power must satisfy new engineering requirements imposed by the environment, with obvious limitations on weight and size and with stringent requirements on reliability.

Electromechanical devices provide *power amplification* of signals for purposes similar to those involving electronic amplifiers; for example, in control systems in which large amounts of power (up to about 20 MW) must be produced with high fidelity over a bandwidth from zero to a few Hertz *dc rotating machines* are used. From this the impression is obtained that electromechanical amplifiers function only at low frequencies; but there are electromechanical devices that provide amplification in the gigacycle-per-second range—*electron beam devices* which, like other physical electronic devices, depend on the small mass of the electron for high-frequency operation.

In current research concerned with controlled thermonuclear fusion the plasma can be regarded for some purposes as a highly conducting gas elevated to such a high temperature that it cannot be contained by solid boundaries. Thus proposed thermonuclear devices attempt to contain the plasma in a magnetic bottle. This illustrates another important application of electro-mechanical dynamics—the *orientation*, *levitation*, or *confinement* of mechanical media. More conventional examples in this category are those that use magnetic or electric fields to levitate the rotor of a gyroscope, to suspend the moving member of an accelerometer, or to position a model in a wind tunnel. Metallurgists employ ac magnetic fields to form a crucible for molten metals that must be free of contamination, and electric fields are proposed for orienting cyrogenic propellants in the zero-gravity environment of space. The use of electric and magnetic fields in shaping malleable metals and solidifying liquids has just begun.

The *propulsion* of vehicles represents still another application of electro-mechanics. Even when the primary source of energy is a rotating shaft from a reciprocating engine or a turbine, as in a locomotive or ship, the problem of transmitting and controlling the power to the wheels or propeller is simplified by converting the power to electrical form with a generator and installing electric motors to propel the vehicle. An important addition to this class of vehicles would be the electric car in which energy is stored in batteries and the wheels are driven by electric motors. Less familiar electromechanical propulsion schemes are being developed, largely for space applications, which make use of magnetohydrodynamic or electrohydrodynamic acceleration of matter to provide thrust. In this regard the particle accelerators required in high-energy physics research should be recognized as electro-mechanical devices.

1.0.2 Objectives

It should be apparent from the discussion of the preceding section that electromechanical dynamics covers a broad range of applications, many of which represent highly developed technologies, whereas others are the subject of research or development. In either case a single application could be the subject of an entire book and in many cases books already exist. Our objective here is to lay a cohesive and unified foundation by treating those concepts and techniques that are fundamental to an understanding of a wide range of electromechanical phenomena. As a consequence, we do not dwell at length on any area of application.

With our basic unified approach it is often difficult to distinguish between those aspects of electromechanics that may be considered research in the scientific sense and those that represent engineering applications. For example, there are many practical uses for a magnetohydrodynamic flow meter, yet the type of theoretical model needed in its study is also pertinent to an understanding of the origin of the earth's magnetic field as it is generated by motion of the molten interior of the earth. In fact, a study of magnetohydrodynamics involves models that are germane to an engineering problem such as the levitation of a molten metal, an applied physics problem such as plasma confinement, or a problem of astrophysical interest such as the dynamics of stellar structures.

The subject of electromechanical dynamics, as we approach it in the following chapters, provides a foundation for a range of interests that extends from the purely scientific to engineering applications and from interactions that occur in systems that can be represented by lumped parameters to those that need continuum representations.

The selection of appropriate mathematical models for electromechanical systems is a process that requires the maturity and insight that can result only from experience with electromechanical phenomena. Of course, the model chosen depends on the nature of the system being studied and the accuracy required. We shall not try to develop a formalism for the largely intuitive process of modeling but rather shall study representative systems with a variety of mathematical models to illustrate the principal phenomena that result from electromechanical interactions. In the course of this study the student should develop facility with the basic models and the mathematical tools used in their analysis and should acquire the insight into the interrelations among the physical phenomena that is necessary for him to be able to develop mathematical models on his own.

1.1 ELECTROMAGNETIC THEORY

The mathematical description of the electrical part of any electromechanical system is based on electromagnetic theory. We therefore assume that the reader is familiar with the basic theory and in particular with magnetostatics and electrostatics.

The subject of electromechanics necessarily includes the behavior of electromagnetic fields in the presence of moving media. In this introductory chapter it therefore seems appropriate to review the laws of electricity and magnetism and to include a discussion of those extensions of the theory required to account for the effects of moving media. This review, however, would represent a digression from our main purpose—the study of electromechanical dynamics. Consequently a discussion is presented in Appendix B for completeness. We can get well into the study of electromechanical dynamics with a few simple extensions of magnetostatic and electrostatic theory. Therefore we cite the electromagnetic equations that form the basis for our study and start to use them immediately. The equations can be accepted as postulates, justified by their relation to ordinary magnetostatic and electrostatic theory and by the fact that they give adequate representation of the electromechanical systems we shall study. As our work progresses from the lumped-parameter models in Chapters 2 to 5 to situations requiring continuum models, the physical significance of the field equations in electromechanical interactions will be more apparent. It is at that point that a meaningful discussion can be made of the most significant effects of moving media on electromagnetic fields, and the reader may find that a study of Appendix B will be most helpful at that time.

1.1.1 Differential Equations

The symbols and units of electromagnetic quantities are defined in Table 1.1. At the outset, we consider two limiting cases of the electromagnetic field equations, which define the dynamics of quasi-static (almost static) magnetic and electric field systems. In spite of the restrictions implied by these limits, our models are adequate for virtually all electromechanical systems of technical importance. A discussion of the quasi-static approximations, which shows how both limiting cases come from the more general electromagnetic theory, is given in Appendix B.

1.1.1a Magnetic Field Systems

The electromagnetic field and source quantities in a magnetic field system are related by the following partial differential equations:

$$\nabla \times \mathbf{H} = \mathbf{J}_f, \tag{1.1.1}$$

$$\nabla \cdot \mathbf{B} = 0, \tag{1.1.2}$$

$$\nabla \cdot \mathbf{J}_f = 0, \tag{1.1.3}$$

$$\mathbf{B} = \mu_0(\mathbf{H} + \mathbf{M}), \tag{1.1.4}$$

$$\nabla \times \mathbf{E} = -\frac{\partial \mathbf{B}}{\partial t}. \tag{1.1.5}$$

Thus in our magnetic field system, even with time-varying sources and deforming media, the magnetic field intensity $\mathbf{H}$ and flux density $\mathbf{B}$ are determined as if the system were magnetostatic. Then the electric field intensity $\mathbf{E}$ is found from the resulting flux density by using (1.1.5). This is the origin of the term quasi-static magnetic field system. In addition to these equations, we need constituent relations that describe how the physical

Table 1.1   Symbols and Units of Electromagnetic Quantities

Symbol	Field Variable Name	MKS Rationalized Units
$\mathbf{H}$	Magnetic field intensity	A/m
$\mathbf{J}_f$	Free current density	A/m^2
$\mathbf{K}_f$	Free surface current density	A/m
$\mathbf{B}$	Magnetic flux density	Wb/m^2
$\mathbf{M}$	Magnetization density	A/m
$\mathbf{E}$	Electric field intensity	V/m
$\mathbf{D}$	Electric displacement	C/m^2
ρ_f	Free charge density	C/m^3
σ_f	Free surface charge density	C/m^2
$\mathbf{P}$	Polarization density	C/m^2
$\mathbf{F}$	Force density	N/m^3
μ_0	Permeability of free space	$4\pi \times 10^{-7}$ H/m
ϵ_0	Permittivity of free space	8.854×10^{-12} F/m

properties of the materials affect the field and source quantities. The magnetization density $\mathbf{M}$ is introduced to account for the effects of magnetizable materials. The most common constitutive law for $\mathbf{M}$ takes the form

$$\mathbf{M} = \chi_m \mathbf{H}, \tag{1.1.6}$$

where χ_m is the magnetic susceptibility. An alternative way of expressing this relation is to define the permeability $\mu = \mu_0(1 + \chi_m)$, where μ_0 is the permeability of free space

$$\mu_0 = 4\pi \times 10^{-7} \text{ H/m}, \tag{1.1.7}$$

in which case it follows from (1.1.4) that the constitutive law of (1.1.6) can also be written as

$$\mathbf{B} = \mu \mathbf{H}. \tag{1.1.8}$$

We shall make considerable use of this simple linear model for magnetizable materials.

Free currents in a stationary material most often arise from conduction induced by the electric field according to Ohm's law:

$$\mathbf{J}_f = \sigma \mathbf{E}, \tag{1.1.9}$$

where σ is the conductivity (mhos/m). A similar constitutive law relates the surface current density $\mathbf{K}_f$ to the electric field intensity $\mathbf{E}_t$ tangential to the surface

$$\mathbf{K}_f = \sigma_s \mathbf{E}_t, \tag{1.1.10}$$

where σ_s is the surface conductivity (mhos). These constitutive laws for the conduction process represent macroscopic models for the migration of charges in materials under the influence of an electric field.

Ideally, quasi-static magnetic field systems are characterized by perfectly conducting ($\sigma \to \infty$) current loops, in which case static conditions ($\partial/\partial t = 0$) result in zero electric field intensity. All practical conductors (except superconductors) have finite conductivity; consequently, a system is modeled as a magnetic field system when the electrical conductivity σ for a current loop is high enough to cause only small departures from the ideal. Thus in Chapter 2 iron structures with coils of wire wound around them are represented as ideal (electrically lossless) magnetic field systems in which the winding resistance is included as an external resistance in series with the winding terminals.

1.1.1b Electric Field Systems

The electromagnetic field and source quantities in an electric field system are related by the following partial differential equations:

$$\nabla \times \mathbf{E} = 0, \tag{1.1.11}$$

$$\nabla \cdot \mathbf{D} = \rho_f, \tag{1.1.12}$$

$$\mathbf{D} = \epsilon_0 \mathbf{E} + \mathbf{P}, \tag{1.1.13}$$

$$\nabla \cdot \mathbf{J}_f = -\frac{\partial \rho_f}{\partial t}, \tag{1.1.14}$$

$$\nabla \times \mathbf{H} = \mathbf{J}_f + \frac{\partial \mathbf{D}}{\partial t}. \tag{1.1.15}$$

Equations 1.1.11 to 1.1.13 describe the fields in an electrostatic system. Hence in our electric field system, even with time-varying sources and geometry, the electric field intensity $\mathbf{E}$ and electric displacement $\mathbf{D}$ are determined as though the system were static. Then the current density $\mathbf{J}_f$ is determined by (1.1.14), which expresses conservation of charge. In turn, the magnetic field intensity $\mathbf{H}$ (if it is of interest) is found from (1.1.15). It is because of the basically electrostatic relationship between the electric field intensity and the free charge density that these equations define the dynamics of a quasi-static electric field system.

Ideally, a quasi-static electric field system is characterized by a set of perfectly conducting ($\sigma \to \infty$) equipotentials separated by perfectly insulating ($\sigma \to 0$) dielectrics, in which case static conditions ($\partial/\partial t = 0$) result in no current density $\mathbf{J}_f$, hence no magnetic field intensity $\mathbf{H}$. Of course, real dielectrics have finite conductivity; thus a system is representable as an electric field system when the electrical conductivity is low enough to cause only a small departure from the ideal. In terms of the lumped-parameter representation to be introduced in Chapter 2, an electric field system is modeled as an ideal circuit consisting of equipotentials separated by perfect insulators with resistances connected externally between terminals to account for the finite conductivity of the dielectric.

In this book the constituent relation for the conduction process usually takes the form of (1.1.9) or (1.1.10). In electric field systems, however, there can be appreciable net charge density, and we must be careful to distinguish between a *net flow of charge*, which occurs in electrically neutral conductors such as metals, and a *flow of net charge*, which occurs in situations such as the drift of negative charge in a vacuum tube. To allow for this differentiation when it is needed a more general form of the conduction constituent relation is used:

$$\mathbf{J}_f = (\rho_{f+}\mu_+ + \rho_{f-}\mu_-)\mathbf{E}, \tag{1.1.16}$$

where ρ_{f+} and ρ_{f-} are the densities of the two species of moving charges and μ_+ and μ_- are the respective mobilities in the field intensity $\mathbf{E}$. When the charge densities and mobilities are constants, (1.1.16) reduces to (1.1.9). In some electric field systems ρ_{f+} and ρ_{f-} are not constant, and (1.1.16) allows us to include the variable charge densities in our conduction model. As questions appear in this regard, it will be helpful to refer to Sections B.1.2 and B.3.3.

To account for the polarization density $\mathbf{P}$ of a dielectric material, we most often use the linear relation

$$\mathbf{P} = \epsilon_0\chi_e\mathbf{E}, \tag{1.1.17}$$

where ϵ_0 is the permittivity of free space

$$\epsilon_0 = 8.854 \times 10^{-12}\,\text{F/m} \tag{1.1.18}$$

and χ_e is the electric susceptibility. In terms of the material permittivity, $\epsilon = \epsilon_0(1 + \chi_e)$ (1.1.17) can also be written

$$\mathbf{D} = \epsilon\mathbf{E}, \tag{1.1.19}$$

where (1.1.13) has been used.

1.1.2   Integral Equations

It is often necessary to have the electromagnetic equations in integral form; for example, boundary conditions are found from integral equations and terminal quantities—voltage and current—are found by integrating field quantities.

In stationary systems the contours, surfaces, and volumes are all fixed in space and the transition from differential to integral equations is simply a matter of using the appropriate integral theorems. In electromechanical dynamics we need integral equations for contours, surfaces, and volumes that are deforming, and the resulting integral equations are different from those found in stationary systems. The formalism of integrating differential equations in the presence of motion is presented in Section B.4. The results are presented here essentially as postulates.

1.1.2a Magnetic Field Systems

The integral forms of (1.1.1) to (1.1.3) and (1.1.5) are

$$\oint_C \mathbf{H} \cdot d\mathbf{l} = \int_S \mathbf{J}_f \cdot \mathbf{n}\, da, \tag{1.1.20}$$

$$\oint_S \mathbf{B} \cdot \mathbf{n}\, da = 0, \tag{1.1.21}$$

$$\oint_S \mathbf{J}_f \cdot \mathbf{n}\, da = 0, \tag{1.1.22}$$

$$\oint_C \mathbf{E}' \cdot d\mathbf{l} = -\frac{d}{dt} \int_S \mathbf{B} \cdot \mathbf{n}\, da. \tag{1.1.23}$$

The contours C, surfaces S, and unit normal vectors $\mathbf{n}$ are defined in the conventional manner, as shown in Fig. 1.1.1. The surfaces of integration S

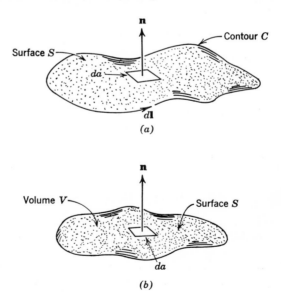

Fig. 1.1.1 (a) Surface S enclosed by the contour C, showing the right-handed relationship between the normal vector $\mathbf{n}$ and the line element $d\mathbf{l}$; (b) surface S enclosing a volume V. The normal vector $\mathbf{n}$ is directed outward, as shown.

for (1.1.21) and (1.1.22) enclose a volume V, whereas those of (1.1.20) and (1.1.23) are enclosed by a contour C.

Equations 1.1.20 to 1.1.23 are valid even when the contours and surfaces are deforming, as demonstrated in Appendix B. Note that in (1.1.23) the electric field intensity is written as $\mathbf{E}'$, and it is this value that would be measured by an observer attached to the deforming contour at the point in question. As demonstrated in Section B.4.1, when $\mathbf{E}' = \mathbf{E} \times (\mathbf{v} \times \mathbf{B})$, where $\mathbf{v}$ is the local velocity of the contour, (1.1.23) results from (1.1.5). More is said about the relation between quantities measured by observers in relative motion in Chapter 6.

In describing magnetic field systems, in addition to (1.1.20) to (1.1.23), we need constituent relations such as (1.1.8) and (1.1.9). We must keep in mind that these constituent relations are defined for stationary media. When there is motion, these equations still hold, but only for an observer moving with the medium. Thus we know that a perfect conductor can support no electric field intensity $\mathbf{E}'$. When the contour of (1.1.23) is fixed to a perfect conductor, the contribution to the contour integral from that portion in the conductor is zero, whether the conductor is moving or not. This is because $\mathbf{E}'$ is the quantity measured by an observer moving with the contour (conductor).

1.1.2b Electric Field Systems

The integral forms of (1.1.11) to (1.1.15) are

$$\oint_C \mathbf{E} \cdot dl = 0, \tag{1.1.24}$$

$$\oint_S \mathbf{D} \cdot \mathbf{n}\, da = \int_V \rho_f\, dV, \tag{1.1.25}$$

$$\oint_S \mathbf{J}'_f \cdot \mathbf{n}\, da = -\frac{d}{dt} \int_V \rho_f\, dV, \tag{1.1.26}$$

$$\oint_C \mathbf{H}' \cdot dl = \int_S \mathbf{J}'_f \cdot \mathbf{n}\, da + \frac{d}{dt} \int_S \mathbf{D} \cdot \mathbf{n}\, da. \tag{1.1.27}$$

These equations are valid for moving and deforming contours C, surfaces S, and volumes V (see Fig. 1.1.1).

Equations 1.1.24 and 1.1.25 are the same as those used to find $\mathbf{E}$ and $\mathbf{D}$ in an electrostatics problem. The current density and magnetic field intensity have been written in (1.1.26) and (1.1.27) as $\mathbf{J}'_f$ and $\mathbf{H}'$ to indicate that they are the values that would be measured by an observer moving with the contour or surface at the point in question. It is shown in Section B.4.2 that

(1.1.26) and (1.1.27) result from integrating (1.1.14) and (1.1.15) when $\mathbf{J}'_f = \mathbf{J}_f - \rho_f \mathbf{v}$ and $\mathbf{H}' = \mathbf{H} - \mathbf{v} \times \mathbf{D}$, where $\mathbf{v}$ is the local velocity of the contour or surface.

1.1.3   Electromagnetic Forces

The force experienced by a test charge q moving with velocity $\mathbf{v}$ is

$$\mathbf{f} = q\mathbf{E} + q\mathbf{v} \times \mathbf{B}. \tag{1.1.28}$$

This is referred to as the Lorentz force and provides a definition of the fields $\mathbf{E}$ and $\mathbf{B}$. For this case of a single moving charge the quantity $q\mathbf{v}$ constitutes a current. Hence the first term in (1.1.28) is the force on a static charge, whereas the second is the force on a current.

In a continuum theory in which we are concerned with a charge density ρ_f and a current density $\mathbf{J}_f$ forces are stated in terms of a force density

$$\mathbf{F} = \rho_f \mathbf{E} + \mathbf{J}_f \times \mathbf{B}. \tag{1.1.29}$$

Free charge and free current densities are used in (1.1.29) to make it clear that this expression does not account for forces due to polarization and magnetization. The terms in (1.1.29) provide a continuum representation of the terms in (1.1.28). The averaging process required to relate the force density of (1.1.29) to the Lorentz force is discussed in Sections B.1.1 and B.1.3. For our present purposes we accept these relations as equivalent and reserve discussion of the conditions under which this assumption is valid for Chapter 8.

In the class of problems undertaken in this book one or the other of the force densities in (1.1.29) is negligible. Hence in the magnetic field systems to be considered the force density is

$$\mathbf{F} = \mathbf{J}_f \times \mathbf{B}, \tag{1.1.30}$$

whereas in the electric field systems

$$\mathbf{F} = \rho_f \mathbf{E}. \tag{1.1.31}$$

In any particular example the validity of these approximations can be tested after the analysis has been completed by evaluating the force that has been ignored and comparing it with the force used in the model.

1.2   DISCUSSION

The equations summarized in Table 1.2 are those needed to describe the electrical side of electromechanical dynamics as presented here. We find that they are of far-reaching physical significance. Nonetheless, they are approximate and their regions of validity should be understood. Furthermore, their

Table 1.2 Summary of Quasi-Static Electromagnetic Equations

	Differential Equations		Integral Equations	
Magnetic field system	$\nabla \times \mathbf{H} = \mathbf{J}_f$	(1.1.1)	$\oint_C \mathbf{H} \cdot d\mathbf{l} = \int_S \mathbf{J}_f \cdot \mathbf{n}\, da$	(1.1.20)
	$\nabla \cdot \mathbf{B} = 0$	(1.1.2)	$\oint_S \mathbf{B} \cdot \mathbf{n}\, da = 0$	(1.1.21)
	$\nabla \cdot \mathbf{J}_f = 0$	(1.1.3)	$\oint_S \mathbf{J}_f \cdot \mathbf{n}\, da = 0$	(1.1.22)
	$\nabla \times \mathbf{E} = -\dfrac{\partial \mathbf{B}}{\partial t}$	(1.1.5)	$\oint_C \mathbf{E}' \cdot d\mathbf{l} = -\dfrac{d}{dt}\int_S \mathbf{B} \cdot \mathbf{n}\, da$	(1.1.23)
			where $\mathbf{E}' = \mathbf{E} + \mathbf{v} \times \mathbf{B}$	
Electric field system	$\nabla \times \mathbf{E} = 0$	(1.1.11)	$\oint_C \mathbf{E} \cdot d\mathbf{l} = 0$	(1.1.24)
	$\nabla \cdot \mathbf{D} = \rho_f$	(1.1.12)	$\oint_S \mathbf{D} \cdot \mathbf{n}\, da = \int_V \rho_f\, dV$	(1.1.25)
	$\nabla \cdot \mathbf{J}_f = -\dfrac{\partial \rho_f}{\partial t}$	(1.1.14)	$\oint_S \mathbf{J}'_f \cdot \mathbf{n}\, da = -\dfrac{d}{dt}\int_V \rho_f\, dV$	(1.1.26)
	$\nabla \times \mathbf{H} = \mathbf{J}_f + \dfrac{\partial \mathbf{D}}{\partial t}$	(1.1.15)	$\oint_C \mathbf{H}' \cdot d\mathbf{l} = \int_S \mathbf{J}'_f \cdot \mathbf{n}\, da + \dfrac{d}{dt}\int_S \mathbf{D} \cdot \mathbf{n}\, da$	(1.1.27)
			where $\mathbf{J}'_f = \mathbf{J}_f - \rho_f \mathbf{v}$	
			$\mathbf{H}' = \mathbf{H} - \mathbf{v} \times \mathbf{D}$	

13

relation to more general electromagnetic theory should also be known. Both topics are discussed in Appendix B. A study of that material may be more appropriate as questions are raised in the course of the developments to follow.

With the equations in Table 1.2 accepted on a postulational basis, we can—and should—proceed forthwith to study electromechanical dynamics.

Chapter 2

LUMPED ELECTROMECHANICAL ELEMENTS

2.0 INTRODUCTION

The purpose of this chapter is to present the techniques of making mathematical models (writing differential equations) for lumped-parameter electromechanical systems. In the context used here lumped-parameter systems are defined as follows: the electromagnetic fields are quasi-static and electrical terminal properties can be described as functions of a finite number of electrical variables. Also, the mechanical effects can be described by a finite number of mechanical variables. Thus the general feature of lumped-parameter electromechanical systems is that field equations can be integrated throughout space to obtain ordinary differential equations.

Electrical parts of the systems are treated by circuit theory generalized to include the effects of electromechanical coupling; the mechanical parts of the systems are treated by the techniques of rigid body mechanics with electromechanical forces included.

The approach followed here is best illustrated by considering the block diagram in Fig. 2.0.1 in which an electromechanical system is separated for analytical purposes into a purely electrical part, a purely mechanical part, and a coupling part. The equations that describe the electrical part of the system are based on Kirchhoff's laws; the equations for the mechanical part of the system are obtained from Newton's laws and the continuity of space. Both sets of equations contain electromechanical coupling terms that arise from the interconnection of the coupling system.

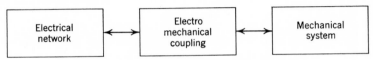

Fig. 2.0.1 An electromechanical system.

15

In what follows we review concepts of circuit theory and derive lumped parameters in a general way to include electromechanical coupling terms. We then review the concepts of rigid-body mechanics. Electromechanical coupling is discussed in Chapter 3.

2.1 CIRCUIT THEORY

The mathematical description of a circuit essentially involves two steps. First, we must be able to describe mathematically the physical properties of each element in the circuit in order to produce expressions for the terminal properties of the elements. Second, we must combine the equations for the elements in a manner prescribed by the interconnections of the elements. This step is performed by using Kirchhoff's laws and the topology of the circuit.* Thus we need only to generalize the description of circuit elements to include the effects of electromechanical interactions.

Conventional circuit theory is the special case of stationary systems in which quasi-static electromagnetic field theory applies. All the concepts of circuit theory can be derived from field theory†; for example, Kirchhoff's current law is derived from the conservation of charge. When we postulate a node that is an interconnection of wires at which no charge can accumulate, the conservation of charge [see (1.1.22) or (1.1.26) with $\rho_f = 0$] becomes

$$\oint_S \mathbf{J}_f \cdot \mathbf{n} \, da = 0, \tag{2.1.1}$$

where the surface S encloses the node. Because current is restricted to the wires, (2.1.1) yields Kirchhoff's current law

$$\sum_k i_k = 0, \tag{2.1.2}$$

where i_k is the current flowing away from the node on the kth wire.

Kirchhoff's voltage law is obtained by recognizing that a voltage is uniquely defined only in a region in which the time rate of change of magnetic flux density is negligible. Thus either (1.1.23) or (1.1.24) becomes

$$\oint_C \mathbf{E} \cdot d\mathbf{l} = 0. \tag{2.1.3}$$

This leads to the Kirchhoff voltage equation which requires that the sum of the voltage drops around a closed loop (contour C) be zero,

$$\sum_k v_k = 0, \tag{2.1.4}$$

---

* E. A. Guillemin, *Introductory Circuit Theory*, Wiley, New York, 1953, Chapters 2 and 4.
† Electrical Engineering Staff, M.I.T., *Electric Circuits*, Technology Press and Wiley, New York, 1943, Chapters 1 and 2.

where v_k is the voltage drop across the kth element in the loop taken in the direction of summation.*

In conventional circuit theory there are three basic types of passive elements: (a) resistances that dissipate electric energy as heat; (b) inductances that store magnetic energy; and (c) capacitances that store electric energy. It is a fact of life that electromechanical coupling of practical significance occurs in elements with appreciable electric or magnetic energy storage. Consequently, we shall consider electromechanical effects in circuit elements that are generalizations of the inductances and capacitances of circuit theory. To be sure, our systems have resistances, but they are treated as purely electrical circuit elements and considered as external to the coupling network.

We proceed now to generalize the concepts of inductance and capacitance to include electromechanical effects. As stated before, we wish to obtain terminal equations suitable for inclusion in a Kirchhoff-law description of a circuit.

2.1.1 Generalized Inductance

From a field point of view an inductor is a quasi-static magnetic field system, as defined in Section 1.1.1a. Thus we start with the field description of a quasi-static magnetic field system and derive the terminal characteristics when parts of the system are in motion.

First it is essential to recognize that in an ideal, lossless magnetic field system there is a perfectly conducting path between the two terminals of each terminal pair, as illustrated schematically in Fig. 2.1.1. We assume that the

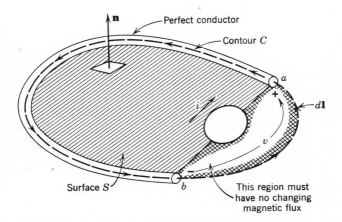

Fig. 2.1.1 Configuration for defining terminal voltage.

* For a discussion of the definition and use of the concept of voltage see Section B.1.4.

terminal pair is excited by the current source i and that the terminal pair is in a region of space in which the time rate of change of magnetic flux density is negligible. This restriction is necessary if we are to be able to describe a terminal voltage unambiguously. The perfect conductor that connects the two terminals is often wound into a coil and the coil may encircle an iron core. The drawing in Fig. 2.1.1 is simplified to illustrate the principles involved.

We must include the possibility that the perfect conductor in Fig. 2.1.1 is moving. We define a contour C that passes through and is fixed to the perfect conductor. That portion of the contour which goes from b to a outside the perfect conductor is fixed and in a region of negligible magnetic flux density. The *terminal voltage* v (see Fig. 2.1.1) is defined in the usual way* as

$$v = -\int_b^a \mathbf{E} \cdot d\mathbf{l};$$

(2.1.5)

it is understood that this line integral is evaluated along the path from b to a that is external to the perfect conductor. We now consider the line integral

$$\oint_C \mathbf{E}' \cdot d\mathbf{l}$$

around the contour of Fig. 2.1.1. The electric field intensity $\mathbf{E}'$ is the field that an observer will measure when he is fixed with respect to the contour. The contour is fixed to the perfect conductor, and, by definition, a perfect conductor can support no electric field.† Consequently, we reach the conclusion that

$$\oint_C \mathbf{E}' \cdot d\mathbf{l} = \int_b^a \mathbf{E} \cdot d\mathbf{l} = -v.$$

(2.1.6)

Thus Faraday's law, (1.1.23) of Table 1.2, yields the terminal voltage

$$v = \frac{d}{dt}\int_S \mathbf{B} \cdot \mathbf{n}\, da,$$

(2.1.7)

where the surface S is enclosed by the contour C in Fig. 2.1.1 and the positive direction of the normal vector $\mathbf{n}$ is defined by the usual right-hand rule, as shown.

Equation 2.1.7 indicates why the external path from b to a in Fig. 2.1.1 must be in a region of negligible time rate of change of magnetic flux density. If it is not, the terminal voltage will depend on the location of the external

---

* See Section B.1.4.

† A more complete discussion of conductors in motion is given in Chapter 6.

contour and will not be defined unambiguously. For convenience we define the *flux linkage* λ of the circuit as

$$\lambda = \int_S \mathbf{B} \cdot \mathbf{n} \, da \qquad (2.1.8)$$

and rewrite (2.1.7) as

$$v = \frac{d\lambda}{dt}. \qquad (2.1.9)$$

In a quasi-static magnetic-field system the magnetic flux density is determined by (1.1.20) to (1.1.22) of Table 1.2 and a constitutive law,

$$\oint_C \mathbf{H} \cdot d\mathbf{l} = \int_S \mathbf{J}_f \cdot \mathbf{n} \, da, \qquad (1.1.20)$$

$$\oint_S \mathbf{B} \cdot \mathbf{n} \, da = 0, \qquad (1.1.21)$$

$$\oint_S \mathbf{J}_f \cdot \mathbf{n} \, da = 0, \qquad (1.1.22)$$

$$\mathbf{B} = \mu_0(\mathbf{H} + \mathbf{M}). \qquad (1.1.4)$$

(The differential forms of these equations can also be employed.) In the solution of any problem the usual procedure is to use (1.1.22) first to relate the terminal current to current density in the system and then (1.1.20), (1.1.21), and (1.1.4) to solve for the flux density $\mathbf{B}$. The resulting flux density is a function of terminal current, material properties (1.1.4), and system geometry. The use of this result in (2.1.8) shows that the flux linkage λ is also a function only of terminal current, material properties, and system geometry.

We are interested in evaluating terminal voltage by using (2.1.9); thus we are interested in time variations of flux linkage λ. If we assume that the system geometry is fixed, except for one movable part whose position can be described instantaneously by a displacement x with respect to a fixed reference, and we further assume that $\mathbf{M}$ is a function of field quantities alone (and therefore a function of current), we can write

$$\lambda = \lambda(i, x). \qquad (2.1.10)$$

In this expression we have indicated explicit functional dependence only on those variables (i and x) that may be functions of time.

We can now use (2.1.10) in (2.1.9) and expand the time derivative to obtain

$$v = \frac{d\lambda}{dt} = \frac{\partial \lambda}{\partial i}\frac{di}{dt} + \frac{\partial \lambda}{\partial x}\frac{dx}{dt}. \qquad (2.1.11)$$

This expression illustrates some general terminal properties of magnetic field systems. We note that the first term on the right of (2.1.11) is proportional to di/dt and is the result of changing current. This term can exist when the system is mechanically stationary and is often referred to as a *transformer voltage*. The second term on the right of (2.1.11) is proportional to dx/dt, which is a mechanical speed. This term exists only when there is relative motion in the system and is conventionally referred to as a *speed voltage*. No matter how many terminal pairs or mechanical displacements a system may have, the voltage at each terminal pair will have terms of the two types contained in (2.1.11).

If we now restrict our system (with one electrical terminal pair and one mechanical displacement) to materials whose magnetization densities are linear with field quantities, we have an *electrically linear* system whose flux linkage can be expressed in terms of an inductance L as

$$\lambda = L(x)i. \tag{2.1.12}$$

This system is electrically linear because the flux linkage is a linear function of current. The variation of flux linkage with geometry, as indicated in general in (2.1.10), is included in (2.1.12) in the function $L(x)$. When the flux linkage is written in the form of (2.1.12), the terminal voltage becomes

$$v = L(x)\frac{di}{dt} + i\frac{dL}{dx}\frac{dx}{dt}. \tag{2.1.13}$$

Once again the first term on the right is the transformer voltage and the second term is the speed voltage.

In the special case of fixed geometry (x constant) the second term on the right of (2.1.13) goes to zero and we obtain

$$v = L\frac{di}{dt}, \tag{2.1.14}$$

which is the terminal relation of an inductance that is conventional in linear circuit theory.

Electromechanical systems often have more than one electrical terminal pair and more than one mechanical displacement. For such a situation the process described is still valid. To illustrate this generalization assume a quasi-static magnetic field system with N electrical terminal pairs and M mechanical variables that are functions of time. There are N electrical currents,

$$i_1, i_2, \ldots, i_N,$$

and M mechanical displacements,

$$x_1, x_2, \ldots, x_M.$$

Because this is a quasi-static magnetic field system, there is a perfectly conducting path between the two terminals of each terminal pair, as illustrated in Fig. 2.1.1. Thus the voltage for any terminal pair is determined by using the contour for that terminal pair with (2.1.6). Then the flux linkage for any terminal pair (say the kth) is given by (2.1.8):

$$\lambda_k = \int_{S_k} \mathbf{B} \cdot \mathbf{n} \, da, \tag{2.1.15}$$

where S_k is the surface enclosed by the contour used with (2.1.6) to evaluate voltage v_k at the kth terminal pair. The voltage v_k is then given by (2.1.7) as

$$v_k = \frac{d\lambda_k}{dt}. \tag{2.1.16}$$

The fields in this more general situation are again described by (1.1.20) to (1.1.22) and (1.1.4). Consequently, the generalization of (2.1.10) is

$$\lambda_k = \lambda_k(i_1, i_2, \ldots, i_N; x_1, x_2, \ldots, x_M), \tag{2.1.17}$$
$$k = 1, 2, \ldots, N.$$

We can now write the generalization of (2.1.11) by using (2.1.17) in (2.1.16) to obtain

$$v_k = \sum_{j=1}^{N} \frac{\partial \lambda_k}{\partial i_j} \frac{di_j}{dt} + \sum_{j=1}^{M} \frac{\partial \lambda_k}{\partial x_j} \frac{dx_j}{dt}, \tag{2.1.18}$$
$$k = 1, 2, \ldots, N.$$

Once again the terms in the first summation are referred to as transformer voltages and the terms in the second summation are referred to as speed voltages.

The preceding development has indicated the formalism by which we obtain lumped-parameter descriptions of quasi-static magnetic field systems. We have treated ideal lossless systems. In real systems losses are primarily resistive losses in wires and losses in magnetic materials.* Even though they may be quite important in system design and operation (efficiency, thermal limitations, etc.), they usually have little effect on the electromechanical interactions. Consequently, the effects of losses are accounted for by electrical resistances external to the lossless electromechanical coupling system.

---

* Losses in magnetic materials result from hysteresis and eddy currents. For a discussion of these effects and their mathematical models see Electrical Engineering Staff, M.I.T., *Magnetic Circuits and Transformers*, Technology Press and Wiley, New York, 1943, Chapters 5, 6, and 13. Eddy currents are discussed in Chapter 7 of this book.

Example 2.1.1. As an example of the calculation of lumped parameters, consider the magnetic field system of Fig. 2.1.2. It consists of a fixed structure made of highly permeable magnetic material with an excitation winding of N turns. A movable plunger, also made of highly permeable magnetic material, is constrained by a nonmagnetic sleeve to move in the x-direction. This is the basic configuration used for tripping circuit breakers, operating valves, and other applications in which a relatively large force is applied to a member that moves a relatively small distance.*

We wish to calculate the flux linkage λ at the electrical terminal pair (as a function of current i and displacement x) and the terminal voltage v for specified time variation of i and x.

To make the analysis of the system of Fig. 2.1.2 more tractable but still quite accurate it is conventional to make the following assumptions:

1. The permeability of the magnetic material is high enough to be assumed infinite.

2. The air-gap lengths g and x are assumed small compared with transverse dimensions $g \ll w$, $x \ll 2w$, so that fringing at the gap edges can be ignored.

3. Leakage flux is assumed negligible; that is, the only appreciable flux passes through the magnetic material except for gaps g and x.

Needed to solve this problem are the quasi-static magnetic field equations (1.1.20) through (1.1.22) and (1.1.4).

We first assume that the terminal current is i. Then by using (1.1.22) we establish that the current at each point along the winding is i. Next, we recognize that the specification of infinitely permeable magnetic material implies that we can write (1.1.4) as

$$\mathbf{B} = \mu \mathbf{H}$$

with $\mu \to \infty$. Thus with finite flux density $\mathbf{B}$ the field intensity $\mathbf{H}$ is zero inside the magnetic

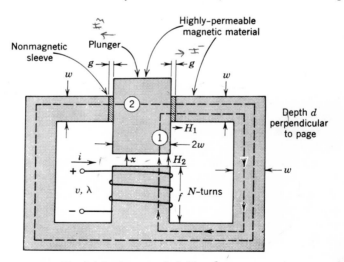

Fig. 2.1.2 A magnetic field system.

---

* A. E. Knowlton, ed., *Standard Handbook for Electrical Engineers*, 9th ed. McGraw-Hill, New York, 1957, Section 5-39 through 5-52.

material. Thus the only nonzero $\mathbf{H}$ occurs in the air gaps g and x, where $\mathbf{M} = 0$, and (1.1.4) becomes

$$\mathbf{B} = \mu_0 \mathbf{H}.$$

The use of (1.1.20) with contour (2) in Fig. 2.1.2 shows that the field intensities in the two gaps g are equal in magnitude and opposite in direction. This is expected from the symmetry of the system. Denoting the magnitude of the field intensity in the gaps g as H_1 and the field intensity in gap x by H_2, we can integrate (1.1.20) around contour (1) in Fig. 2.1.2 to obtain

$$H_1 g + H_2 x = Ni, \tag{a}$$

where H_2 is taken positive upward and H_1 is taken positive to the right. We now use (1.1.21) with a surface that encloses the plunger and passes through the gaps to obtain

$$\mu_0 H_1 (2wd) - \mu_0 H_2 (2wd) = 0. \tag{b}$$

We combine (a) and (b) to obtain

$$H_1 = H_2 = \frac{Ni}{g + x}.$$

The flux through the center leg of the core is simply the flux crossing the air gap x and is

$$\phi = \mu_0 H_2 (2wd) = \frac{2wd\mu_0 Ni}{g + x}.$$

In the absence of leakage flux this same flux links the N-turn winding N times; that is, when we evaluate

$$\int_S \mathbf{B} \cdot \mathbf{n} \, da$$

over a surface enclosed by the wire of the N-turn winding, we obtain the flux linkage λ as

$$\lambda = N\phi = \frac{2wd\mu_0 N^2 i}{g + x}. \tag{c}$$

Note that because λ is a linear function of i the system is electrically linear and we can write (c) as

$$\lambda = L(x)i, \tag{d}$$

where

$$L(x) = \frac{2wd\mu_0 N^2}{g + x}. \tag{e}$$

When we assume that the current i and displacement x are specified functions of time, we can use (d) with (2.1.13) to evaluate the terminal voltage as

$$v = \frac{2wd\mu_0 N^2}{g + x} \frac{di}{dt} - \frac{2wd\mu_0 N^2 i}{(g + x)^2} \frac{dx}{dt}.$$

The first term is the transformer voltage that will exist if x is fixed and i is varying. The second term is the speed voltage that will exist if i is constant and x is varying.

Example 2.1.2. As a second example, consider the system in Fig. 2.1.3 which has two electrical terminal pairs and the mechanical displacement is rotational. This system consists

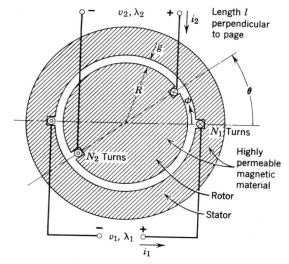

Fig. 2.1.3 Doubly excited magnetic field system.

of a fixed annular section of highly permeable magnetic material that is concentric with a cylindrical piece of the same material of the same axial length. Mounted in axial slots in the material are coils labeled with the numbers of turns and current directions. The angular position of the inner structure (rotor) relative to the outer structure (stator) is indicated by an angle θ which can vary with time. Current is fed to the coil on the rotor through sliding contacts (brushes that make contact with slip rings).

The system in Fig. 2.1.3 represents the basic method of construction of many rotating machines. In our solution we discuss how this configuration is used with some variations to achieve the lumped parameters desired for rotating-machine operation.

We wish to calculate the two flux linkages λ_1 and λ_2 as functions of the currents i_1 and i_2 and the angular displacement θ. The voltages at the two terminal pairs are also to be found, assuming that i_1, i_2, and θ are specified functions of time.

Electromechanical systems of the type illustrated in Fig. 2.1.3 are normally constructed with relative dimensions and materials that allow reasonably accurate calculation of lumped parameters when the following assumptions are made:

1. The permeability of the magnetic material is high enough to be assumed infinite.

2. The radial air-gap length g is small enough compared with the radius R and axial length l to allow the neglect of fringing fields at the ends and of radial variation of magnetic field intensity in the air gap.

3. The slots containing the windings are small enough both radially and circumferentially to perturb the fields a negligible amount; that is, the coils are considered to be infinitely thin.

Equations 1.1.20 and 1.1.21 are used to write the radial fields in the air gap in terms of the angular variable ϕ defined in Fig. 2.1.3. If we define the magnetic field as positive when directed radially outward and consider $0 < \theta < \pi$,

$$H_r = \frac{N_1 i_1 - N_2 i_2}{2g}, \qquad \text{for} \quad 0 < \phi < \theta,$$

$$H_r = \frac{N_1 i_1 + N_2 i_2}{2g}, \qquad \text{for} \quad \theta < \phi < \pi,$$

$$H_r = -\frac{N_1 i_1 - N_2 i_2}{2g}, \qquad \text{for} \quad \pi < \phi < \pi + \theta,$$

$$H_r = -\frac{N_1 i_1 + N_2 i_2}{2g}, \qquad \text{for} \quad \pi + \theta < \phi < 2\pi.$$

The flux linkages with the two windings can be found from the integrals

$$\lambda_1 = \int_0^\pi N_1 \mu_0 H_r l R \, d\phi,$$

$$\lambda_2 = \int_\theta^{\pi+\theta} N_2 \mu_0 H_r l R \, d\phi.$$

Evaluation of these integrals yields

$$\lambda_1 = L_1 i_1 + L_m i_2,$$

$$\lambda_2 = L_m i_1 + L_2 i_2,$$

where

$$L_1 = N_1^2 L_0, \qquad L_2 = N_2^2 L_0,$$

$$L_m = L_0 N_1 N_2 \left(1 - \frac{2\theta}{\pi}\right), \qquad \text{for} \quad 0 < \theta < \pi,$$

$$L_0 = \frac{\mu_0 l R \pi}{2g}.$$

Similar arguments show that for $-\pi < \theta < 0$ the terminal relations have the same form except that

$$L_m = L_0 N_1 N_2 \left(1 + \frac{2\theta}{\pi}\right)$$

Note that only the mutual inductance L_m is a function of angular displacement θ because the geometry seen by each coil individually does not change with θ; thus the self-inductances are constants. The mutual inductance is sketched as a function of θ in Fig. 2.1.4.

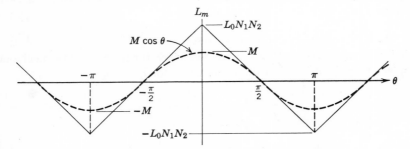

Fig. 2.1.4 Mutual inductance L_m as a function of θ.

In the design of rotating machines, especially for operation on alternating currents, it is desirable to have a system similar to that in Fig. 2.1.3 but to modify it in such a way that the mutual inductance varies cosinusoidally with $\theta (L_m = M \cos \theta)$. This is accomplished by putting additional slots and windings at different positions around the periphery of both members. By using a proper distribution of slots and numbers of turns the dependence of L_m can be made the cosinusoidal function shown by the dashed curve in Fig. 2.1.4. In many later examples we assume that this design process has been followed.

When the two currents i_1 and i_2 and the angular position θ are functions of time and the mutual inductance is expressed as $L_m = M \cos \theta$, we can write the terminal voltages as

$$v_1 = \frac{d\lambda_1}{dt} = L_1 \frac{di_1}{dt} + M \cos \theta \frac{di_2}{dt} - i_2 M \sin \theta \frac{d\theta}{dt},$$

$$v_2 = \frac{d\lambda_2}{dt} = L_2 \frac{di_2}{dt} + M \cos \theta \frac{di_1}{dt} - i_1 M \sin \theta \frac{d\theta}{dt}.$$

Note that the first term in each expression is a derivative with a constant coefficient, whereas the last two terms are derivatives with time-varying coefficients.

So far we have described lumped-parameter magnetic field systems by expressing the flux linkages as functions of the currents and displacements. Although this is a natural form for deriving lumped parameters, we shall find it convenient later to express lumped parameters in different forms. For example, we often use the lumped parameters in a form that expresses the current as a function of flux linkages and displacements. Assuming that the flux linkages are known as functions of currents and displacements, we are merely required to solve a set of simultaneous algebraic equations.

Consider the situation of an electrically linear system with one electrical terminal pair and one displacement. The flux linkage for this system has been described in (2.1.12) and it is a simple matter to solve this expression for i to obtain

$$i = \frac{\lambda}{L(x)}. \tag{2.1.19}$$

For an electrically linear system with two electrical terminal pairs we can write the expressions for the two flux linkages as

$$\lambda_1 = L_1 i_1 + L_m i_2, \tag{2.1.20}$$

$$\lambda_2 = L_m i_1 + L_2 i_2. \tag{2.1.21}$$

It is assumed that the three inductances are functions of the mechanical displacements. Solutions of these equations for i_1 and i_2 are

$$i_1 = \frac{L_2}{L_1 L_2 - L_m{}^2} \lambda_1 - \frac{L_m}{L_1 L_2 - L_m{}^2} \lambda_2, \tag{2.1.22}$$

$$i_2 = -\frac{L_m}{L_1 L_2 - L_m{}^2} \lambda_1 + \frac{L_1}{L_1 L_2 - L_m{}^2} \lambda_2. \tag{2.1.23}$$

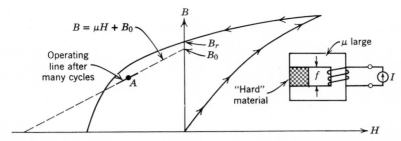

Fig. 2.1.5 Hard magnetic material magnetized and then demagnetized by the current I.

For the more general (and possibly not electrically linear) case for which flux linkages are expressed by (2.1.17) we can, at least in theory, solve these N simultaneous equations to obtain the general functional form

$$i_k = i_k(\lambda_1, \lambda_2, \ldots, \lambda_N; x_1, x_2, \ldots x_M),$$

$$k = 1, 2, \ldots, N. \tag{2.1.24}$$

Although we have generalized the concept of inductance to the point at which we can describe an electrically nonlinear system, the full, nonlinear expressions are rarely used in the analysis of electromechanical devices. This is so because devices that involve mechanical motion normally have air gaps (where the material is electrically linear) and the fields in the air gaps predominate (see the last two examples). It is worthwhile, however, to understand the origins of lumped parameters and how to describe nonlinear systems because there are some devices in which nonlinearities predominate.

In our examples of magnetic field systems we have considered only a "soft" magnetic material with a flux density (or more accurately a magnetization density **M**) that is ideally a linear function of a magnetic field intensity. A different type of magnetic material often used in electromechanical systems is the "hard" or permanent magnet material. In these materials the flux density is, in general, not given by $\mathbf{B} = \mu\mathbf{H}$. Figure 2.1.5 shows the type of curve that would result if a hard magnetic material were subjected to a field intensity H by means of an extremely large current applied as shown.* When the current (i.e., H) is removed, there is a residual flux density B_r. Then, if the sample is removed from the magnetic circuit and subjected to other magnetic fields (of limited strength), the B–H curve settles down to operate about some point such as A in Fig. 2.1.5. To a good approximation we can often model this relation by the straight line shown in Fig. 2.1.5.

$$B = \mu H + B_0. \tag{2.1.25}$$

* See, for example, Electrical Engineering Staff, M.I.T., *op. cit.*, Chapter 4.

The calculation of terminal relations is now the same as described, except that in the permanent magnet (2.1.25) is used rather than (1.1.8).

Example 2.1.3. The system shown in Fig. 2.1.2 is excited electrically by removing the N turns and placing a permanent magnet of length f in the magnetic circuit. Then the analysis of Example 2.1.1 is altered by the integration of (1.1.20) around the contour 1. If, in the section of length f, the material is characterized by (2.1.25), (a) of Example 2.1.1 is replaced by

$$H_1 g + H_2 x + \frac{fB}{\mu} = \frac{fB_0}{\mu}, \tag{a}$$

where B is the flux density in the magnet. Equation 1.1.21, however, again shows that B is the same in the magnet as it is in each of the air gaps. Hence

$$B = \mu_0 H_1 = \mu_0 H_2 \tag{b}$$

and (a) shows that

$$B = \frac{fB_0}{(\mu/\mu_0)(g + x) + f}. \tag{c}$$

Note from (a) that we can replace the permanent magnet with an equivalent current source I driving N turns, as shown in Fig. 2.1.2, but in which

$$i = I = \frac{fB_0}{N\mu},$$

and in the magnetic circuit there is a magnetic material of permeability μ and length f. This model allows us to compute forces of electrical origin for systems involving permanent magnets on the same basis as those excited by currents through electrical terminal pairs.

2.1.2 Generalized Capacitance

To derive the terminal characteristics of lumped-parameter electric field systems we start with the quasi-static equations given in Table 1.2. The equations we need are (1.1.24) to (1.1.26) and (1.1.13):

$$\oint_C \mathbf{E} \cdot d\mathbf{l} = 0, \tag{1.1.24}$$

$$\oint_S \mathbf{D} \cdot \mathbf{n} \, da = \int_V \rho_f \, dV, \tag{1.1.25}$$

$$\mathbf{D} = \epsilon_0 \mathbf{E} + \mathbf{P}, \tag{1.1.13}$$

$$\oint_S \mathbf{J}_f' \cdot \mathbf{n} \, da = -\frac{d}{dt} \int_V \rho_f \, dV. \tag{1.1.26}$$

We can use the differential forms of these equations alternatively, although the integral forms are more appropriate for the formalism of this section.

It is essential to recognize that an ideal, lossless electric field system consists of a set of equipotential bodies with no conducting paths between them.

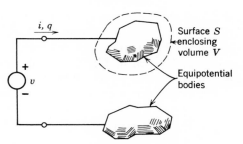

Fig. 2.1.6 A simple electric field system.

Terminals are brought out so that excitation may be applied to the equipotential bodies. It is conventional to select one equipotential body as a reference and designate its voltage as zero. The potentials of the other bodies are then specified with respect to the reference.

As a simple example of finding the terminal relations for an electric field system, consider the two equipotential bodies in Fig. 2.1.6. We assume that the voltage v is impressed between the two equipotential bodies and wish to find the current i. We choose a surface S (see Fig. 2.1.6) which encloses only the upper equipotential body and apply the conservation of charge (1.1.26). The only current density on the surface S occurs where the wire cuts through it. At this surface there is no free charge density ρ_f, hence $J_f = J'_f$, so that

$$\oint_S \mathbf{J}'_f \cdot \mathbf{n} \, da = -i. \tag{2.1.26}$$

The minus sign results because the normal vector $\mathbf{n}$ is directed outward from the surface.

The total charge q on the upper equipotential body in Fig. 2.1.6 is

$$q = \int_V \rho_f \, dV, \tag{2.1.27}$$

where V is a volume that includes the body and is enclosed by the surface S. Use of the conservation of charge (1.1.26) with (2.1.26) and (2.1.27) yields the terminal current

$$i = \frac{dq}{dt}. \tag{2.1.28}$$

Equation 2.1.28 simply expresses the fact that a current i leads to an accumulation of charge on the body. For a quasi-static system in which we impose voltage constraints the field quantities and the charge density ρ_f are determined by (1.1.24), (1.1.25) and (1.1.13), and all are functions of the applied voltages, the material properties (polarization), and the geometry. Thus, because (2.1.27) is an integral over space, the charge q is a function of the applied voltages, material properties, and geometry.

If we again consider the system in Fig. 2.1.6 and specify that the time variation of the geometry is uniquely specified by a mechanical displacement x with respect to a fixed reference, we can write the charge in the general functional form

$$q = q(v, x). \tag{2.1.29}$$

In writing the charge in this way we have indicated explicit functional dependence on only those variables (v and x) that may be functions of time.

We can now use (2.1.29) in (2.1.28) to obtain the terminal current as

$$i = \frac{\partial q}{\partial v}\frac{dv}{dt} + \frac{\partial q}{\partial x}\frac{dx}{dt}. \tag{2.1.30}$$

The first term exists only when the voltage is changing with time and the second term exists only when there is relative mechanical motion.

If we consider a system whose polarization density $\mathbf{P}$ is a linear function of field quantities, the system is *electrically linear* and the functional dependence of (2.1.29) can be written in the form

$$q = C(x)v. \tag{2.1.31}$$

The capacitance C contains the dependence on geometry. For a system whose charge is expressible by (2.1.31) the terminal current is

$$i = C(x)\frac{dv}{dt} + v\frac{dC}{dx}\frac{dx}{dt}. \tag{2.1.32}$$

In the special case in which the geometry does not vary with time (x is constant), (2.1.32) reduces to

$$i = C\frac{dv}{dt}, \tag{2.1.33}$$

which is the terminal equation used for a capacitance in linear circuit theory.

Now that we have established the formalism for calculating the terminal properties of lumped-parameter electric field systems by treating the simplest case, we can, as we did for the magnetic field system in the preceding section, generalize the equations to describe systems with any number of electrical terminal pairs and mechanical displacements. We assume a system with $N + 1$ equipotential bodies. We select one of them as a reference (zero) potential and apply voltages to the other N terminals. There are then N terminal voltages,

$$v_1, v_2, \ldots, v_N.$$

We assume that there are M mechanical displacements that uniquely specify the time variation of the geometry

$$x_1, x_2, \ldots, x_M.$$

Although we write these displacements as if they were translational, they can equally well be rotational (angular).

For the integration of (2.1.26) we select a surface S_k that encloses the kth equipotential body. Then (2.1.27) is integrated over the enclosed volume V_k and the conservation of charge expression (1.1.26) is used to express the current into the terminal connected to the kth equipotential as

$$i_k = \frac{dq_k}{dt}, \tag{2.1.34}$$

where

$$q_k = \int_{V_k} \rho_f \, dV. \tag{2.1.35}$$

Because the system is quasi-static, the fields are functions only of the applied voltages, the material properties, and the displacements. Thus we can generalize the functional form of (2.1.29) for our multivariable problem to

$$q_k = q_k(v_1, v_2, \ldots, v_N; x_1, x_2, \ldots, x_M), \tag{2.1.36}$$

$$k = 1, 2, \ldots, N.$$

From (2.1.36) and (2.1.34), the k'th terminal current follows as

$$i_k = \sum_{j=1}^{N} \frac{\partial q_k}{\partial v_j} \frac{dv_j}{dt} + \sum_{j=1}^{M} \frac{\partial q_k}{\partial x_j} \frac{dx_j}{dt}, \tag{2.1.37}$$

$$k = 1, 2, \ldots, N.$$

If we specify that our multivariable system is electrically linear (a situation that occurs when polarization $\mathbf{P}$ is a linear function of electric field intensity) we can write the function of (2.1.36) in the form

$$q_k = \sum_{j=1}^{N} C_{kj}(x_1, x_2, \ldots, x_M) v_j, \tag{2.1.38}$$

$$k = 1, 2, \ldots, N.$$

Equations 2.1.36 and 2.1.38 can be inverted to express the voltages as functions of the charges and displacements. This process was illustrated for magnetic field systems by (2.1.19) through (2.1.24).

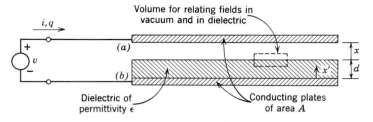

Fig. 2.1.7 A parallel-plate capacitor.

Example 2.1.4. Consider the simple parallel-plate capacitor of Fig. 2.1.7. It consists of two rectangular, parallel highly conducting plates of area A. Between the plates is a rectangular slab of dielectric material with constant permittivity ϵ,

$$\mathbf{D} = \epsilon\mathbf{E}.$$

The lower plate and the dielectric are fixed and the upper plate can move and has the instantaneous position x with respect to the top of the dielectric. The transverse dimensions are large compared with the plate separation. Thus fringing fields can be neglected. The terminal voltage is constrained by the source v which is specified as a function of time.

We wish to calculate the instantaneous charge on the upper plate and the current to the upper plate.

To solve this problem we need the given relation between $\mathbf{D}$ and $\mathbf{E}$, (1.1.24) and (1.1.25), and the definition of the voltage of point a with respect to point b

$$v = -\int_b^a \mathbf{E} \cdot d\mathbf{l}$$

With the neglect of fringing fields, the field quantities $\mathbf{D}$ and $\mathbf{E}$ will have only vertical components. We take them both as being positive upward. In the vacuum space

$$D_v = \epsilon_0 E_v$$

and in the dielectric

$$D_d = \epsilon E_d.$$

We assume that the dielectric has no free charge; consequently, we use (1.1.25) with a rectangular box enclosing the dielectric-vacuum interface as illustrated in Fig. 2.1.7 to obtain

$$\epsilon_0 E_v = \epsilon E_d.$$

We now use the expression for the voltage to write

$$v = -\int_0^d \frac{\epsilon_0}{\epsilon} E_v \, dx' - \int_d^{x+d} E_v \, dx'.$$

Integration of these expressions yields the vacuum electric field intensity

$$E_v = -\frac{v}{x + (\epsilon_0/\epsilon)d}.$$

We now use (1.1.25) with a rectangular surface enclosing the upper plate to obtain

$$q = A\epsilon_0 E_v = \frac{\epsilon_0 A v}{x + (\epsilon_0/\epsilon)d}$$

As would be expected from the linear constitutive law used in the derivation, the system is electrically linear. The charge can be expressed as

$$q = C(x)v,$$

where

$$C(x) = \frac{\epsilon_0 A}{x + (\epsilon_0/\epsilon)d}.$$

When voltage v and displacement x are specified functions of time, we can write the terminal current as

$$i = \frac{dq}{dt} = \frac{\epsilon_0 A}{x + (\epsilon_0/\epsilon)d}\frac{dv}{dt} - \frac{\epsilon_0 A v}{[x + (\epsilon_0/\epsilon)d]^2}\frac{dx}{dt}.$$

Note that the first term will exist when the geometry (x) is fixed and the voltage is varying and that the second term will exist when the voltage is constant and the geometry is varying. This illustrates once again how mechanical motion can generate a time-varying current.

Example 2.1.5. As an example of a multiply excited electric field system, consider the system in Fig. 2.1.8 which is essentially a set of three parallel-plate capacitors immersed in vacuum. Of the three plates, one is fixed and two are movable, as indicated. The dimensions and variables are defined in Fig. 2.1.8.

We wish to calculate the charges q_1 and q_2 on the two movable plates and the currents i_1 and i_2 to those plates. We neglect fringing at the edges of the plates and assume that the voltages v_1 and v_2 are specified.

We designate the electric field intensities in the three regions as E_1, E_2, and E_m, with the positive directions as indicated in Fig. 2.1.8. The electric field intensities have constant

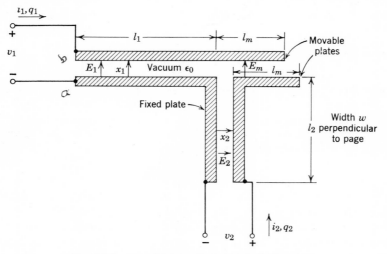

Fig. 2.1.8 A multiply excited electric field system.

magnitudes in the three regions; consequently, our definition of voltage applied in the three regions yields

$$E_1 = -\frac{v_1}{x_1},$$

$$E_2 = -\frac{v_2}{x_2},$$

$$E_m = \frac{v_2 - v_1}{x_1}.$$

We now use (1.1.25) with a rectangular surface enclosing the top plate to obtain

$$q_1 = -l_1 w\epsilon_0 E_1 - (l_m - x_2)w\epsilon_0 E_m$$

and with a rectangular box enclosing the right-hand movable plate to obtain

$$q_2 = -l_2 w\epsilon_0 E_2 + (l_m - x_2)w\epsilon_0 E_m.$$

These two expressions are electrically linear and can be written in the forms

$$q_1 = C_1 v_1 - C_m v_2, \tag{a}$$

$$q_2 = -C_m v_1 + C_2 v_2, \tag{b}$$

where

$$C_1 = \frac{\epsilon_0 w[l_1 + (l_m - x_2)]}{x_1}, \tag{c}$$

$$C_2 = \epsilon_0 w\left(\frac{l_2}{x_2} + \frac{l_m - x_2}{x_1}\right), \tag{d}$$

$$C_m = \frac{\epsilon_0 w(l_m - x_2)}{x_1}. \tag{e}$$

With v_1, v_2, x_1, and x_2 given as specified functions of time, we can write the terminal currents as

$$i_1 = C_1\frac{dv_1}{dt} - C_m\frac{dv_2}{dt} + v_1\left(\frac{\partial C_1}{\partial x_1}\frac{dx_1}{dt} + \frac{\partial C_1}{\partial x_2}\frac{dx_2}{dt}\right) - v_2\left(\frac{\partial C_m}{\partial x_1}\frac{dx_1}{dt} + \frac{\partial C_m}{\partial x_2}\frac{dx_2}{dt}\right),$$

$$i_2 = -C_m\frac{dv_1}{dt} + C_2\frac{dv_2}{dt} - v_1\left(\frac{\partial C_m}{\partial x_1}\frac{dx_1}{dt} + \frac{\partial C_m}{\partial x_2}\frac{dx_2}{dt}\right) + v_2\left(\frac{\partial C_2}{\partial x_1}\frac{dx_1}{dt} + \frac{\partial C_2}{\partial x_2}\frac{dx_2}{dt}\right).$$

A comparison of these results with those of the preceding example illustrates how quickly the expressions become longer and more complex as the numbers of electrical terminal pairs and mechanical displacements are increased.

2.1.3 Discussion

In the last two sections we specified the process by which we can obtain the electrical terminal properties of lumped-parameter, magnetic field and electric field systems. The general forms of the principal equations are summarized in Table 2.1. The primary purpose of obtaining terminal relations is to be able to include electromechanical coupling terms when writing circuit

Table 2.1 Summary of Terminal Variables and Terminal Relations

Magnetic field system   Electric field system

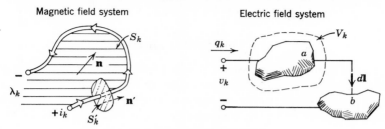

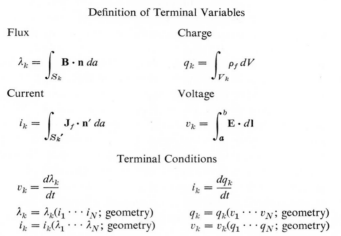

Definition of Terminal Variables

Flux   Charge

$$\lambda_k = \int_{S_k} \mathbf{B} \cdot \mathbf{n}\, da \qquad q_k = \int_{V_k} \rho_f\, dV$$

Current   Voltage

$$i_k = \int_{S_k'} \mathbf{J}_f \cdot \mathbf{n}'\, da \qquad v_k = \int_a^b \mathbf{E} \cdot d\mathbf{l}$$

Terminal Conditions

$$v_k = \frac{d\lambda_k}{dt} \qquad\qquad i_k = \frac{dq_k}{dt}$$

$$\lambda_k = \lambda_k(i_1 \cdots i_N;\text{ geometry}) \qquad q_k = q_k(v_1 \cdots v_N;\text{ geometry})$$
$$i_k = i_k(\lambda_1 \cdots \lambda_N;\text{ geometry}) \qquad v_k = v_k(q_1 \cdots q_N;\text{ geometry})$$

equations. After a review of rigid-body mechanics and a look at some energy considerations, we shall address ourselves to the problem of writing coupled equations of motion for electromechanical systems.

2.2 MECHANICS

We now discuss lumped-parameter modeling of the mechanical parts of systems. In essence, we shall consider the basic notions of rigid-body mechanics, including the forces of electric origin.

Just as in circuit theory, there are two steps in the formulation of equations of motion for rigid-body mechanical systems. First, we must specify the kinds of elements and their mathematical descriptions. This is analogous to defining terminal relations for circuit elements in circuit theory. Next, we must specify the laws that are used for combining the mathematical descriptions of elements into equations of motion. In mechanics these are Newton's second law and the continuity of space (often called geometrical compatibility) and they are analogous to Kirchhoff's laws in circuit theory.

In the two sections to follow we first define mechanical elements and then specify the laws and illustrate the formulation of equations of motion.

2.2.1　Mechanical Elements

In general, a mechanical system, which, for the moment, we define as an interconnected system of ponderable bodies in relative motion, will exhibit kinetic energy storage in moving masses, potential energy storage due to gravitational fields or elastic deformations, and mechanical losses due to friction of various types. Any component of a system will exhibit all three effects to varying degrees; as a practical matter of analysis and design, however, we can often represent mechanical systems as interconnections of ideal elements, each of which exhibits only one of these effects. This process is analogous to that of defining ideal circuit elements in circuit theory and has its justification in derivations from continuum mechanics. These derivations are not made in a formal way; however, in our treatment of continuum mechanics in later chapters the connections between the continuum theory and ideal, lumped-parameter, mechanical elements will become clear.

We consider three types of ideal mechanical elements: (a) elements that store kinetic energy—for translational systems these are masses and for rotational systems they are moments of inertia; (b) elements that store potential energy—for both translational and rotational systems these are springs; (c) elements that dissipate mechanical energy as heat—for both translational and rotational systems these are mechanical dampers. We define the nomenclature by which we describe each element before we combine them into systems. In the process we introduce the concept of mechanical circuits and mechanical circuit elements, which are simply pictorial representations of mathematical relations somewhat analogous to the circuits of electrical systems.* Mechanical circuits are of value for two reasons: they provide a formalism for writing the equations of motion and they emphasize the concept of mechanical terminal pairs.

The mechanical variables used in describing mechanical elements and systems are force and displacement. The displacement is always measured with respect to a reference position. In a way analogous to that used in circuit theory, we define ideal mechanical sources.

First, we define a position source as in Fig. 2.2.1. Here we represent a a simple physical situation in which the motion of the two objects (Fig. 2.2.1a) is restricted to the vertical. Thus there are two *mechanical nodes* whose positions x_1 and x_2 are measured with respect to a fixed reference. The

---

* M. F. Gardner, and J. L. Barnes, *Transients in Linear Systems*, Vol. I, Wiley, New York, 1942, Chapter 2. (Various conventions are used for drawing mechanical circuits. One alternative is given in the above.)

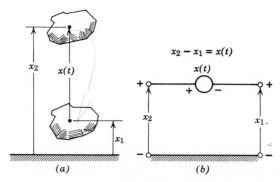

Fig. 2.2.1 A position source: (a) physical; (b) schematic.

position source $x(t)$ constrains the relative positions of the two nodes to

$$x_2 - x_1 = x(t); \tag{2.2.1}$$

the sign is determined by the $+$ and $-$ signs associated with the source. In Fig. 2.2.1b we give the circuit representation of the position source. The circuit is a pictorial representation of the scalar equation (2.2.1) and as such is completely analogous to the representations in circuit theory. Because (2.2.1) is valid regardless of other mechanical elements attached to the nodes, the ideal position source can supply an arbitrary amount of force.

In a similar way we can define a velocity source $v(t)$ that constrains the relative velocity of the two nodes to

$$\frac{dx_2}{dt} - \frac{dx_1}{dt} = v(t). \tag{2.2.2}$$

The circuit is as shown in Fig. 2.2.1b with x replaced by v.

A different kind of ideal mechanical source is a force source for which nomenclature is given in Fig. 2.2.2. In the physical representation of Fig. 2.2.2a motion is constrained to the vertical and the force $f(t)$ is vertical. The position of the arrow indicates the direction of positive force, and the convention we use here is that, with the arrow as shown and a positive $f(t)$, the force tends to push the two mechanical nodes apart exactly as if one were standing on node x_1 and pushing upward on node x_2 with the hands. The circuit representation of this force source is given in Fig. 2.2.2b. In the circuit our convention is that with the arrow as shown $[f(t)$ positive] the force tends to increase x_2 and decrease x_1.

The sources of Figs. 2.2.1 and 2.2.2 have been specified for translational systems. We can also specify analogous sources and circuits for rotational

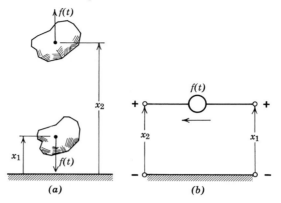

Fig. 2.2.2 A force source: (a) physical; (b) schematic.

systems. These extensions of our definitions should be clear from Figs. 2.2.3 and 2.2.4, in which θ_1 and θ_2 measure the angular displacements of the two disks, with respect to fixed references, and the torque T is applied between them.

In the examples we shall consider we shall encounter either pure translation or rotation about a fixed axis. Consequently, the geometry of motion as described so far is adequate for our purposes. We now describe ideal, passive, lumped-parameter, mechanical elements.

2.2.1a The Spring*

An *ideal* spring is a device with negligible mass and mechanical losses whose deformation is a single-valued function of the applied force. A *linear*

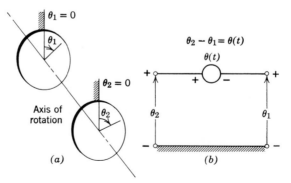

Fig. 2.2.3 An angular position source: (a) physical; (b) schematic.

* For a comprehensive treatise on the subject see A. M. Wahl, *Mechanical Springs*, 2nd ed., McGraw-Hill, New York, 1963.

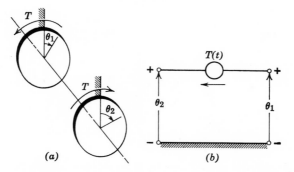

Fig. 2.2.4 A torque source: (*a*) physical; (*b*) schematic.

ideal spring has deformation *proportional* to force. In our treatment we are concerned almost exclusively with linear springs. We represent a spring physically as in Fig. 2.2.5*a* and in mechanical circuits as the symbol of Fig. 2.2.5*b*. The force f at one end of the spring must always be balanced by an equal and opposite force f at the other end. The force is thus transmitted through the spring much as current is transmitted through an inductance. In the circuit of Fig. 2.2.5*b* the applied force f is represented as a force source.

The spring of Fig. 2.2.5 has a spring constant K and the force is a linear function of the *relative* displacement of the two ends of the spring. Thus

$$f = K(x_2 - x_1 - l), \tag{2.2.3}$$

where l is the value of the relative displacement for which the force is zero.

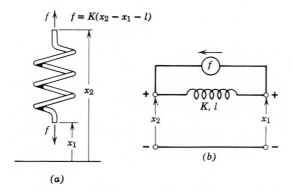

Fig. 2.2.5 A linear ideal spring for translational motion held in equilibrium by a force f: (*a*) physical system; (*b*) circuit.

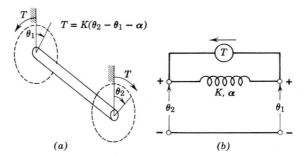

Fig. 2.2.6 A linear ideal torsional spring: (a) physical system; (b) circuit.

It is always possible, although in many cases not convenient, to define reference positions for measuring x_1 and x_2 such that $l = 0$.

We can also have linear ideal torsional springs in rotational systems. The mathematical and circuit representations are analogous to those of a translational spring and are evident in Fig. 2.2.6. The torque is a linear function of the relative angular displacement of the two ends

$$T = K(\theta_2 - \theta_1 - \alpha). \tag{2.2.4}$$

Note that the K in (2.2.3) has different dimensions than the K in (2.2.4).

2.2.1b The Mechanical Damper

The mechanical damper is analogous to electrical resistance in that it dissipates energy as heat. An *ideal* damper is a device that exhibits no mass or spring effect and exerts a force that is a function of the relative velocity between its two nodes. A *linear* ideal damper has a force proportional to the relative velocity of the two nodes. In all cases a damper produces a force that opposes the relative motion of the two nodes.

A linear damper (often called a viscous damper) is usually constructed in such a way that friction forces result from the viscous drag of a fluid under laminar flow conditions.* Two examples of viscous dampers, one for linear and one for rotary motion, are shown in Fig. 2.2.7 along with the mechanical circuits. Note that the force f (or torque T) is the force (or torque) that must be applied by an external agent to produce a positive relative velocity of the two nodes. For the linear-motion damper the terminal relation is

$$f = B \frac{d}{dt}(x_2 - x_1) \tag{2.2.5}$$

---

* For more detail on viscous laminar flow see Chapter 14.

and for the rotary-motion damper it is analogous (Fig. 2.2.7):

$$T = B \frac{d}{dt} (\theta_2 - \theta_1). \tag{2.2.6}$$

Note that the damping constant B has different dimensions for the two systems. In each case both displacements are measured with respect to references that are fixed.

Mechanical friction occurs in a variety of situations under many different physical conditions. Sometimes friction is unwanted but must be tolerated and accounted for analytically, as, for example, in bearings, sliding electrical contacts, and the aerodynamic drag on a moving body. In other cases friction is desired and is designed into equipment. Examples are vibration dampers and shock absorbers. Although in some cases a linear model is a useful approximation, in many others it is inadequate. The subject of friction

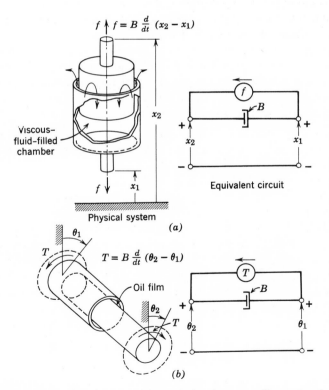

Fig. 2.2.7 Mechanical dampers: (*a*) translational system; (*b*) rotational system.

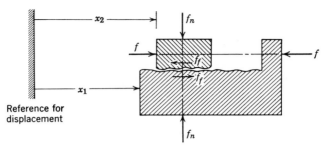

Fig. 2.2.8 Coulomb friction between members in contact.

is lengthy and complex*; most practical devices, however, can be modeled as described or by one of two nonlinear models that we now discuss.

The first of these additional models is coulomb friction which is characteristic of sliding contacts between dry materials. See Fig. 2.2.8 in which the blocks are assumed to have negligible mass. If we apply constant, equal and opposite, normal forces f_n, as shown, and then apply equal and opposite forces f, as shown, the blocks may or may not move relatively, depending on the friction coefficient of the surface. If we vary the force f, which must be balanced by the friction force f_f for steady motion, and measure the resultant steady relative velocity, we can plot the friction coefficient (f_f/f_n) as a function of relative velocity (see Fig. 2.2.9). The quantity μ_s is the coefficient of static friction and μ_d is the coefficient of sliding friction. When we

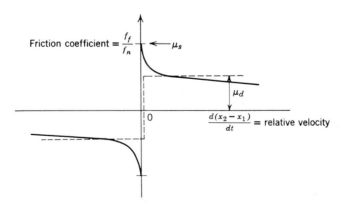

Fig. 2.2.9 Typical coulomb friction characteristic.

* See, for example, G. W. Van Stanten, *Introduction to a Study of Mechanical Vibration,* 3rd ed., Macmillan, New York, 1961, Chapter 14.

approximate this curve by the piecewise linear dashed line of Fig. 2.2.9, we can represent coulomb friction mathematically by the relation

$$f = \frac{f_n\mu_d(d/dt)(x_2 - x_1)}{|(d/dt)(x_2 - x_1)|} . \quad (2.2.7)$$

It is important to remember that coulomb friction, like all other forms of friction, produces a force that tends to oppose the relative motion of the nodes in the system.

Coulomb friction can also occur in rotational systems, in which case an expression analogous to (2.2.7) can be used for a mathematical description.

The final model of friction that we shall consider is that resulting primarily from the drag of a viscous fluid in turbulent flow.* This type of friction can be represented with fair accuracy by a model that makes the force (or torque) proportional to the square of relative velocity (or relative angular velocity). Such an expression is

$$f = \pm B_s\left[\frac{d}{dt}(x_2 - x_1)\right]^2. \quad (2.2.8)$$

Once again the force produced by the friction opposes the relative mechanical motion. Two examples in which square-law damping occurs are given in Fig. 2.2.10. The linear motion damper of Fig. 2.2.10a has the configuration characteristic of dashpots for making time-delay relays and for automobile shock absorbers. The square-law rotational damping of Fig. 2.2.10b occurs frequently in high-speed rotating machines in which the fluid is air or some other gaseous coolant.

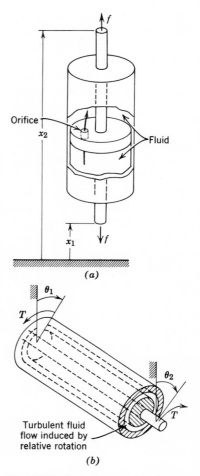

Fig. 2.2.10 Typical square-law dampers: (a) orifice and piston damper; (b) damping due to rotation.

2.2.1c The Mass

The final ideal mechanical element we need to consider is the element that stores kinetic energy but has no spring or damping effects. For translational

* See, for example, H. Schlichting, *Boundary Layer Theory*, 4th ed., McGraw-Hill, New York, 1960, Chapter 21.

systems this is a mass and for rotational systems a moment of inertia. After we have reviewed the plane motion of a point mass, we shall generalize to translation of a rigid body of finite size and to rotation of a rigid body about a fixed axis.

The motion of a point that has associated with it a constant amount of mass M is described by Newton's second law*:

$$\mathbf{f} = M \frac{d\mathbf{v}}{dt}, \tag{2.2.9}$$

where $\mathbf{f}$ is the force vector acting on the mass point and $\mathbf{v}$ is the absolute vector velocity of the point. It should be clearly recognized that $\mathbf{v}$ must be measured in relation to a fixed or nonaccelerating point or frame of reference. Such a reference system is called an *inertial reference*.

In motion occurring on the surface of the earth the earth is often considered to be approximately an inertial reference and $\mathbf{v}$ is measured in relation to the earth. When dealing with the motion of long-range missiles, orbital vehicles, and spacecraft, the earth cannot be considered to be a nonaccelerating reference and velocities are then measured with respect to the fixed stars.

When the velocity of a mass begins to approach the velocity of light, the Newtonian equation of motion in the form of (2.2.9) becomes invalid because the mass of a given particle of matter increases with velocity, according to the theory of relativity.† The present considerations are limited to velocity levels small compared with the velocity of light, so that Newton's law (2.2.9) will apply. This is consistent with the approximations we have made in defining the quasi-static electromagnetic field equations.

If we now consider the two-dimensional motion of a point mass M, we can define an orthogonal inertial reference system as in Fig. 2.2.11a and write Newton's second law in component form as

$$f_x = M \frac{d^2 x}{dt^2}, \tag{2.2.10}$$

$$f_y = M \frac{d^2 y}{dt^2}. \tag{2.2.11}$$

We can also represent these two equations by the mechanical circuit of Fig. 2.2.11b. Each degree of freedom of a point mass M is represented by a node with mass M. A force that tends to increase the displacement of a

---

* For a review of the fundamental concepts involved in Newton's laws, see for example R. R. Long, *Engineering Science Mechanics*, Prentice-Hall, Englewood Cliffs, N.J., 1963, Chapter 2.

† Long, *ibid.*, Chapter 10.

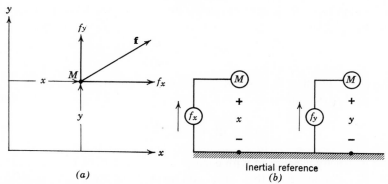

Fig. 2.2.11 Plane motion of a point mass: (*a*) physical; (*b*) circuit representation.

node is represented by an arrow pointing toward the node. The extension of these representations to three-dimensional motion is straightforward.

In order to obtain a representation for a mass element more general than a point mass, we need to review briefly the dynamics of rigid bodies. We consider first the translational motion of a rigid body.

A rigid body, by definition, is one in which any line drawn in or on the body remains constant in length and all angles drawn in or on the body remain constant. In Fig. 2.2.12 we represent a rigid body with a mass density ρ (kilograms per cubic meter) that may vary from point to point in the body but remains constant in time at any point in the body. We define an inertial coordinate system (x, y, z) and specify the position vector $\mathbf{r}$ of an arbitrary point p that is fixed in the body.

The instantaneous acceleration of the point p is

$$\mathbf{a}_p = \frac{d^2\mathbf{r}}{dt^2}. \tag{2.2.12}$$

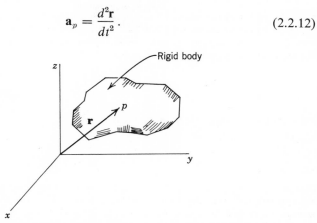

Fig. 2.2.12 Geometry for analyzing the translation of a rigid body.

Thus the infinitesimal element of mass $\rho \, dV$ at point p will have an acceleration force

$$d\mathbf{f}_n = \rho \, dV \frac{d^2\mathbf{r}}{dt^2}. \tag{2.2.13}$$

The force $d\mathbf{f}_n$ consists of two components: $d\mathbf{f}$ from sources external to the body and $d\mathbf{f}_i$ from sources within the body. Thus (2.2.13) can be written as

$$d\mathbf{f} + d\mathbf{f}_i = \rho \, dV \frac{d^2\mathbf{r}}{dt^2}. \tag{2.2.14}$$

The mass density associated with each point p in the rigid body is constant. Hence, when we integrate this expression throughout the volume of the body and recognize that the internal forces integrate to zero,* we obtain the result

$$\mathbf{f} = M \frac{d^2\mathbf{r}_m}{dt^2}, \tag{2.2.15}$$

where $\mathbf{f}$ is the total external force applied to the body,

$$M = \int_V \rho \, dV \text{ is a constant and is the total mass of the body,}$$

$$\mathbf{r}_m = \frac{\int_V \rho\mathbf{r} \, dV}{M} \text{ is the position vector of the center of mass of the body.}$$

From the result of (2.2.15) it is clear that the translational motion of a rigid body can be described completely by treating the body as if all the mass were concentrated at the center of mass. Consequently, (2.2.10) and (2.2.11)

---

* To illustrate that the internal forces integrate to zero consider an ensemble of N interacting particles. An internal force is applied between two particles: $\mathbf{f}_{ij} = -\mathbf{f}_{ji}$, where $\mathbf{f}_{ij}$ is the force on the ith particle due to the source connected between the ith and jth particles. The total internal force on the ith particle is

$$\mathbf{f}_i = \sum_{\substack{j=1 \\ j \neq i}}^{N} \mathbf{f}_{ij}.$$

The total internal force on the ensemble is

$$\mathbf{f} = \sum_{i=1}^{N} \mathbf{f}_i = \sum_{i=1}^{N} \sum_{\substack{j=1 \\ j \neq i}}^{N} \mathbf{f}_{ij}.$$

Because $\mathbf{f}_{ij} = -\mathbf{f}_{ji}$, we conclude that each term in this summation is canceled by an equal and opposite term and the net internal force is zero. If we let $N \to \infty$, the nature of the result is unchanged; thus we conclude that the integral of internal forces over the volume of a rigid body must be zero.

and Fig. 2.2.11, which were defined for a point mass, hold equally well for describing the motion of the center of mass of a rigid body.

Our rotational examples involve rotation about a fixed axis only. Thus we treat only the mechanics of rigid bodies rotating about fixed axes.* For this purpose we consider the system of Fig. 2.2.13. The body has mass density ρ that may vary with space in the body but at a point p fixed in the material is constant. We select a rectangular coordinate system whose z-axis coincides with the axis of rotation. The instantaneous angular velocity of the body is

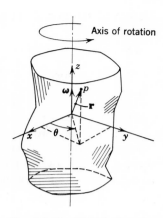

$$\boldsymbol{\omega} = \mathbf{i}_z \frac{d\theta}{dt}. \qquad (2.2.16)$$

Fig. 2.2.13 Rigid-body rotation.

At the point p with coordinates (x, y, z) the element of mass $\rho\, dV$ will have the instantaneous velocity

$$\mathbf{v} = \boldsymbol{\omega} \times \mathbf{r}, \qquad (2.2.17)$$

where $\mathbf{r} = \mathbf{i}_x x + \mathbf{i}_y y + \mathbf{i}_z z$ is the radius vector from the origin to the mass element.

The acceleration force on this mass element is

$$d\mathbf{f}_n = \rho\, dV \frac{d\mathbf{v}}{dt} = \rho\, dV\left[\frac{d\boldsymbol{\omega}}{dt} \times \mathbf{r} + \boldsymbol{\omega} \times (\boldsymbol{\omega} \times \mathbf{r})\right], \qquad (2.2.18)$$

where $d\mathbf{f}_n$ contains both internal and external forces [see (2.2.14)] and the last term has been written by using (2.2.17). We use the identity for the triple vector product

$$\mathbf{a} \times (\mathbf{b} \times \mathbf{c}) = \mathbf{b}(\mathbf{a} \cdot \mathbf{c}) - \mathbf{c}(\mathbf{a} \cdot \mathbf{b}) \qquad (2.2.19)$$

to write (2.2.18) in the form

$$d\mathbf{f}_n = \rho\, dV\left[\frac{d\boldsymbol{\omega}}{dt} \times \mathbf{r} + \boldsymbol{\omega}(\boldsymbol{\omega} \cdot \mathbf{r}) - \mathbf{r}(\boldsymbol{\omega} \cdot \boldsymbol{\omega})\right]. \qquad (2.2.20)$$

To find the acceleration torque on this mass element we write

$$d\mathbf{T}_n = \mathbf{r} \times d\mathbf{f}_n. \qquad (2.2.21)$$

---

* For a treatment of the general case of simultaneous translation and rotation in three dimensions, see, for example, Long, *op. cit.*, Chapter 6.

Using (2.2.20) in (2.2.21) and simplifying, we find that

$$dT + dT_i = \rho \, dV \left\{ i_z(x^2 + y^2)\frac{d^2\theta}{dt^2} - i_x \left[xz\frac{d^2\theta}{dt^2} - yz\left(\frac{d\theta}{dt}\right)^2 \right] \right.$$
$$\left. - i_y \left[yz\frac{d^2\theta}{dt^2} + xz\left(\frac{d\theta}{dt}\right)^2 \right] \right\}, \quad (2.2.22)$$

where dT = the torque from external sources,
      dT_i = the torque from internal sources.

To find the total acceleration torque on the body we must integrate (2.2.22) throughout the volume V of the body. For this purpose we find it convenient to define the moment of inertia about the z-axis as

$$J_z = \int_V (x^2 + y^2)\rho \, dV \quad (2.2.23)$$

and the products of inertia*

$$J_{xz} = \int_V xz\rho \, dV, \quad (2.2.24)$$

$$J_{yz} = \int_V yz\rho \, dV. \quad (2.2.25)$$

When we use these parameters and integrate (2.2.22) throughout the volume V of the body, the internal torque integrates to zero [see (2.2.14) and (2.2.15) and the associated footnote for arguments similar to those required here], and we obtain for the total acceleration torque T applied by external sources

$$\mathbf{T} = i_z J_z \frac{d^2\theta}{dt^2} - i_x \left[J_{xz}\frac{d^2\theta}{dt^2} - J_{yz}\left(\frac{d\theta}{dt}\right)^2 \right] - i_y \left[J_{yz}\frac{d^2\theta}{dt^2} + J_{xz}\left(\frac{d\theta}{dt}\right)^2 \right]. \quad (2.2.26)$$

With the restriction to rotation about a fixed axis, only the first term in this expression affects the dynamics of the body. Thus we write the z component of (2.2.26) as

$$T_z = J_z \frac{d^2\theta}{dt^2} \quad (2.2.27)$$

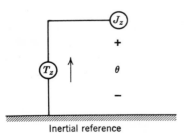

Inertial reference

Fig. 2.2.14 Circuit representation of a moment of inertia.

and represent this element in a mechanical circuit as in Fig. 2.2.14. Note that this circuit has exactly the same form as that adopted earlier for representing mass in a translational system (see Fig. 2.2.11).

* See, for example, I. H. Shames, *Engineering Mechanics*, Prentice-Hall, Englewood Cliffs, N.J., 1960, pp. 187–188.

The last two terms on the right of (2.2.26) (the x- and y-components) represent a torque that must be applied by bearings and support structure to maintain the axis of rotation fixed. It should be clear from the definitions of the products of inertia in (2.2.24) and (2.2.25) that certain axes of symmetry make these products of inertia zero. Such axes are called principal axes.* When rotation occurs about a principal axis (the body is dynamically balanced), no bearing torque is necessary to maintain the axis of rotation fixed.

Now that we have completed the definitions of the elements that will make up the mechanical parts of our electromechanical systems, we have only to describe how we combine elements to obtain complete equations of motion.

2.2.2 Mechanical Equations of Motion

When electrical circuit elements are interconnected, Kirchhoff's loop and node relations must be satisfied. The sum of the voltage differences around any loop must be zero and the sum of all currents into any node must be zero.

Similar relations must hold in networks composed of interconnected ideal mechanical elements. Consider first a *mechanical node*. A mechanical node is a location in a mechanical system which has a certain position relative to a reference position and a particular mass associated with it. A node appears in the mechanical circuit as a circle in which two or more terminals of ideal elements are connected. Figure 2.2.15 shows a simple mechanical system with one node p having mass M connected to two springs, a damper, and a force source. The motion of this system is completely specified by one coordinate x which is the instantaneous position of node p. The system is said to have one *degree of freedom*. In general, the number of degrees of freedom in a mechanical system equals the number of nodes it has.

The forces acting in the passive elements of Fig. 2.2.15a are all vertical and may be described by the scalar quantities f_1, f_2, and f_3 and shown also in the free-body diagram of the mass shown in Fig. 2.2.15b and in the circuit of Fig. 2.2.15c. The convention used here is that forces are drawn as *applied to* the node. The arrow directions on f_1, f_2, and f_3 are such that when they are positive they tend to *decrease* the displacement of the node. Hence they act out of the node in the circuit. This convention is adopted because we can express f_1 and f_2 [see (2.2.3)] as

$$f_1 = K_1(x - l_1) \tag{2.2.28}$$

$$f_2 = K_2(x - l_2) \tag{2.2.29}$$

and can express f_3 [see (2.2.5)] as

$$f_3 = B \frac{dx}{dt}. \tag{2.2.30}$$

* *Ibid.*, pp. 195–197.

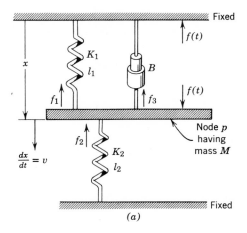

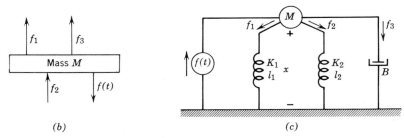

Fig. 2.2.15 System showing forces at a node: (a) system; (b) free body diagram of mass M; (c) circuit.

Newton's second law (2.2.10) requires that the *algebraic sum of all forces applied to a node in the positive x-direction must equal the acceleration force for the mass of the node.* For the example in Fig. 2.2.15 this requires that

$$f(t) - f_1 - f_2 - f_3 = M \frac{d^2x}{dt^2}. \tag{2.2.31}$$

Note that forces acting in the $+x$-direction "flow" into the node in Fig. 2.2.15c. Substitution from (2.2.28) through (2.2.30) into (2.2.31) yields the differential equation

$$f(t) - K_1(x - l_1) - K_2(x - l_2) - B \frac{dx}{dt} = M \frac{d^2x}{dt^2}. \tag{2.2.32}$$

Thus, if the system constants are known and $f(t)$ is specified, this differential equation can be solved to find $x(t)$; (2.2.32) is the equation of motion for the system in Fig. 2.2.15.

We can generalize (2.2.31) to describe any mechanical node with mass M and displacement x and with n forces applied by sources and passive elements.

$$\sum_{i=1}^{n} f_i = M \frac{d^2x}{dt^2}. \tag{2.2.33}$$

We must exercise caution to include the correct sign on each force in the summation.

In a rotational system the nodes have moments of inertia; thus the summation of torques applied to a node must equal the acceleration torque of the moment of inertia associated with the node. For a node with n torques applied the expression is

$$\sum_{i=1}^{n} T_i = J \frac{d^2\theta}{dt^2}. \tag{2.2.34}$$

Once again care must be exercised in attaching the correct sign to each torque in the summation.

As an example of the application of (2.2.34), consider the rotational system in Fig. 2.2.16a for which the mechanical circuit is shown in Fig. 2.2.16b.

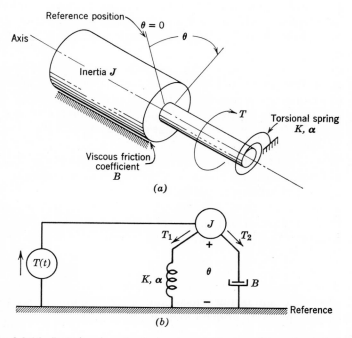

Fig. 2.2.16 Rotational mechanical system: (a) system; (b) mechanical circuit.

We represent the torques *applied to* the node in the $-\theta$-direction by the passive elements as T_1 and T_2. Reference to (2.2.4) and (2.2.6) shows that these torques can be expressed as

$$T_1 = K(\theta - \alpha), \tag{2.2.35}$$

$$T_2 = B\frac{d\theta}{dt}. \tag{2.2.36}$$

By use of these expressions with the source and arrow directions in Fig. 2.2.16b (2.2.34) yields the equation of motion

$$T(t) - K(\theta - \alpha) - B\frac{d\theta}{dt} = J\frac{d^2\theta}{dt^2}. \tag{2.2.37}$$

Once again, torques acting in the $+\theta$-direction "flow" into the node. When the constants are known and $T(t)$ is specified, this differential equation can be used to find the response $\theta(t)$.

An important point should be made here. In a mechanical system the reference or "ground" is usually considered fixed; this is necessary if any masses are involved. If the reference is fixed and elements are attached to the reference, it implies that forces not usually considered are available to prevent the ground point from moving. The surface of the earth, for example, is often taken as a reference, and although the earth will move a certain amount when a net force is exerted on it this movement is extremely small and can be neglected.

Equations 2.2.33 and 2.2.34, which are analogous for our forms of mechanical equivalent circuits to Kirchhoff's current law, are used almost exclusively for formulating equations of motion for mechanical systems. A second relation for mechanical systems analogous to Kirchhoff's voltage law is seldom used in a formal way but must at all times be satisfied. This second relation is called geometrical compatibility or continuity of space. To illustrate this concept with an example we use the system in Fig. 2.2.17. This system has three mechanical nodes (p, q, and r) whose velocities (v_1, v_2, and v_3) are measured in relation to the fixed point g.

The mechanical circuit of Fig. 2.2.17b has two independent mechanical loops. From examination of Fig. 2.2.17a it is evident that the velocity of p must be equal to the velocity of q, plus the velocity of p relative to q.

$$v_1 + (v_2 - v_1) - v_2 = 0. \tag{2.2.38}$$

This condition, which is identically satisfied, states that in the left-hand loop of Fig. 2.2.17b the sum of the velocity differences around the loop must be zero. Similarly, for the right-hand loop of Fig. 2.2.17b

$$v_2 + (v_3 - v_2) - v_3 = 0. \tag{2.2.39}$$

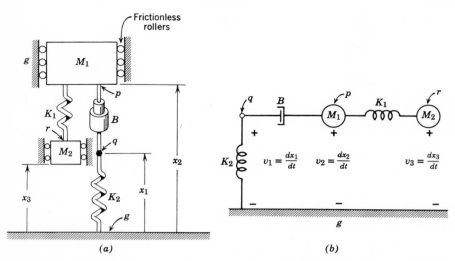

Fig. 2.2.17 Mechanical system and its network diagram: (*a*) system; (*b*) mechanical equivalent circuit.

We can generalize from this example to state that for a mechanical loop with n elements geometrical compatibility requires that

$$\sum_{i=1}^{n} (v_{i+1} - v_i) = 0, \tag{2.2.40}$$

where $(v_{i+1} - v_i)$ is the velocity difference across the ith element taken positive in the direction of summation. An equivalent relation for rotational systems can be obtained by summing angular velocity differences around a loop.

In establishing the loop equations it is preferable to work with *velocity differences* as above. If displacements are used, the geometric compatibility equations will contain constant terms, such as unstretched lengths of springs, and will be more complicated than (2.2.40).

As stated earlier, the geometric compatibility relation is not often explicitly used in formulating equations of motion. Nonetheless, it must be satisfied.

Example 2.2.1. Consider the simplified model of an automobile suspension system shown in Fig. 2.2.18*a*. The tire surface is excited by variations in the road surface. We wish to formulate equations suitable for determining the motion of the auto mass M_1 and the force on the tires.

The mechanical circuit is shown in Fig. 2.2.18*b*. The road acts as a position source applied to node 1, as shown. We assume that the references for measuring displacements of the two springs are chosen so that the equilibrium lengths are zero. In the circuit of

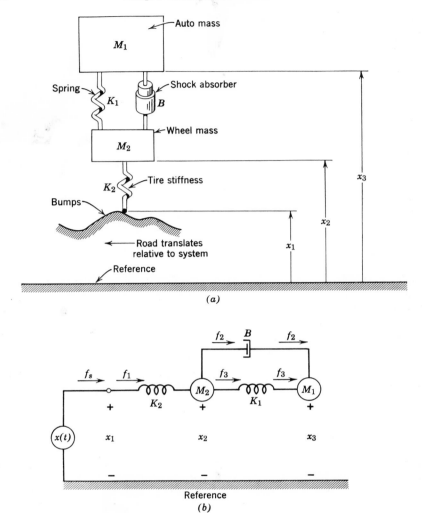

Fig. 2.2.18 One-dimensional model of auto suspension: (a) system; (b) equivalent circuit.

Fig. 2.2.18b three passive ideal mechanical elements (excluding masses) appear. The equations for these ideal elements are

$$f_1 = K_2(x_1 - x_2), \tag{a}$$

$$f_2 = B\left(\frac{dx_2}{dt} - \frac{dx_3}{dt}\right), \tag{b}$$

$$f_3 = K_1(x_2 - x_3). \tag{c}$$

These equations may be combined at nodes 2 and 3 according to (2.2.33) to eliminate the forces at those nodes (which are not of interest).

$$K_2(x_1 - x_2) = B\left(\frac{dx_2}{dt} - \frac{dx_3}{dt}\right) + K_1(x_2 - x_3) + M_2 \frac{d^2x_2}{dt^2}, \tag{d}$$

$$B\left(\frac{dx_2}{dt} - \frac{dx_3}{dt}\right) + K_1(x_2 - x_3) = M_1 \frac{d^2x_3}{dt^2}. \tag{e}$$

With the specified position source

$$x_1 = x(t), \tag{f}$$

(d) and (e) can be solved for x_2 and x_3. Then the force f_s applied to the tires by the road can be found from (a) as

$$f_s = f_1 = K_2(x_1 - x_2). \tag{g}$$

Note that the forces acting on the reference in the network diagram *do not balance* but equal f_s. It is presumed that the force transmitted to the earth by the automobile tires will not move the earth.

2.3 DISCUSSION

In this chapter we have laid the foundation for studying lumped-parameter electromechanics by reviewing the derivations of lumped electric circuit elements, by generalizing the derivations to include the effects of mechanical motion, and by reviewing the basic definitions and techniques of rigid-body mechanics. The stage is now set to include the electromechanical coupling network of Fig. 2.0.1 and to study some general properties of electromechanical systems, including the techniques for obtaining complete equations of motion.

PROBLEMS

2.1. A piece of infinitely permeable magnetic material completes the magnetic circuit in Fig. 2P.1 in such a way that it is free to move in the x- or y-direction. Under the assumption that the air gaps are short compared with their cross-sectional dimensions (i.e., that the fields are as shown), find $\lambda(x, y, i)$. For what range of x and y is this expression valid?

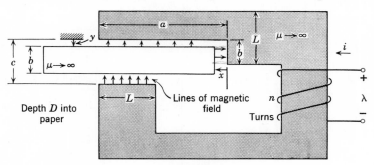

Fig. 2P.1

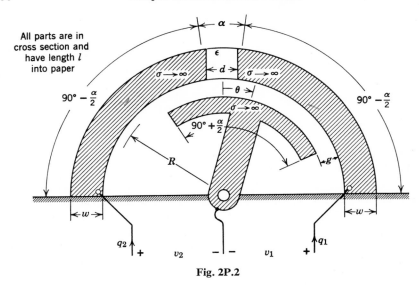

Fig. 2P.2

2.2. Three pieces of infinitely conducting material are arranged as shown in Fig. 2P.2. The two outer pieces are stationary and are separated by a block of insulating material of permittivity ϵ. The inner piece is free to rotate an angle θ. The gap g is much less than the average radius R, which implies that the fields are approximately those of a plane-parallel geometry. Neglect the fringing fields. Find $q_1(v_1, v_2, \theta)$, $q_2(v_1, v_2, \theta)$.

2.3. The cross section of a cylindrical solenoid used to position the valve mechanism of a hydraulic control system is shown in Fig. 2P.3. When the currents i_1 and i_2 are equal, the plunger is centered horizontally ($x = 0$). When the coil currents are unbalanced, the plunger moves a distance x. The nonmagnetic sleeves keep the plunger centered radially. The

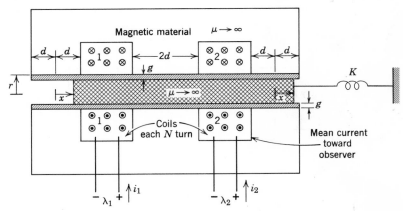

Fig. 2P.3

displacement x is limited to the range $-d < x < d$. Show that the electrical terminal relations are

$$\lambda_1 = L_{11}i_1 + L_{12}i_2,$$
$$\lambda_2 = L_{12}i_1 + L_{22}i_2,$$

where

$$L_{11} = L_0 \left[3 - 2\left(\frac{x}{d}\right) - \left(\frac{x}{d}\right)^2 \right],$$

$$L_{22} = L_0 \left[3 + 2\left(\frac{x}{d}\right) - \left(\frac{x}{d}\right)^2 \right],$$

$$L_{12} = L_0 \left[1 - \left(\frac{x}{d}\right)^2 \right].$$

What is L_0 in terms of the system geometry?

2.4. (a) Write the differential equation governing the motion of mass M acted on by the force source f and the linear damper with coefficient B (Fig. 2P.4).

(b) Calculate and make a dimensioned sketch of dx/dt and x as functions of time for $t > 0$ when the force source is the impulse (u_0 = unit impulse) $f = I_0 u_0(t)$. (This is like hitting the mass with a hammer.)

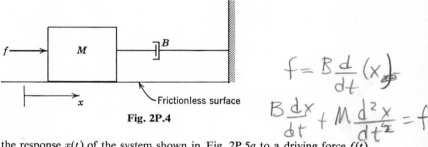

Fig. 2P.4

Frictionless surface

$$f = B\frac{d}{dt}(x)$$
$$B\frac{dx}{dt} + M\frac{d^2x}{dt^2} = f$$

2.5. (a) Find the response $x(t)$ of the system shown in Fig. 2P.5a to a driving force $f(t)$ which is

(1) an impulse $\qquad f(t) = I_0 u_0(t),$
(2) a step $\qquad f(t) = F_0 u_{-1}(t).$

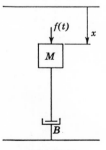

Fig. 2P.5a

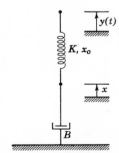

Fig. 2P.5b

(b) Find the response $x(t)$ of the system shown in Fig. 2P.5b to a driving displacement $y(t)$ which is

(1) $$y(t) = Au_0(t),$$
(2) $$y(t) = Y_0 u_{-1}(t).$$

2.6. The mechanical system shown in Fig. 2P.6 is set into motion by a forcing function $f(t)$. This motion is translational only. The masses M_2 and M_3 slip inside the cans as shown. Note that the upper can is attached to the mass M_1.

(a) Draw the mechanical circuit with nodes and parameters designated.
(b) Write three differential equations in x_1, x_2, and x_3 to describe the motion.

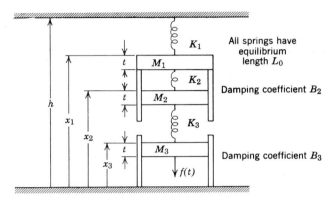

Fig. 2P.6

2.7. In the system in Fig. 2P.7 the two springs have zero force when both x_1 and x_2 are zero. A mechanical force f is applied to node 2 in the direction shown. Write the equations governing the motion of the nodes 1 and 2. What are the natural frequencies involved?

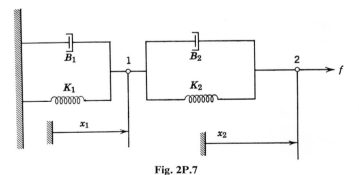

Fig. 2P.7

2.8. The velocity of the point P shown in Fig. 2P.8 is

$$\mathbf{v} = \mathbf{i}_r \frac{dr}{dt} + \mathbf{i}_\theta r \frac{d\theta}{dt}.$$

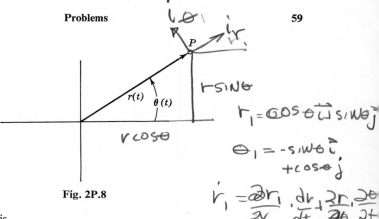

Fig. 2P.8

Show that the acceleration is

$$\frac{d\mathbf{v}}{dt} = \mathbf{i}_r \left[\frac{d^2 r}{dt^2} - r\left(\frac{d\theta}{dt}\right)^2 \right] + \mathbf{i}_\theta \left(r\frac{d^2\theta}{dt^2} + 2\frac{dr}{dt}\frac{d\theta}{dt} \right),$$

where

$$-r\left(\frac{d\theta}{dt}\right)^2 = \text{centripetal acceleration,}$$

$$2\frac{dr}{dt}\frac{d\theta}{dt} = \text{Coriolis acceleration.}$$

Hint. Remember in carrying out the time derivatives that $\mathbf{i}_r$ and $\mathbf{i}_\theta$ are functions of time. In fact, you will wish to show that

$$\frac{d\mathbf{i}_r}{dt} = \mathbf{i}_\theta \frac{d\theta}{dt}, \qquad \frac{d\mathbf{i}_\theta}{dt} = -\mathbf{i}_r \frac{d\theta}{dt}.$$

Chapter 3

LUMPED-PARAMETER ELECTROMECHANICS

3.0 INTRODUCTION

Having reviewed the derivations of lumped electric circuit elements and rigid-body mechanical elements and generalized these concepts to allow inclusion of electromechanical coupling, we are now prepared to study some of the consequences of this coupling.

In the analysis of lumped-parameter electromechanical systems experience has shown that sufficient accuracy is obtained in most cases by making a lossless model of the coupling system. Thus energy methods are used to provide simple and expeditious techniques for studying the coupling process.

After introducing the method of calculating the energy stored in an electromechanical coupling field, we present energy methods for obtaining forces of electric origin. We shall then study the energy conversion process in coupling systems and finally discuss the formalism of writing equations of motion for complete electromechanical systems. The techniques for analyzing the dynamic behavior of lumped-parameter electromechanical systems are introduced and illustrated in Chapter 5.

3.1 ELECTROMECHANICAL COUPLING

There are four technically important forces of electric origin.

1. The force resulting from an electric field acting on free charge.
2. The force resulting from an electric field acting on polarizable material.
3. The force resulting from a magnetic field acting on a moving free charge (a current).
4. The force resulting from a magnetic field acting on magnetizable material.

60

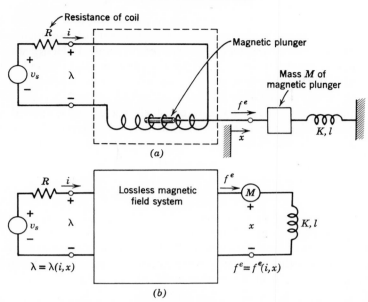

Fig. 3.1.1 (a) A magnetic field electromechanical system; (b) its representation in terms of terminal pairs. Note that the coupling network does not include mechanical energy storages (M) or electrically dissipative elements (R).

Because of the restriction of our treatment to quasi-static systems, the fields that give rise to forces in a particular element are electric or magnetic, but not both. Thus we can consider separately the forces due to electric fields and the forces due to magnetic fields.

To illustrate how the coupling can be taken into account suppose the problem to be considered is the magnetic field system shown in Fig. 3.1.1. The electromechanical coupling occurs between one electrical terminal pair with the variables i and λ and one mechanical terminal pair composed of the node x acted on by the electrical force f^e. It has been demonstrated in Sections 2.1.1 and 2.1.2 that the electrical terminal variables are related by an electrical terminal relation expressible in the form

$$\lambda = \lambda(i, x). \tag{3.1.1}$$

This relation tells us the value of λ, given the values of i and x. We can say, given the *state* (i, x) of the magnetic field system enclosed in the box, that the value of λ is known.

We now make a crucial assumption, motivated by the form of the electrical equation: given the current i and position x, the force of electric origin has a certain single value

$$f^e = f^e(i, x); \tag{3.1.2}$$

that is, the force f^e exerted by the system in the box on the mechanical node is a function of the state (i, x). This is reasonable if the box includes only those elements that store energy in the magnetic field. Hence all purely electrical elements (inductors that do not involve x, capacitors, and resistors) and purely mechanical elements (all masses, springs, and dampers) are connected to the terminals externally.

Note that f^e is defined as the force of electrical origin applied to the mechanical node in a direction that tends to increase the relative displacement x. Because (3.1.1) can be solved for i to yield

$$i = i(\lambda, x), \tag{3.1.3}$$

the force f^e can also be written as

$$f^e = f^e(\lambda, x). \tag{3.1.4}$$

It is well to remember that the functions of (3.1.2) and (3.1.4) are different because the variables are different; however, for a particular set of i, λ, x the force f^e will have the same numerical value regardless of the equation used.

In a similar way the mechanical force of electric origin for an electric field system (see Fig. 3.1.2) can be written as

$$f^e = f^e(q, x) \tag{3.1.5}$$

or

$$f^e = f^e(v, x). \tag{3.1.6}$$

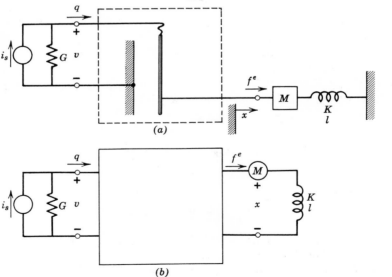

Fig. 3.1.2   (a) An electric field electromechanical system; (b) its representation in terms of terminal pairs. Note that the coupling network does not include mechanical energy storage elements (M) or electrically dissipative elements (G).

When the mechanical motion is rotational, the same ideas apply. We replace force f^e by torque T^e and displacement x by angular displacement θ.

Although the systems of Figs. 3.1.1 and 3.1.2 have only one electrical and one mechanical terminal pair, the discussion can be generalized to any arbitrary number of terminal pairs. For instance, if an electric field system has N electrical terminal pairs and M mechanical terminal pairs for which the terminal relations are specified by (2.1.36), then (3.1.6) is generalized to

$$f_i^e = f_i^e(v_1, v_2, \ldots, v_N; x_1, x_2, \ldots, x_M),$$
$$i = 1, 2, \ldots, M, \tag{3.1.7}$$

where the subscript i denotes the mechanical terminal pair at which f_i^e is applied to the external system by the coupling field. The other forms of f^e can be generalized in the same way.

The next question to be considered is how to determine the force f^e for a particular system. One method is to solve the field problem, find force densities, and then perform a volume integration to find the total force. This process, described in Chapter 8, supports our assumption that f^e has the form of (3.1.2) and (3.1.5). It is often impractical, however, to solve the field problem. A second method of determining f^e is experimental; that is, if the device exists, we can measure f^e as a function of the variables (i and x, λ and x, v and x, or q and x) on which it depends, plot the results, and fit an analytical curve to obtain a function in closed form. This method also has obvious disadvantages.

It is shown in the next section that when the electrical terminal relations are known and the coupling system can be represented as lossless the force f^e can be found analytically. Because electrical lumped parameters are usually easier to calculate and/or measure than mechanical forces, this often provides the most convenient way of determining the mechanical forces of electric origin f_i^e.

3.1.1 Energy Considerations

It will be useful to study some of the general properties of lossless electric and magnetic field energy storages that are functions of geometry. In these considerations we use the conservation of energy (first law of thermodynamics) repeatedly.

As an example, consider again the magnetic field system of Fig. 3.1.1. The system *symbolically* enclosed in the box contains only a magnetic field whose value and therefore energy storage is affected by both electrical and mechanical variables. This coupling network is assumed to be lossless, which means that energy put into the system by the electrical and mechanical terminal pairs is stored in the magnetic field and can be recovered completely through the terminals. Such a system is often called conservative. We use lossless and conservative as synonyms.

When the total energy stored in the magnetic field is denoted by W_m, the conservation of power for the system can be written as

$$\frac{dW_m}{dt} = i \frac{d\lambda}{dt} - f^e \frac{dx}{dt}. \tag{3.1.8}$$

The term dW_m/dt is the time rate of increase in magnetic energy stored, the term $i(d\lambda/dt)$ is the power input at the electrical terminals, and $[-f^e(dx/dt)]$ is the power input at the mechanical terminals. The minus sign on the mechanical power results because f^e is defined as acting on (into) the mechanical node.

Multiplication of (3.1.8) by dt yields an equation for conservation of energy

$$dW_m = i \, d\lambda - f^e \, dx. \tag{3.1.9}$$

From (3.1.3) and (3.1.4), it is evident that only two of the four variables (i, λ, f^e, x) can be set independently without violating the internal physics of the system. There are further restrictions that the external mechanical and electrical systems impose on the terminal pairs of the box (mechanical and electrical circuit equations). If, however, we think of the coupling network as being temporarily disconnected from the electrical and mechanical circuits, we can choose two *independent variables*, say (λ, x), which through the terminal relations stipulate i and f^e. Our choice of λ and x is motivated by (3.1.9), which shows how incremental changes in these variables are related to incremental changes in the magnetic stored energy W_m. The evaluation of the change in W_m when λ and/or x are varied by finite amounts requires an integration of (3.1.9). This is a line integration through variable space. For the example being considered (Fig. 3.1.1) there are two independent variables (λ, x); thus variable space is two-dimensional, as illustrated in Fig. 3.1.3. Independence of variables is indicated by orthogonality of axes. Suppose it is

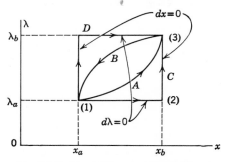

Fig. 3.1.3 Two-dimensional variable space.

desired to find the change in stored energy when the independent variables are changed from the point (λ_a, x_a) to the point (λ_b, x_b). To evaluate a line integral we must specify the path of integration; an infinite number of possible paths exist between the two points. A property of a conservative system, however, is that its stored energy is a function of its *state* (i.e., of the particular values of λ and x that exist) and does not depend on what succession of variable values or what path through variable space was used to reach that state. A consequence of this property is that if the system variables are made to change along path A from (λ_a, x_a) to (λ_b, x_b) in Fig. 3.1.3 and then along path B back to (λ_a, x_a), the net change in stored energy W_m during the process is zero.

In a conservative system the change in stored energy between any two points in variable space is independent of the path of integration. Thus we can select the path that makes the integration easiest. As an example, consider the evaluation of the change in energy between points (λ_a, x_a) and (λ_b, x_b) in Fig. 3.1.3. Along segment 1–2, $d\lambda = 0$; and along segment 2–3, $dx = 0$. Thus, using path C, integration of (3.1.9) takes on the particular form

$$W_m(\lambda_b, x_b) - W_m(\lambda_a, x_a) = -\int_{x_a}^{x_b} f^e(\lambda_a, x)\, dx + \int_{\lambda_a}^{\lambda_b} i(\lambda, x_b)\, d\lambda. \quad (3.1.10)$$

If, alternatively, we wish to evaluate the integral along path D in Fig. 3.1.3, the result is

$$W_m(\lambda_b, x_b) - W_m(\lambda_a, x_a) = \int_{\lambda_a}^{\lambda_b} i(\lambda, x_a)\, d\lambda - \int_{x_a}^{x_b} f^e(\lambda_b, x)\, dx. \quad (3.1.11)$$

The energy difference as evaluated by (3.1.10) and (3.1.11) must, of course, be the same.

The integrations given in (3.1.10) and (3.1.11) have a simple physical significance. The integrations of (3.1.10) represent putting energy into the network in two successive steps. First we put the system together mechanically (integrate on x) while keeping λ constant. In general, this operation requires doing work against the force f^e, and this is the contribution of the first integral in (3.1.10) to the energy stored in the coupling network. Then we put energy in through the electrical terminals, keeping the geometry (x) fixed. The second integral is the energy supplied by an electrical source which provides the excitation λ. In (3.1.11) these successive steps are reversed in order.

We always define electrical terminal pairs that account for the excitation of all electric or magnetic fields in the system. Then, when the electrical terminal variables are zero ($\lambda_a = 0$ in the present example), we can say that there is no force of electrical origin. The difference between (3.1.10) and (3.1.11) with $\lambda_a = 0$ is crucial, for in the first the contribution of f^e to the integration is zero$[f^e(0, x) = 0]$, whereas in the second we must know f^e to carry out the integration; that is, by first integrating on the mechanical variables and then on the electrical variables we can determine W_m from the electrical terminal relations. Physically, this simply means that if we put the system together mechanically when no force is required we can account for all the energy stored by putting it in through the electrical terminal pairs.

An example of a system in which there will be energy stored in the network and a force of electrical origin even with no external electrical excitation is the permanent magnet device of Example 2.1.3. In that example, however, it was shown that we could replace the permanent magnet with an externally excited terminal pair; hence this case imposes no restriction on our development.

We can also study electric field systems using the conservation of energy. For the example in Fig. 3.1.2, with the electrical energy stored in the system denoted by W_e, the conservation of power can be written as

$$\frac{dW_e}{dt} = v \frac{dq}{dt} - f^e \frac{dx}{dt}, \tag{3.1.12}$$

and multiplication by dt yields the conservation of energy

$$dW_e = v \, dq - f^e \, dx. \tag{3.1.13}$$

A comparison of (3.1.9) and (3.1.13) shows that the description of lossless magnetic field systems can be used directly for electric field systems by replacing W_m by W_e, i by v, and λ by q. All the mathematical processes are exactly the same.

These examples are systems with one electrical and one mechanical terminal pair. The results can be extended to systems with any arbitrary number of terminal pairs; for example, consider an electric field system with N electrical terminal pairs and M rotational mechanical terminal pairs. Then the conservation of energy can be written as

$$\frac{dW_e}{dt} = \sum_{i=1}^{N} v_i \frac{dq_i}{dt} - \sum_{i=1}^{M} T_i^e \frac{d\theta_i}{dt}, \tag{3.1.14}$$

where v_i and q_i are the voltage and charge associated with the ith electrical terminal pair, T_i^e and θ_i are the torque and angular displacement at the ith mechanical terminal pair, and W_e represents the total electric energy stored in the system.

Multiplication of (3.1.14) by dt yields

$$dW_e = \sum_{i=1}^{N} v_i \, dq_i - \sum_{i=1}^{M} T_i^e \, d\theta_i. \tag{3.1.15}$$

For this system there will be N electrical terminal relations of the general form

$$v_i = v_i(q_1, q_2, \ldots, q_N; \theta_1, \theta_2, \ldots, \theta_M); i = 1, 2, \ldots, N \quad (3.1.16)$$

and M mechanical terminal relations

$$T_i^e = T_i^e(q_1, q_2, \ldots, q_N; \theta_1, \theta_2, \ldots, \theta_M); i = 1, 2, \ldots, M. \quad (3.1.17)$$

As a result of the use of (3.1.16) and (3.1.17), (3.1.15) is expressed as a function of $(N + M)$ independent variables, the N charges and M angles. Thus the stored energy can be written in general as

$$W_e = W_e(q_1, q_2, \ldots, q_N; \theta_1, \theta_2, \ldots, \theta_M) \quad (3.1.18)$$

and W_e can be obtained by integrating (3.1.15) along any convenient path through the $(N + M)$-dimensional variable space.

Further generalization of these ideas to magnetic field systems and translational mechanical terminal pairs is straightforward and is not carried out here (see Table 3.1). Example 3.1.1 illustrates the line integration that has been described.

3.1.2 Mechanical Forces of Electric Origin

Now that we have specified the formalism by which we calculate stored energy, we shall derive mechanical forces of electric origin by using the conservation of energy.

3.1.2a Force-Energy Relations

To start with a simple example, we consider again the magnetic field system of Fig. 3.1.1 which was described mathematically by (3.1.3), (3.1.4), and (3.1.9). From these expressions it is clear that the magnetic stored energy W_m is expressible as a function of the two independent variables λ and x.

$$W_m = W_m(\lambda, x). \quad (3.1.19)$$

We shall find that if the system is to be conservative the energy must be a single-valued function of the independent variables (λ, x) with finite second partial derivatives. Making this restriction on W_m we can formally take the total differential of (3.1.19) to obtain

$$dW_m = \frac{\partial W_m}{\partial \lambda} d\lambda + \frac{\partial W_m}{\partial x} dx, \quad (3.1.20)$$

where the partial derivatives are taken by using λ and x as independent variables. When (3.1.20) is subtracted from (3.1.9), the result is

$$0 = \left(i - \frac{\partial W_m}{\partial \lambda}\right) d\lambda - \left(f^e + \frac{\partial W_m}{\partial x}\right) dx. \quad (3.1.21)$$

Table 3.1 Energy Relations for an Electromechanical Coupling Network with N Electrical and M Mechanical Terminal Pairs*

Magnetic Field Systems		Electric Field Systems	

Conservation of Energy

$$dW_m = \sum_{j=1}^{N} i_j\, d\lambda_j - \sum_{j=1}^{M} f_j^e\, dx_j \quad\text{(a)}\qquad\qquad dW_e = \sum_{j=1}^{N} v_j\, dq_j - \sum_{j=1}^{M} f_j^e\, dx_j \quad\text{(b)}$$

$$dW_m' = \sum_{j=1}^{N} \lambda_j\, di_j + \sum_{j=1}^{M} f_j^e\, dx_j \quad\text{(c)}\qquad\qquad dW_e' = \sum_{j=1}^{M} q_j\, dv_j + \sum_{j=1}^{M} f_j^e\, dx_j \quad\text{(d)}$$

Forces of Electric Origin, $j = 1, \ldots, M$

$$f_j^e = -\,\frac{\partial W_m(\lambda_1, \ldots, \lambda_N; x_1, \ldots, x_M)}{\partial x_j} \quad\text{(e)}\qquad\qquad f_j^e = -\,\frac{\partial W_e(q_1, \ldots, q_N; x_1, \ldots, x_M)}{\partial x_j} \quad\text{(f)}$$

$$f_j^e = \frac{\partial W_m'(i_1, \ldots, i_N; x_1, \ldots, x_M)}{\partial x_j} \quad\text{(g)}\qquad\qquad f_j^e = \frac{\partial W_e'(v_1, \ldots, v_N; x_1, \ldots, x_M)}{\partial x_j} \quad\text{(h)}$$

Relation of Energy to Coenergy

$$W_m + W_m' = \sum_{j=1}^{N} \lambda_j i_j \quad\text{(i)}\qquad\qquad W_e + W_e' = \sum_{j=1}^{N} v_j q_j \quad\text{(j)}$$

Energy and Coenergy from Electrical Terminal Relations

$$W_m = \sum_{j=1}^{N} \int_0^{\lambda_j} i_j(\lambda_1, \ldots, \lambda_{j-1}, \lambda_j', 0, \ldots, 0; x_1, \ldots, x_M)\, d\lambda_j' \quad\text{(k)}\qquad\qquad W_e = \sum_{j=1}^{N} \int_0^{q_j} v_j(q_1, \ldots, q_{j-1}, q_j', 0, \ldots, 0; x_1, \ldots, x_M)\, dq_j' \quad\text{(l)}$$

$$W_m' = \sum_{j=1}^{N} \int_0^{i_j} \lambda_j(i_1, \ldots, i_{j-1}, i_j', 0, \ldots, 0; x_1, \ldots, x_M)\, di_j' \quad\text{(m)}\qquad\qquad W_e' = \sum_{j=1}^{N} \int_0^{v_j} q_j(v_1, \ldots, v_{j-1}, v_j', 0, \ldots, 0; x_1, \ldots, x_M)\, dv_j' \quad\text{(n)}$$

* The mechanical variables f_j and x_j can be regarded as the jth force and displacement or the jth torque T_j and angular displacement θ_j.

68

The variables λ and x are independent. Thus $d\lambda$ and dx can have arbitrary values, and the equation must be satisfied by requiring the coefficients of $d\lambda$ and dx to be zero:

$$i = \frac{\partial W_m(\lambda, x)}{\partial \lambda}, \tag{3.1.22}$$

$$f^e = -\frac{\partial W_m(\lambda, x)}{\partial x}. \tag{3.1.23}$$

If the stored energy is known, the electrical and mechanical terminal relations can now be calculated.

Equations 3.1.22 and 3.1.23 can be generalized to describe a system with arbitrary numbers of electrical and mechanical terminal pairs (see Table 3.1). To illustrate this generalization we consider again the electric field system of N electrical terminal pairs and M rotational terminal pairs which was described mathematically by (3.1.14) to (3.1.18). We now take the total differential of (3.1.18),

$$dW_e = \sum_{i=1}^{N} \frac{\partial W_e}{\partial q_i} dq_i + \sum_{i=1}^{M} \frac{\partial W_e}{\partial \theta_i} d\theta_i. \tag{3.1.24}$$

Subtraction of (3.1.24) from (3.1.15) yields

$$0 = \sum_{i=1}^{N} \left(v_i - \frac{\partial}{\partial q_i}^e \right) dq_i - \sum_{i=1}^{M} \left(T_i^e + \frac{\partial W_e}{\partial \theta_i} \right) d\theta_i. \tag{3.1.25}$$

All N of the q_i's and M of the θ_i's are independent. Thus each coefficient of dq_i and $d\theta_i$ must be equal to zero:

$$v_i = \frac{\partial W_e}{\partial q_i}; \qquad i = 1, 2, \ldots, N, \tag{3.1.26}$$

$$T_i^e = -\frac{\partial W_e}{\partial \theta_i}; \qquad i = 1, 2, \ldots, M. \tag{3.1.27}$$

These expressions are generalizations of (3.1.22) and (3.1.23) to describe systems with arbitrary numbers of terminal pairs. They indicate that when the stored energy W_e is known as a function of the independent variables all terminal relations can be calculated (see Table 3.1).

It is usually easier in practice to determine the electrical terminal relations by calculation or measurement than it is to determine the mechanical terminal relations or the stored energy. We have seen that the electrical terminal relations are sufficient to evaluate the stored energy if we choose a path of integration in variable space that keeps electrical excitations zero while mechanical variables are brought to their final values. Once the stored energy is known, the force f^e can be calculated as a derivative of the stored

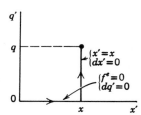

Fig. 3.1.4 Variable space for system of Fig. 3.1.2.

energy [see (3.1.23) or (3.1.27)]. Thus the properties of a coupling system can be determined completely if the electrical terminal relations are known and the system is represented by a conservative model.

To illustrate these ideas consider the electric field system of Fig. 3.1.2 for which the electrical terminal relation is

$$v = v(q, x). \qquad (3.1.28)$$

The path of integration in the q-x plane to be used in evaluating stored energy W_e is shown in Fig. 3.1.4. If we use (3.1.13), the energy at point (q, x) is

$$W_e(q, x) = \int_0^x -f^e(0, x')\, dx' + \int_0^q v(q', x)\, dq'. \qquad (3.1.29)$$

In this expression and in Fig. 3.1.4 the primes denote running variables and (q, x) represents the fixed end point of the line integration. The first term on the right of (3.1.29) is zero because f^e is the force of interaction between charges and electric fields, and with no charge $(q = 0)$ f^e must be zero. Thus (3.1.29) can be written for this particular path of integration in the simpler form

$$W_e(q, x) = \int_0^q v(q', x)\, dq'. \qquad (3.1.30)$$

This result can be generalized in a straightforward way to magnetic field coupling systems, rotational mechanical systems, and multiterminal-pair systems. The generalized force and energy relations are summarized in Table 3.1. This table is intended to illustrate the generality and interrelations of the equations. These general equations are *not* intended for use in the solution of most problems. The concepts and techniques are simple enough that it is good practice to start from the conservation of energy and derive the forces in each problem. In this way we can be certain that fundamental physical laws are satisfied.

Example 3.1.1. To illustrate the use of this technique consider again the electric field system that was treated earlier in Example 2.1.5 and represented by Fig. 2.1.8. That figure is reproduced here as Fig. 3.1.5 for convenience. The electrical terminal relations were derived in Example 2.1.5 and are expressible in the forms

$$v_1 = S_1(x_1, x_2)q_1 + S_m(x_1, x_2)q_2, \qquad (a)$$

$$v_2 = S_m(x_1, x_2)q_1 + S_2(x_1, x_2)q_2, \qquad (b)$$

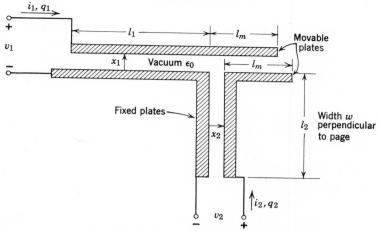

Fig. 3.1.5. Multiply excited electric field system.

where we have solved (a) and (b) of Example 2.1.5 for v_1 and v_2, and therefore have

$$S_1 = \frac{C_2}{C_1 C_2 - C_m^2},$$

$$S_2 = \frac{C_1}{C_1 C_2 - C_m^2},$$

$$S_m = \frac{C_m}{C_1 C_2 - C_m^2};$$

C_1, C_2, and C_m are the functions of x_1 and x_2 given by (c), (d), and (e) of Example 2.1.5.

The system is first assembled mechanically with q_1 and q_2 zero, during which process no energy is put into the system. Next, charges q_1 and q_2 are brought to their final values with x_1 and x_2 fixed. This step requires an integration along a path in the q_1-q_2 plane. The path chosen for this example is shown in Fig. 3.1.6. Along this path the running variables are related by

$$q_2' = \frac{q_2}{q_1} q_1';$$

thus the necessary integral takes the form

$$W_e(q_1, q_2, x_1, x_2) = \int_0^{q_1} \left[v_1\left(q_1', \frac{q_2}{q_1}q_1', x_1, x_2\right) dq_1' \right.$$
$$\left. + v_2\left(q_1', \frac{q_2}{q_1}q_1', x_1, x_2\right)\frac{q_2}{q_1} dq_1' \right]. \quad (c)$$

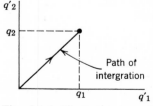

Fig. 3.1.6 Illustrating a path for line integration in variable space for Example 3.1.1.

Substitution of (a) and (b) into (c) and evaluation of the integral yields

$$W_e(q_1, q_2, x_1, x_2) = \tfrac{1}{2}S_1(x_1, x_2)q_1^2 + S_m(x_1, x_2)q_1q_2 + \tfrac{1}{2}S_2(x_1, x_2)q_2^2. \quad (d)$$

From this expression we can now evaluate the mechanical forces of electric origin f_1^e and f_2^e (mechanical terminal relations); thus

$$f_1^e(q_1, q_2, x_1, x_2) = -\frac{\partial W_e}{\partial x_1} = -\tfrac{1}{2}q_1^2 \frac{\partial S_1}{\partial x_1} - q_1 q_2 \frac{\partial S_m}{\partial x_1} - \tfrac{1}{2}q_2^2 \frac{\partial S_2}{\partial x_1}, \qquad (e)$$

$$f_2^e(q_1, q_2, x_1, x_2) = -\frac{\partial W_e}{\partial x_2} = -\tfrac{1}{2}q_1^2 \frac{\partial S_1}{\partial x_2} - q_1 q_2 \frac{\partial S_m}{\partial x_2} - \tfrac{1}{2}q_2^2 \frac{\partial S_2}{\partial x_2}. \qquad (f)$$

Because S_1, S_2, and S_m are known as functions of x_1 and x_2 for this example, the derivatives in (e) and (f) can be calculated; this is straightforward differentiation, however, and is not carried out here.

3.1.2b   Force-Coenergy Relations

So far in the magnetic field examples the flux linkage λ has been used as the independent variable, with current i described by the terminal relation. Similarly, in electric field examples charge q has been used as the independent variable, with voltage v described by the terminal relation. These choices were natural because of the form of the conservation of energy equations (3.1.9) and (3.1.13). Note that in Example 3.1.1 we were required to find $v_1(q_1, q_2)$ and $v_2(q_1, q_2)$. It would have been more convenient if we had been able to use $q_1(v_1, v_2)$ and $q_2(v_1, v_2)$, for this is the form these equations took in Example 2.1.5. We consider next how this can be done.

It should be possible to analyze systems using current as the independent electrical variable for magnetic field systems and voltage as the independent variable for electric field systems. In fact, it is often more convenient to make this choice. Alternatively, it is sometimes convenient to use a hybrid set of variables consisting of both currents and flux linkages in magnetic field systems and voltages and charges in electric field systems. Such hybrid sets of variables are used in Chapter 5.

To illustrate this change of independent variables consider once again the magnetic field system described in Fig. 3.1.1, with the restriction that the current i is to be used as the independent variable. The conservation of energy as expressed by (3.1.9) is still a fundamental relation:

$$dW_m = i \, d\lambda - f^e \, dx. \qquad (3.1.9)$$

The electrical terminal relation is (3.1.1),

$$\lambda = \lambda(i, x), \qquad (3.1.1)$$

and the mechanical terminal relation is (3.1.2),

$$f^e = f^e(i, x). \qquad (3.1.2)$$

Equation 3.1.9 can be written in a form that involves di and dx by first using the rule of differentiation,

$$i \, d\lambda = d(\lambda i) - \lambda \, di. \qquad (3.1.31)$$

Then the energy equation (3.1.9) is

$$dW'_m = \lambda\, di + f^e\, dx, \tag{3.1.32}$$

where

$$W'_m = \lambda i - W_m. \tag{3.1.33}$$

The energy equation (3.1.32) now has the required form in which changes in the function W'_m are accounted for by changes in the independent variables (i, x). The function $W'_m(i, x)$ is called the *coenergy* and is defined in terms of the energy $W_m(i, x)$ and terminal relations $\lambda(i, x)$ by (3.1.33).*

Remember that (3.1.32) physically represents conservation of energy for the coupling network. The form of this equation is similar to that of (3.1.9) and our arguments now parallel those of Section 3.1.2a. Because $W'_m = W'_m(i, x)$,

$$dW'_m = \frac{\partial W'_m}{\partial i}\, di + \frac{\partial W'_m}{\partial x}\, dx. \tag{3.1.34}$$

We subtract (3.1.34) from (3.1.32) to obtain

$$0 = \left(\lambda - \frac{\partial W'_m}{\partial i}\right) di + \left(f^e - \frac{\partial W'_m}{\partial x}\right) dx. \tag{3.1.35}$$

Because di and dx are independent (arbitrary),

$$\lambda = \frac{\partial W'_m(i, x)}{\partial i}, \tag{3.1.36}$$

$$f^e = \frac{\partial W'_m(i, x)}{\partial x}. \tag{3.1.37}$$

If the stored energy (hence coenergy) is known, the electrical and mechanical terminal relations can be calculated. Comparison of (3.1.37) and (3.1.23) shows the change in the form of the force expression when the electrical variable chosen as independent is changed from λ to i.

The result of (3.1.37) can be generalized to a system with any number of terminal pairs in a straightforward manner (see Table 3.1). For a magnetic field system with N electrical terminal pairs and M translational mechanical terminal pairs the conservation of energy equation becomes

$$dW_m = \sum_{j=1}^{N} i_j\, d\lambda_j - \sum_{j=1}^{M} f_j^{\,e}\, dx_j. \tag{3.1.38}$$

We now use the generalization of (3.1.31),

$$\sum_{j=1}^{N} i_j\, d\lambda_j = \sum_{j=1}^{N} d(i_j\lambda_j) - \sum_{j=1}^{N} \lambda_j\, di_j, \tag{3.1.39}$$

* This manipulation, which represents conservation of energy in terms of new independent variables, is called a Legendre transformation in classical mechanics and thermodynamics.

to replace the first term on the right-hand side of (3.1.38). Rearranging terms, we obtain

$$dW'_m = \sum_{j=1}^{N} \lambda_j \, di_j + \sum_{j=1}^{M} f_j^e \, dx_j, \tag{3.1.40}$$

where

$$W'_m = \sum_{j=1}^{N} i_j \lambda_j - W_m \tag{3.1.41}$$

and W'_m is the coenergy. The independent variables are $(i_1, i_2, \ldots, i_N;$ $x_1, x_2, \ldots, x_M)$. We assume that the λ's and W_m in (3.1.41) are written in terms of these variables, hence that W'_m is a function of these variables. Then

$$dW'_m = \sum_{j=1}^{N} \frac{\partial W'_m}{\partial i_j} \, di_j + \sum_{j=1}^{M} \frac{\partial W'_m}{\partial x_j} \, dx_j, \tag{3.1.42}$$

and when we subtract (3.1.42) from (3.1.40) and require that the coefficient of each di_j and each dx_j be zero

$$\lambda_j = \frac{\partial W'_m}{\partial i_j} ; \qquad j = 1, 2, \ldots, N, \tag{3.1.43}$$

$$f_j^e = \frac{\partial W'_m}{\partial x_j} ; \qquad j = 1, 2, \ldots, M. \tag{3.1.44}$$

This same process of generalization can be carried out for an electric field system (see Table 3.1); for instance, for the system of N electrical terminal pairs and M rotational mechanical terminal pairs for which the torque was found in (3.1.27) the use of the voltage as the independent variable instead of charge leads to the result

$$T_i^e = \frac{\partial W'_e(v_1, v_2, \ldots, v_N; \theta_1, \theta_2, \ldots, \theta_M)}{\partial \theta_i}, \tag{3.1.45}$$

where

$$W'_e = \sum_{j=1}^{N} v_j q_j - W_e. \tag{3.1.46}$$

This expression is obtained by a straightforward process of exactly the same form as that used for the general magnetic field system (3.1.38) to (3.1.44).

It is not necessary to find the coenergy by first determining the energy; for example, we can integrate (3.1.32) to find W'_m just as we integrated (3.1.9) to find W_m. In general, we evaluate W'_m by selecting a path of integration through variable space for (3.1.40) that changes the x'_j's with all electrical excitations zero and then changes electrical excitations with mechanical displacements held fixed.

For a better understanding of the meaning of coenergy consider the

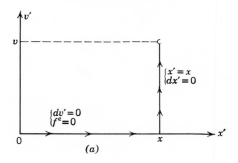

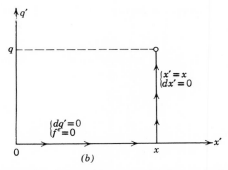

Fig. 3.1.7 Paths of integration in variable space: (a) for evaluating coenergy; (b) for evaluating energy.

simple electric field system presented earlier in Fig. 3.1.2. The coenergy is evaluated by the integration of

$$dW'_e = q \, dv + f^e \, dx. \tag{3.1.47}$$

[This is the energy equation (3.1.13) with $v \, dq = d(vq) - q \, dv$ and $W'_e = qv - W_e$.] We use the path of integration defined in Fig. 3.1.7a to reduce this integration to

$$W'_e = \int_0^v q(v', x) \, dv'. \tag{3.1.48}$$

In the case of electrical linearity

$$q(v, x) = C(x)v, \tag{3.1.49}$$

and (3.1.48) becomes

$$W'_e = \tfrac{1}{2}Cv^2. \tag{3.1.50}$$

It follows that

$$f^e = \frac{\partial W'_e(v, x)}{\partial x} = \tfrac{1}{2}v^2 \frac{dC}{dx}. \tag{3.1.51}$$

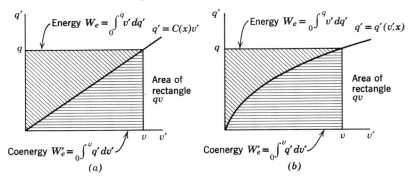

Fig. 3.1.8 Illustration of energy and coenergy: (a) electrically linear system; (b) electrically nonlinear system.

We can compare this result with what we find if we integrate (3.1.13) along the path of Fig. 3.1.7b to find the energy

$$W_e = \int_0^q v(q', x)\, dq', \tag{3.1.52}$$

which from (3.1.49) is

$$W_e(q, x) = \frac{q^2}{2C(x)}. \tag{3.1.53}$$

Now, when we use (3.1.49) to eliminate q from this expression, we see that the coenergy and energy are *numerically* equal. This is a consequence of the electrical linearity, as may be seen by observing Fig. 3.1.8a, in which (3.1.48) and (3.1.52) are the areas in the q'-v' plane indicated. (Remember that, by definition, in our system with one electrical terminal pair $W_e' + W_e = qv$.) When the areas are separated by a straight line (3.1.49), the integrals are obviously equal. On the other hand, when the areas are not separated by a straight line, the system is electrically nonlinear and energy and coenergy are not equal. An example of electrical nonlinearity is shown in Fig. 3.1.8b.

Energy and coenergy have the same numerical values in an electrically linear system. We have, however, consistently made use of the energy expressed as a function of (q, x) or (λ, x) and the coenergy expressed as a function of (v, x) or (i, x). These functions are quite different in mathematical form, even when the system is electrically linear [compare (3.1.50) and (3.1.53)].

A word of caution is called for at this point. A partial derivative is taken with respect to one independent variable holding the other independent variables fixed. In order for this process to be correct, it is easiest to perform the differentiation when the function to be differentiated is written without explicit dependence on dependent variables. To be more specific, consider the capacitance $C(x)$ of plane parallel plates with area A and spacing x (Fig. 3.1.2). Then

$$C(x) = \frac{A\epsilon}{x} \qquad (3.1.54)$$

and (3.1.51) gives

$$f^e = -\frac{v^2 A\epsilon}{2x^2} . \qquad (3.1.55)$$

The minus sign tells us that f^e acts on the upper plate (node) in the $(-x)$ direction. This we expect, for positive charges on the top plate are attracted by negative charges on the bottom plate. We can obtain the same result by using the energy and the translational form of (3.1.27).

$$f^e = -\frac{\partial W_e(q, x)}{\partial x} . \qquad (3.1.56)$$

From (3.1.53) and (3.1.54)

$$f^e = -\frac{q^2}{2A\epsilon} . \qquad (3.1.57)$$

In view of (3.1.49) and (3.1.54) this result and (3.1.55) are identical. Suppose, however, that we blindly apply (3.1.56) to the energy of (3.1.53) with q replaced by Cv. The magnitude of the resulting force will be correct, but the sign will be wrong. For electrically nonlinear systems the magnitude of the force will also be wrong if the partial differentiation is not carried out correctly.

The generalized force and coenergy equations are summarized in Table 3.1. This table is intended to illustrate the generality of the equations and their interrelations. The general equations are *not* recommended for use in solving problems. It is better to rederive the equations in each case to make certain that fundamental physical laws are satisfied. Equations (k) to (n) in Table 3.1 for evaluating energy and coenergy are written by using a path of integration that brings each electrical variable from zero to its final value in sequence $j = 1$ to $j = N$.

3.1.2c Reciprocity

The mathematical description of a conservative electromechanical coupling system must satisfy a *reciprocity* condition that is a generalization of the reciprocity conventionally discussed in electric circuit theory.* To illustrate reciprocity for a simple example, consider the magnetic field system of Fig. 3.1.1 for which the terminal relations are expressed as derivatives of stored

---

* E. A. Guillemin, *Introductory Circuit Theory*, Wiley, New York, 1953, pp. 148–150 and 429.

energy in (3.1.22) and (3.1.23):

$$i = \frac{\partial W_m(\lambda,\, x)}{\partial \lambda}, \tag{3.1.22}$$

$$f^e = -\frac{\partial W_m(\lambda,\, x)}{\partial x}. \tag{3.1.23}$$

We now differentiate (3.1.22) with respect to x and (3.1.23) with respect to λ. Then, because

$$\frac{\partial^2 W_m}{\partial \lambda\, \partial x} = \frac{\partial^2 W_m}{\partial x\, \partial \lambda},$$

the reciprocity relation results:

$$\frac{\partial i(\lambda,\, x)}{\partial x} = -\frac{\partial f^e(\lambda,\, x)}{\partial \lambda}. \tag{3.1.58}$$

The process used in obtaining the reciprocity condition (3,1.58) shows that the condition is necessary for the system to be conservative. This same condition can also be shown to be sufficient to ensure that the system is conservative. The proof requires a straightforward but involved integration and is not carried out here primarily because it is a standard inclusion in some thermodynamics texts.*

The reciprocity condition of (3.1.58) can be generalized to describe a conservative system with any number of terminal pairs. Consider again the electric-field system with N electrical terminal pairs and M rotational mechanical terminal pairs whose terminal relations are described by (3.1.26) and (3.1.27):

$$v_i = \frac{\partial W_e}{\partial q_i}; \qquad i = 1, 2, \ldots, N, \tag{3.1.26}$$

$$T_i^e = -\frac{\partial W_e}{\partial \theta_i}; \qquad i = 1, 2, \ldots, M. \tag{3.1.27}$$

When we take appropriate partial derivatives of these equations and recognize that the order of differentiation is immaterial, we obtain the general reciprocity conditions:

$$\frac{\partial v_i}{\partial q_j} = \frac{\partial v_j}{\partial q_i}, \qquad i, j = 1, 2, \ldots, N, \tag{3.1.59}$$

$$\frac{\partial T_i^e}{\partial \theta_j} = \frac{\partial T_j^e}{\partial \theta_i}, \qquad i, j = 1, 2, \ldots, M, \tag{3.1.60}$$

$$\frac{\partial v_i}{\partial \theta_j} = -\frac{\partial T_j^e}{\partial q_i}; \qquad \begin{array}{l} i = 1, 2, \ldots, N, \\ j = 1, 2, \ldots, M. \end{array} \tag{3.1.61}$$

* See, for instance, W. P. Allis and M. A. Herlin, *Thermodynamics and Statistical Mechanics*, McGraw-Hill, 1952, pp. 6–9.

Note that for an electrically linear system (3.1.59) reduces to $C_{ij} = C_{ji}$ which is the usual form of the reciprocity relation for linear capacitive circuits.*

Although the reciprocity conditions must always be satisfied for a conservative system, they are not often used in the analysis and design of electromechanical systems. Their primary usefulness is twofold. First, they provide a rapid check on results to identify certain kinds of mathematical error; and, second, they provide a mathematical framework for identifying the classes of nonlinear functions with which we can approximate the terminal relations of multiterminal-pair, electrically nonlinear, systems. If the reciprocity conditions are not satisfied, the mathematical description will imply sources and/or sinks of energy in the coupling field that can lead to nonphysical results.

3.1.3   Energy Conversion

The fact that in lumped-parameter electromechanics we are dealing with lossless coupling systems in which stored energy is a state function (single-valued function of the independent variables) can be quite useful in assessing energy conversion properties of electromechanical systems. This is especially true of systems that operate cyclically. For any conservative coupling system we can write the conservation of energy as

$$\begin{bmatrix} \text{electrical energy} \\ \text{input} \end{bmatrix} + \begin{bmatrix} \text{mechanical energy} \\ \text{input} \end{bmatrix} = \begin{bmatrix} \text{change in} \\ \text{stored energy} \end{bmatrix}. \quad (3.1.62)$$

For a complete cycle of operation, that is, for a situation in which the independent variables return to the values from which they started, the net change in stored energy is zero. Thus for a cyclic process (3.1.62) becomes

$$\begin{bmatrix} \text{net electrical} \\ \text{energy input} \\ \text{for one cycle} \end{bmatrix} + \begin{bmatrix} \text{net mechanical} \\ \text{energy input} \\ \text{for one cycle} \end{bmatrix} = 0. \quad (3.1.63)$$

We need to calculate only the electrical or mechanical energy input to find the net conversion of energy between electrical and mechanical forms.

Example 3.1.2. The device shown schematically in Fig. 3.1.9 is used to illustrate the energy conversion properties of a cyclically operating system.† It contains a cylindrical stator of highly permeable magnetic material with polar projections on which coils are wound. The two coils are connected in series in the polarity shown to form one electrical terminal pair. This machine also contains a rotor, made of highly permeable magnetic

---

* Guillemin, *loc. cit.*

† For more detail on this type of machine (called a two-pole, single-phase, salient-pole synchronous machine) see Section 4.2.

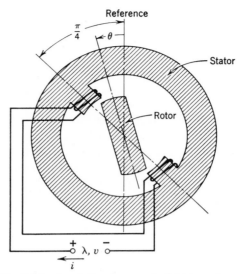

Fig. 3.1.9   A rotational magnetic field transducer.

material, which has the shape shown in end view in Fig. 3.1.9 and which can rotate about the axis with the instantaneous angle θ.

It is determined experimentally that the machine is electrically linear and that the electrical terminal relation can be approximated by the inductance

$$L = L_0 + L_2 \sin 2\theta, \tag{a}$$

where L_0 and L_2 are positive constants and $L_0 > L_2$. Note that this inductance is a maximum at $\theta = \pi/4$ and $\theta = 5\pi/4$, as we expected, because the air gaps between rotor and stator iron are smallest for these angles. Also, the inductance is a minimum for $\theta = -\pi/4$ and $\theta = 3\pi/4$, in which case the air gaps are largest. In practice, the rotor and stator are shaped so that the periodic variation of inductance with angle closely approaches the ideal of (a).

With the inductance thus specified, we can write the electrical terminal relation as

$$\lambda = Li = (L_0 + L_2 \sin 2\theta)i. \tag{b}$$

We can now use (b) to evaluate the magnetic coenergy by using (m) of Table 3.1,

$$W'_m = \tfrac{1}{2}(L_0 + L_2 \sin 2\theta)i^2, \tag{c}$$

and (g) in Table 3.1 to find the torque of electric origin,

$$T^e = \frac{\partial W'_m}{\partial \theta} = L_2 i^2 \cos 2\theta. \tag{d}$$

We can now represent the electromechanical coupling symbolically, as in Fig. 3.1.10. The box includes only the magnetic field energy storage of the machine. All purely electrical properties (winding resistance and losses in the magnetic material) and all purely mechanical properties (moment of inertia and friction) can be represented as lumped elements connected externally to the terminals of the coupling system.

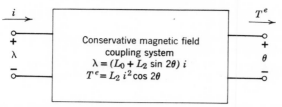

Fig. 3.1.10 Representation of the coupling field of the system in Fig. 3.1.9.

In an actual application there would be lumped electrical and mechanical elements, in addition to those inherent in the machine, connected to the coupling network. Our purpose here is to study the energy conversion properties of the coupling system; consequently, we will excite the terminals with ideal sources and there will be no need to consider passive elements connected to the terminals.

We now excite the electrical terminal pair of the coupling system with a sinusoidal current source

$$i = I \cos \omega t \tag{e}$$

and the mechanical terminal pair with the position source

$$\theta = \omega t, \tag{f}$$

where ω is a positive constant. With these terminal constraints and with steady-state operation, we wish to calculate the electromechanical energy conversion per cycle of operation.

Because they are constrained independently, current i and angle θ are the logical choices as independent variables. We can sketch the path of operation for one cycle in the i-θ plane, as shown in Fig. 3.1.11. Note that $\theta = 0$ and $\theta = 2\pi$ represent the same geometry; thus, although the trajectory in Fig. 3.1.11 does not close on itself, it nonetheless represents one cycle of operation in which the final physical state is the same as the initial physical state. The arrows indicate the direction that the operating point travels in the i-θ plane.

When we apply (3.1.63) to this system for a complete cycle of operation, we obtain,

$$\oint i\, d\lambda - \oint T^e\, d\theta = 0, \tag{g}$$

wherein $\oint$ indicates an integral around a closed cycle. The first term represents the net

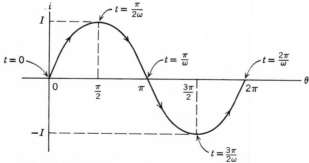

Fig. 3.1.11 Trajectory of operating point in i-θ plane.

electrical energy input over a cycle and the second (with the minus sign) represents the net mechanical energy input. Because there is no net change in stored energy, we need to calculate only the first or second term to find energy converted. To be thorough in our study we shall consider both terms.

We first look at the trajectory of the operating point in a λ-i plane. We can express it as two parametric equations (time is the parameter) by using (b) and (e):

$$\lambda = I(L_0 + L_2 \sin 2\omega t) \cos \omega t, \tag{h}$$

$$i = I \cos \omega t. \tag{i}$$

Alternatively, we can use trigonometric identities* to eliminate t from the two equations and obtain

$$\lambda = i\left[L_0 \pm \frac{2L_2 i}{I}\left(1 - \frac{i^2}{I^2}\right)^{1/2}\right]. \tag{j}$$

The double-valued character of this equation makes it easier to plot the trajectory by using the parametric equations (h) and (i). This trajectory is shown in Fig. 3.1.12, plotted for the relative parameter values

$$L_2 = \tfrac{1}{2}L_0.$$

Next, we can look at the trajectory of the operating point in the T^e-θ plane. We use (d), (e), and (f) to write

$$T^e = L_2 I^2 \cos^2 \theta \cos 2\theta. \tag{k}$$

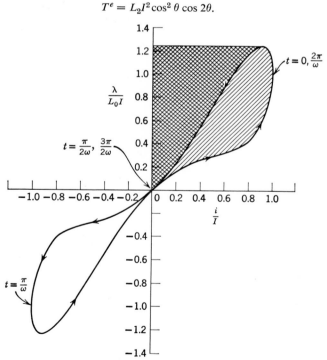

Fig. 3.1.12 Trajectory of operation in the λ-i plane for $L_2 = \tfrac{1}{2}L_0$.

* $\sin 2\omega t = 2 \sin \omega t \cos \omega t$; $\sin \omega t = \pm\sqrt{1 - \cos^2 \omega t}$.

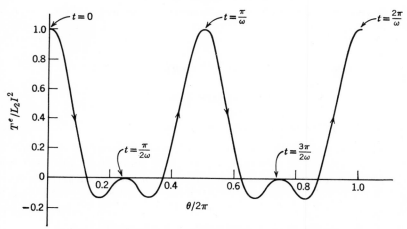

Fig. 3.1.13 Trajectory of operating point in T^e-θ plane.

This trajectory is shown in Fig. 3.1.13. Note once again that although the curve does not close on itself it represents a full cycle of operation because $\theta = 0$ and $\theta = 2\pi$ represent the same state. The direction of travel of the operating point is indicated on the curve.

We can now calculate the energy converted per cycle. First, evaluating

$$\oint i\,d\lambda = \text{net electrical input power,}$$

we can see graphically in Fig. 3.1.12 that the integral of $i\,d\lambda$ around the trajectory yields the area enclosed by the loop; furthermore, this area is positive. There is net conversion of energy from electrical to mechanical form. Under these conditions the machine is operating as a motor.

We can evaluate the energy converted per cycle by calculating the area enclosed by the loop in the first quadrant of Fig. 3.1.12 and multiplying the answer by two. This integral can best be performed parametrically by writing

$$i = I\cos\theta,$$

$$\lambda = I(L_0 + L_2\sin 2\theta)\cos\theta,$$

$$d\lambda = (-IL_0\sin\theta + 2L_2I\cos 2\theta\cos\theta - L_2I\sin 2\theta\sin\theta)\,d\theta.$$

Some trigonometric manipulation allows us to put $d\lambda$ in the form

$$d\lambda = I(-L_0\sin\theta - 2L_2\cos\theta + 4L_2\cos^3\theta - 2L_2\cos\theta\sin^2\theta)\,d\theta.$$

We can now write for the area of the loop in the first quadrant of Fig. 3.1.12

$$\frac{W_c}{2} = \int_{-\pi/2}^{\pi/2} i(\theta)\,d\lambda(\theta) = \int_{-\pi/2}^{\pi/2} I^2(-L_0\sin\theta\cos\theta - 2L_2\cos^2\theta + 4L_2\cos^4\theta$$
$$- 2L_2\cos^2\theta\sin^2\theta)\,d\theta,$$

where W_c is the energy converted per cycle. Evaluation of this integral yields

$$W_c = \frac{\pi}{2} L_2 I^2.$$

We can also calculate the mechanical output energy per cycle from

$$\int_0^{2\pi} T^e \, d\theta = \int_0^{2\pi} L_2 I^2 \cos^2 \theta \cos 2\theta \, d\theta = \frac{\pi}{2} L_2 I^2,$$

which is equal to the electric input energy per cycle as it should be.

The ideas of energy bookkeeping illustrated by Example 3.1.2 can be extended to systems with arbitrary numbers of terminal pairs. For more than two variables the graphical representation of operation in variable space (Fig. 3.1.11) is difficult; it is possible, however, to represent the path of operation at each terminal pair (Figs. 3.1.12 and 3.1.13). Such techniques are especially suitable for systems that operate cyclically.

3.2 EQUATIONS OF MOTION

In the preceding sections of this chapter we have described in detail the various elements that make up lumped-parameter electromechanical systems. Our approach is to isolate the coupling system (either electric or magnetic field) and analyze its properties. We can then write Kirchhoff's laws for the electrical parts of the system by introducing electromechanical coupling effects through the terminal relations of the coupling system. Similarly, we write Newton's second law and continuity of space for the mechanical parts of the system, including electromechanical coupling effects in the terminal relations of the coupling system. We now present examples in which our objective is to write the complete equations of motion for electromechanical systems.

Example 3.2.1.   We consider again the magnetic field system shown in Fig. 3.2.1. The electrical terminal relation of the coupling system was calculated in Example 2.1.1. Now we include the type of electrical and mechanical elements that will normally be present in applications of this transducer. The resistance R represents the winding resistance plus any additional series resistance in the external circuit. This system is of the form conventionally used to actuate relays, valves, etc.; consequently, the source $v_s(t)$ is usually a positive or negative step. The spring K is used to open the gap x to its maximum width when the current is zero. The linear damper B represents friction between the nonmagnetic sleeve and the plunger, although in some cases additional damping is added externally either to slow down the mechanical motion (as in a time-delay relay) or to reduce the bouncing that may occur when the plunger reaches $x = 0$.

In Example 2.1.1, with suitable assumptions, the flux linkages of this device were calculated to be

$$\lambda = \frac{L_0 i}{1 + x/g}, \tag{a}$$

$$L_0 = 2w \frac{d u_0 N^2}{g}$$

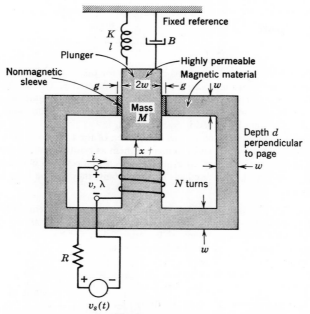

Fig. 3.2.1 A magnetic field electromechanical system.

where $L_0 = 2wd\mu_0 N^2/g$ is the coil inductance with the variable gap closed ($x = 0$). We wish to write the complete equations of motion.

We have a single electrical loop and a single mechanical node; consequently, we can write two equations in which the current i and displacement x are the dependent variables.

Applying Kirchhoff's voltage law to the electrical loop and using the terminal voltage of the coupling system as derived in Example 2,1,1, we obtain

$$v_s(t) = iR + \frac{L_0}{1 + x/g}\frac{di}{dt} - \frac{L_0(i)}{g(1 + x/g)^2}\frac{dx}{dt}.$$ (b)

To write Newton's second law for the mechanical node we need the force of electric origin. We first write the magnetic coenergy [see (m) in Table 3.1] as

$$W'_m = \int_0^i \lambda(i', x)\, di'$$

and use (a) to write

$$W'_m = \frac{1}{2}\frac{L_0 i^2}{1 + x/g}$$ (c)

We now find the force by using (g) in Table 3.1.

$$f^e = -\frac{1}{2}\frac{L_0 i^2}{g(1 + x/g)^2}.$$ (d)

This is a force source applied to the mechanical node x.

We can now write Newton's law for the mechanical node as

$$-\frac{1}{2}\frac{L_0 i^2}{g(1+x/g)^2} = M\frac{d^2x}{dt^2} + B\frac{dx}{dt} + K(x-l). \tag{e}$$

Equations b and e are the equations of motion for this system. Note that there are two equations with two dependent variables (unknowns) i and x. The driving function is the source voltage $v_s(t)$. If we specify the explicit variation of v_s with time and also specify initial conditions, we, at least in theory, can solve (b) and (e) for i and x. The dynamic behavior of this system is studied in Section 5.1.2.

In the above analysis no account has been taken of the two mechanical stops that limit the mechanical motion. It is easiest to include them as position sources; in practical cases, however, the stops may also have some elastic effects that result in bouncing of the plunger at the ends of its travel. If such effects are important, they can be included in a straight-forward manner.

Example 3.2.2. In this example we wish to consider a system with more than one electrical terminal pair and more than one mechanical node. For this purpose we use the basic electric field coupling system of Example 2.1.5, shown in Fig. 3.2.2, along with suitable external electrical and mechanical elements.

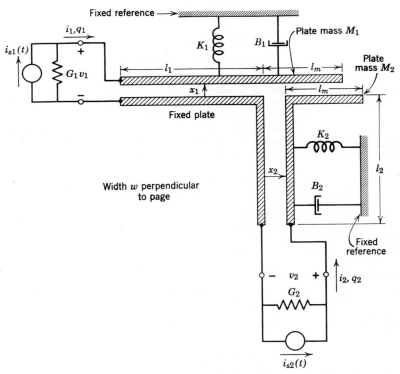

Fig. 3.2.2 Multiply excited electric field-coupled electromechanical system.

The electrical terminal relations were derived for this system in Example 2.1.5 and are

$$q_1 = C_1 v_1 - C_m v_2, \tag{a}$$

$$q_2 = -C_m v_1 + C_2 v_2, \tag{b}$$

where

$$C_1 = \frac{\epsilon_0 w[l_1 + (l_m - x_2)]}{x_1}, \qquad C_1(x_1, x_2) \tag{c}$$

$$C_2 = \epsilon_0 w \left(\frac{l_2}{x_2} + \frac{l_m - x_2}{x_1} \right), \qquad C_2(x_1, x_3) \tag{d}$$

$$C_m = \frac{\epsilon_0 w(l_m - x_2)}{x_1}. \tag{e}$$

We write Kirchhoff's current law for the two electrical nodes as

$$i_{s1}(t) = G_1 v_1 + \frac{dq_1}{dt}, \tag{f}$$

$$i_{s2}(t) = G_2 v_2 + \frac{dq_2}{dt}. \tag{g}$$

Using (a) to (e), we express these equations explicitly in terms of the unknowns as

$$i_{s1}(t) = G_1 v_1 + \frac{\epsilon_0 w[l_1 + (l_m - x_2)]}{x_1} \frac{dv_1}{dt} - \frac{\epsilon_0 w(l_m - x_2)}{x_1} \frac{dv_2}{dt}$$

$$- \frac{\epsilon_0 w[l_1 + (l_m - x_2)]}{x_1^2} v_1 \frac{dx_1}{dt} - \frac{\epsilon_0 w}{x_1} v_1 \frac{dx_2}{dt} + \frac{\epsilon_0 w(l_m - x_2)}{x_1^2} v_2 \frac{dx_1}{dt} + \frac{\epsilon_0 w}{x_1} v_2 \frac{dx_2}{dt} \tag{h}$$

$$i_{s2}(t) = G_2 v_2 - \frac{\epsilon_0 w(l_m - x_2)}{x_1} \frac{dv_1}{dt} + \epsilon_0 w \left(\frac{l_2}{x_2} + \frac{l_m - x_2}{x_1} \right) \frac{dv_2}{dt} + \frac{\epsilon_0 w(l_m - x_2)}{x_1^2} v_1 \frac{dx_1}{dt}$$

$$+ \frac{\epsilon_0 w}{x_1} v_1 \frac{dx_2}{dt} - \frac{\epsilon_0 w(l_m - x_2)}{x_1^2} v_2 \frac{dx_1}{dt} - \epsilon_0 w \left(\frac{l_2}{x_2^2} + \frac{1}{x_1} \right) v_2 \frac{dx_2}{dt}. \tag{i}$$

Before we can write equations for the mechanical nodes we must calculate the forces of electric origin. Because we want the explicit electrical variables to be the voltages, we use (n) in Table 3.1 to evaluate the coenergy as

$$W_e' = \tfrac{1}{2} C_1 v_1^2 - C_m v_1 v_2 + \tfrac{1}{2} C_2 v_2^2. \tag{j}$$

We now use (h) in Table 3.1 to evaluate the forces

$$f_1^e = \frac{\partial W_e'}{\partial x_1} = \tfrac{1}{2} v_1^2 \frac{\partial C_1}{\partial x_1} - v_1 v_2 \frac{\partial C_m}{\partial x_1} + \tfrac{1}{2} v_2^2 \frac{\partial C_2}{\partial x_1}, \tag{k}$$

$$f_2^e = \frac{\partial W_e'}{\partial x_2} = \tfrac{1}{2} v_1^2 \frac{\partial C_1}{\partial x_2} - v_1 v_2 \frac{\partial C_m}{\partial x_2} + \tfrac{1}{2} v_2^2 \frac{\partial C_2}{\partial x_2}. \tag{l}$$

We carry out the indicated differentiations and include these two forces as sources in writing Newton's second law for the two mechanical nodes.

$$-\tfrac{1}{2}v_1{}^2\,\frac{\epsilon_0 w[l_1 + (l_m - x_2)]}{x_1{}^2} - v_1 v_2\,\frac{\epsilon_0 w(l_m - x_2)}{x_1{}^2} - \tfrac{1}{2}v_2{}^2\,\frac{\epsilon_0 w(l_m - x_2)}{x_1{}^2}$$

$$= M_1\frac{d^2 x_1}{dt^2} + B_1\frac{dx_1}{dt} + K_1 x_1, \quad \text{(m)}$$

$$-\tfrac{1}{2}v_1{}^2\,\frac{\epsilon_0 w}{x_1} - v_1 v_2\,\frac{\epsilon_0 w}{x_1} - \tfrac{1}{2}v_2{}^2\epsilon_0 w\left(\frac{l_2}{x_2{}^2} + \frac{1}{x_1}\right) = M_2\frac{d^2 x_2}{dt^2} + B_2\frac{dx_2}{dt} + K_2 x_2. \quad \text{(n)}$$

Equations (h), (i), (m), and (n) are the four equations of motion for the system in Fig. 3.2.2. Several important aspects of these equations should be examined. First, we note that all four equations are coupled, that is, each equation contains all four dependent variables. We also note that there is no external coupling between electrical terminal pairs and between mechanical terminal pairs; thus all the coupling occurs through the electric fields. We note further that the coupling between the two mechanical terminal pairs [see (m) and (n)] results in terms that are functions of mechanical positions and voltages. Thus these coupling terms appear essentially as nonlinear elements whose properties depend on the electrical variables (voltages).

3.3 DISCUSSION

In this chapter we have learned some of the general properties of conservative electromechanical coupling networks. In the process we have indicated techniques for finding mechanical forces of electric origin once electrical terminal relations are known. We have also introduced techniques for studying the energy conversion properties of coupling fields and illustrated the method of writing complete equations of motion for electromechanical systems. In Chapter 5 we complete our study of lumped-parameter electromechanical systems by introducing techniques for solving the equations of motion and by emphasizing some of the more important phenomena that occur in these systems.

PROBLEMS

3.1. A simple plunger-type solenoid for the operation of relays, valves, etc., is represented in Fig. 3P.1. Assume that it is a conservative system and that its electrical equation of state is

$$\lambda = \frac{L_0 i}{1 + x/a}.$$

(a) Find the force that must be *applied to* the plunger to hold it in equilibrium at a displacement x and with a current i.

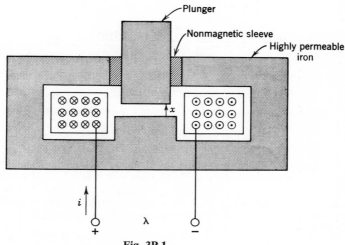

Fig. 3P.1

(b) Make a labeled sketch of the force of part (a) as a function of x with constant i.

(c) Make a labeled sketch of the force of part (a) as a function of x with constant λ.

3.2. An electrically linear electric field system with two electrical terminal pairs is illustrated in Fig. 3P.2. The system has the electrical equations of state $v_1 = S_{11}q_1 + S_{12}q_2$ and $v_2 = S_{21}q_1 + S_{22}q_2$. (See Example 3.1.1 for a physical case of this type.)

(a) Calculate the energy input to the system over each of the three paths A, B, and C in the q_1-q_2 plane illustrated in Fig. 3P.2b.

(b) What is the relation between coefficients S_{12} and S_{21} to make these three values of energy the same?

(c) Derive the result of (b) by assuming that the system is conservative and applying reciprocity.

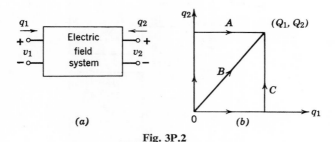

Fig. 3P.2

3.3. A slab of dielectric slides between plane parallel electrodes as shown. The dielectric obeys the constitutive law $\mathbf{D} = \alpha(\mathbf{E} \cdot \mathbf{E})\mathbf{E} + \epsilon_0\mathbf{E}$, where ϵ_0 is the permittivity of free space and α is a constant. Find the force of electrical origin on the slab. Your answer should take the form $f^e = f^e(v, x)$.

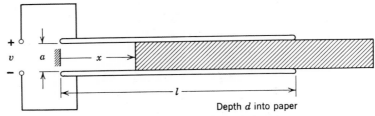

Fig. 3P.3

3.4. A magnetic circuit, including a movable plunger, is shown in Fig. 3P.4. The circuit is excited by an N-turn coil and consists of a perfectly permeable yoke and plunger with a variable air gap $x(t)$ and a fixed nonmagnetic gap d. The system, with the cross section shown, has a width w into the paper. The following parts lead to a mathematical formulation of the equations of motion for the mass M, given the excitation $I(t)$.

(a) Find the terminal relation for the flux $\lambda(i, x)$ linked by the electrical terminal pair. Ignore fringing in the nonmagnetic gaps. Note that the coil links the flux through the magnetic material N times.

(b) Find the energy $W_m(\lambda, x)$ stored in the electromechanical coupling. This should be done by making use of part (a).

(c) Use the energy function $W_m(\lambda, x)$ to compute the force of electrical origin f^e acting on the plunger.

(d) Write an electrical (circuit) equation of motion involving λ and x as the only dependent variables and $I(t)$ as a driving function.

(e) Write the mechanical equation of motion for the mass. This differential equation should have λ and x as the only dependent variables, hence taken with the result of (d) should constitute a mathematical formulation appropriate for analyzing the system dynamics.

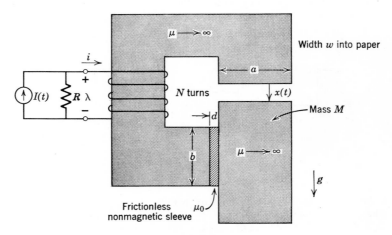

Fig. 3P.4

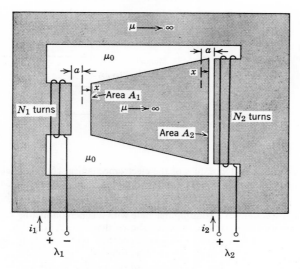

Fig. 3P.5

3.5. A magnetic circuit with a movable element is shown in Fig. 3P.5. With this element centered, the air gaps have the same length (a). Displacements from this centered position are denoted by x.

(a) Find the electrical terminal relations $\lambda_1(i_1, i_2, x)$ and $\lambda_2(i_1, i_2, x)$ in terms of the parameters defined in the figure.

(b) Compute the coenergy $W'_m(i_1, i_2, x)$ stored in the electromechanical coupling.

3.6. An electrically nonlinear magnetic field coupling network illustrated in Fig. 3P.6 has the equations of state

$$i = I_0 \left[\frac{\lambda/\lambda_0 + (\lambda/\lambda_0)^3}{1 + x/a} \right], \qquad f^e = \frac{I_0}{a} \left[\frac{\frac{1}{2}\lambda^2/\lambda_0 + \frac{1}{4}\lambda^4/\lambda_0^3}{(1 + x/a)^2} \right],$$

where I_0, λ_0, and a are positive constants.

(a) Prove that this system is conservative.

(b) Evaluate the stored energy at the point λ_1, x_1 in variable space.

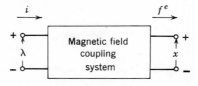

Fig. 3P.6

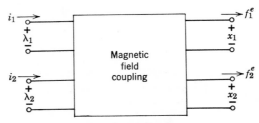

Fig. 3P.7

3.7. The electrical terminal variables of the electromechanical coupling network shown in Fig. 3P.7 are known to be $\lambda_1 = ax_1i_1^3 + bx_1x_2i_2$ and $\lambda_2 = bx_1x_2i_1 + cx_2i_2^3$, where a, b, and c are constants. What is the coenergy $W'_m(i_1, i_2, x_1, x_2)$ stored in the coupling network?

3.8. A schematic diagram of a rotating machine with a superconducting rotor (moment of inertia J) is shown in Fig. 3P.8. Tests have shown that $\lambda_1 = i_1L_1 + i_2L_m \cos\theta$ and $\lambda_2 = i_1L_m \cos\theta + i_2L_2$, where $\theta(t)$ is the angular deflection of the shaft to which coil (2) is attached. The machine is placed in operation as follows:

(a) With the (2) terminals open circuit and the shaft at $\theta = 0$, $I(t)$ is raised to I_0.

(b) Terminals (2) are shorted to conserve the flux λ_2 regardless of $\theta(t)$ or $i_1(t)$.

(c) $I(t)$ is now made a given driving function.

Write the equation of motion for the shaft. Your answer should be one equation involving only $\theta(t)$ as an unknown. Damping can be ignored.

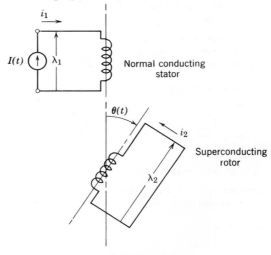

Fig. 3P.8

3.9. The electric terminal variables of the electromechanical coupling system shown in Fig. 3P.9 are known to be $\lambda_1 = ax_1^2i_1^3 + bx_2^2x_1i_2$ and $\lambda_2 = bx_2^2x_1i_1 + cx_2^2i_2^3$, where a, b, and c are constants.

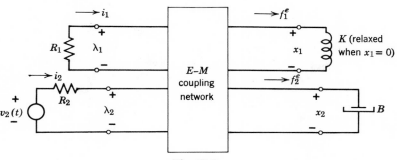

Fig. 3P.9

(a) What is the coenergy $W'_m(i_1, i_2, x_1, x_2)$ stored in the coupling network?
(b) Find the forces $f_1{}^e$ and $f_2{}^e$.
(c) Write the *complete* set of equations for the system with the terminal constraints shown.

3.10. The following equations of state describe the conservative, magnetic field coupling system of Fig. 3P.10 for the ranges of variables of interest $(i_1 > 0, i_2 > 0)$. $\lambda_1 = L_0 i_1 + A i_1 i_2{}^2 x$ and $\lambda_2 = A i_1{}^2 i_2 x + L_0 i_2$, where L_0 and A are positive constants.

(a) Find the force applied by the coupling system on the external mechanical circuit as a function of i_1, i_2, and x.
(b) Write the *complete* set of differential equations for the system by using i_1, i_2, and x as dependent variables.

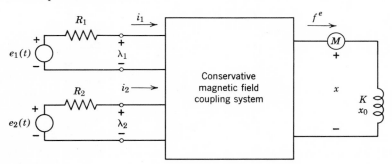

Fig. 3P.10

3.11. Two coils are free to rotate as shown in Fig. 3P.11. Each coil has a moment of inertia J. Measurements have shown that $\lambda_1 = L_1 i_1 + M i_2 \cos \theta \cos \psi$ and $\lambda_2 = M i_1 \cos \theta \cos \psi + L_2 i_2$, where L_1, L_2, and M are constants. Because the system is electrically linear, we know that the coenergy $W'_m(i_1, i_2, \psi, \theta)$ is given by $W'_m = \frac{1}{2} L_1 i_1{}^2 + M \cos \theta \cos \psi i_1 i_2 + \frac{1}{2} L_2 i_2{}^2$. The coils are driven by the external circuits, where I_1 and I_2 are known functions of time

(a) What are the torques of electrical origin $T_1{}^e$ and $T_2{}^e$ that the electrical system exerts on the coils?
(b) Write the *complete* equations of motion that define $\theta(t)$ and $\psi(t)$.

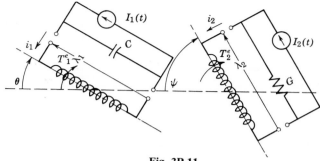

Fig. 3P.11

3.12. A magnetic field system has three electrical terminal pairs and two mechanical terminal pairs as shown in Fig. 3P.12. The system is electrically linear and may be described by the relations $\lambda_1 = L_{11}i_1 + L_{12}i_2 + L_{13}i_3$, $\lambda_2 = L_{21}i_1 + L_{22}i_2 + L_{23}i_3$, and $\lambda_3 = L_{31}i_1 + L_{32}i_2 + L_{33}i_3$. Each of the inductances L_{ij} ($i = 1, 2, 3; j = 1, 2, 3$) may be functions of the mechanical variables x_1 and x_2. *Prove* that if the system is conservative, $L_{12} = L_{21}$, $L_{13} = L_{31}$, and $L_{23} = L_{32}$. To do this recall that for a conservative system the energy (or coenergy) does not depend on the path of integration but only on the end point.

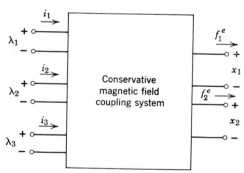

Fig. 3P.12

3.13. Electrostatic voltmeters are often constructed as shown in Fig. 3P.13a. N pairs of pie-shaped plates form the stator and rotor of a variable capacitor (Fig. 3P.13a shows six pairs of rotor plates and six pairs of stator plates). The rotor plates are attached to a conducting shaft that is free to rotate through an angle θ. In the electrostatic voltmeter a pointer is attached to this shaft so that the deflection θ is indicated on a calibrated scale (not shown).

(a) Determine $q(v, \theta)$, where q is the charge on the stator and v is the voltage applied between the rotor and stator. The device is constructed so that fringing fields can be ignored and the area of the plates is large compared with the cross section of the shaft. In addition, it is operated in a region of θ in which the plates overlap but not completely.

(b) Find the torque of electrical origin on the rotor.

(c) The shaft is attached to a torsional spring which has the deflection θ when

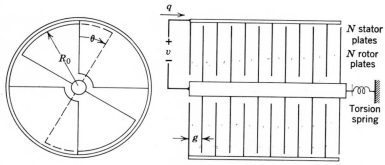

Fig. 3P.13a

subjected to a torque T_m, where θ and T_m are related by $T_m = K(\theta - \alpha)$. The shaft has a moment of inertia J and is subject to a damping torque $B\,d\theta/dt$. Write the torque equation for the shaft.

(d) The circuit of Fig. 3P.13b is attached to the terminals. Write the electrical equation for the system. [The results of parts (c) and (d) should constitute two equations in two unknowns.]

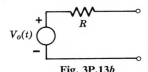

Fig. 3P.13b

(e) A "zero adjust" knob on the electrostatic voltmeter is used to set α in such a way that a pointer attached to the shaft indicates 0 when $\theta = \alpha$. A constant voltage $v = V_0$ is attached to the terminals. What is the static deflection of the pointer $(\theta - \alpha)$ as a function of V_0?

3.14. A fixed cylindrical capacitor of length L is made of a solid perfectly conducting inner rod of radius a which is concentric with a perfectly conducting outer shell of radius b. An annular half cylinder (inner radius a, outer radius b) of dielectric with permittivity ϵ and length L is free to move along the axis of the capacitor as shown in Fig. 3P.14 (ignore fringing).

(a) Find the charge on the outer cylinder $q = q(v, x)$, where v is the voltage between the inner and outer conductors and x is the displacement of the half cylinder of dielectric (assume $L > x > 0$).

(b) Write the conservation of power for this system in terms of the terminal voltage and current, the electric energy stored, the force of electric origin, and the velocity of the dielectric.

(c) Find the electric energy stored in terms of q and x.

(d) Find the electric coenergy in terms of v and x.

(e) Find the force of electric origin exerted by the fields on the dielectric.

Suppose one end of the dielectric is attached to a spring of constant K, which is relaxed when $x = l$.

(f) Write the differential equation of motion for the dielectric, assuming that it has mass M and slides without friction.

(g) If a constant voltage V_0 is established between the conductors, find x.

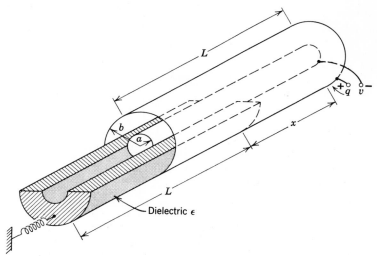

Fig. 3P.14

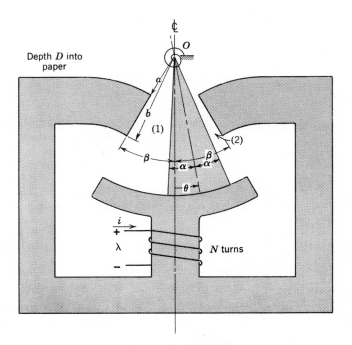

Fig. 3P.15

96

3.15. A magnetic transducer is shown in Fig. 3P.15. A wedge-shaped infinitely permeable piece of metal is free to rotate through the angle θ $(-(\beta - \alpha) < \theta < \beta - \alpha)$. The angle θ is the deflection of the wedge center line from the center line of the device. A magnetic field is produced in regions (1) and (2) by means of the infinitely permeable yoke and the N-turn winding.

(a) Find λ (i, θ). (You may assume that the fringing fields at the radii $r = a$ and $r = b$ from the origin O are of negligible importance.)

(b) Compute the magnetic coenergy stored in the electromechanical coupling $W'_m(i, \theta)$.

(c) Use the conservation of energy to find the torque T^e exerted by the magnetic field on the wedge.

(d) The wedge has a moment of inertia J about O and is constrained by a torsion spring that exerts the torque $T_m = K\theta$. Write the equation of motion for the wedge, assuming that i is a given function of time.

(e) If $i = I_0 = $ constant, show that the wedge can be in static equilibrium at $\theta = 0$.

3.16. A plane electrode is free to move into the region between plane-parallel electrodes, as shown in Fig. 3P.16. The outer electrodes are at the same potential, whereas the inner electrode is at a potential determined by the constant voltage source V_0 in series with the output of an amplifier driven by a signal proportional to the displacement of the movable electrode itself. Hence the voltage of the inner electrode relative to that of the outer electrodes is $v = -V_0 + Ax$, where A is a given feedback gain. Find the force of electrical origin $f^e(x)$. (Note that this force is only a function of position, since the voltage is a known function of x.)

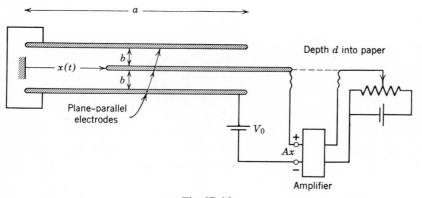

Fig. 3P.16

3.17. In Fig. 3P.17 we have a slab of magnetic material positioned between three pole faces. The nonlinear magnetic material is such that the constituent relation is given by $\mathbf{B} = \alpha(\mathbf{H} \cdot \mathbf{H})\mathbf{H} + \mu_0\mathbf{H}$, where α is a known constant.

(a) Show that

$$\lambda_1 = L_0\left(1 + \frac{d}{g}\right)i_1 + L_0\beta\left(1 - \frac{x}{l}\right)i_1{}^3 + L_0\frac{d}{g}i_2.$$

and

$$\lambda_2 = L_0\frac{d}{g}i_1 + L_0\beta\left(\frac{x - g}{l}\right)i_2{}^3 + L_0\left(1 + \frac{d}{g}\right)i_2,$$

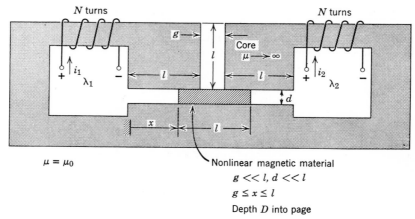

$$\mu = \mu_0$$

Nonlinear magnetic material

$$g \ll l, d \ll l$$
$$g \leq x \leq l$$

Depth D into page

Fig. 3P.17

where

$$L_0 = \frac{\mu_0 N^2 l D}{d},$$

$$\beta = \frac{\alpha}{\mu_0}\left(\frac{N}{d}\right)^2,$$

and

$$g \leq x \leq l$$

(b) Determine an expression for the magnetic coenergy $W'_m = W'_m(i_1, i_2, x)$.

(c) What is the force of magnetic origin f^e acting on the nonlinear magnetic material?

3.18. A slab of dielectric material is positioned between three perfectly conducting plates shown in Fig. 3P.18. The dielectric is such that the displacement vector $\mathbf{D}$ is related to the electric field $\mathbf{E}$ through the relation $\mathbf{D} = \alpha(\mathbf{E} \cdot \mathbf{E})\mathbf{E} + \epsilon_0 \mathbf{E}$, where α is a known positive constant. The slab and adjacent plates have a width (into paper) w.

(a) With the slab at the position x, find the electrical terminal relations. Ignore fringing fields and assume that the slab is always well within the plates

$$q_r = q_r(v_r, v_l, x) \text{ and } q_l = q_l(v_r, v_l, x).$$

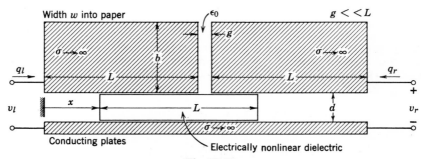

Fig. 3P.18

(b) Find the electrical coenergy $W'_e(v_r, v_l, x)$ stored between the plates.

(c) What is the force of electrical origin f^e on the slab of dielectric?

3.19. A perfectly conducting plate of length $2\alpha R$ and depth D is attached to the end of a conducting bar that rotates about the axis O, shown in Fig. 3P.19. A pair of conducting electrodes forms half cylinders, coaxial with the axis O. The gap $\Delta \ll R$. We ignore fringing fields in the present analysis.

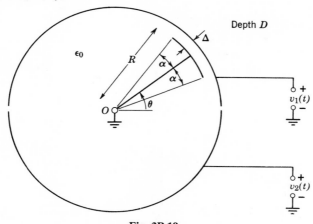

Fig. 3P.19

(a) Make a dimensioned plot of the coenergy $W'_e(\theta, v_1, v_2)$ as a function of θ.

(b) Make a dimensioned plot of the torque exerted by the electric fields on the rotor.

(c) In terms of this torque, write a differential equation for $\theta(t)$. You may assume that the rotor has an inertia J but is not impeded by a viscous damping force.

3.20. A parallel-plate capacitor has its bottom plate fixed and its top plate free to move vertically under the influence of the externally applied mechanical force f. A slab of the dielectric of thickness d is between the plates shown in Fig. 3P.20a. With plate area A and displacement x, the electrical terminal relation (neglecting fringing fields; see Example 2.1.4) is

$$q(v, x) = \frac{\epsilon A}{d(1 + \epsilon x/\epsilon_0 d)} v.$$

(a) The capacitor is charged to a value of charge $q = Q$ and the terminals are open-circuited. Calculate, sketch, and label the externally applied force $f(Q, x)$ necessary to hold the plate in equilibrium and the terminal voltage $v(Q, x)$ as functions of x for the range $0 < x < 2(\epsilon_0/\epsilon)d$.

(b) A battery of constant voltage V is connected to the terminals of the capacitor. Calculate, sketch, and label the externally applied force $f(V, x)$ necessary to hold the plate in equilibrium and the charge $q(V, x)$ as functions of x for the range $0 < x < 2(\epsilon_0/\epsilon)d$.

(c) By the use of suitable electrical and mechanical sources the system of Fig. 3P.20a is made to traverse the closed cycle in q-x plane shown in Fig. 3P.20b in the direction indicated by the arrows. Calculate the energy converted per cycle and specify whether the conversion is from electrical to mechanical or vice versa.

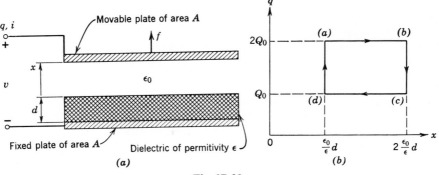

Movable plate of area A

q, i

f

x

v

ϵ_0

d

Fixed plate of area A

Dielectric of permitivity ϵ

(a)

q

$2Q_0$

(a) (b)

Q_0

(d) (c)

$\frac{\epsilon_0}{\epsilon}d$ $2\frac{\epsilon_0}{\epsilon}d$ x

(b)

Fig. 3P.20

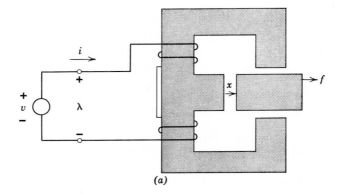

i

$+$

$+$

v

λ

x

f

$-$

(a)

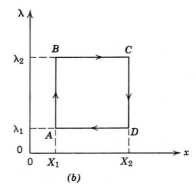

λ

λ_2 B C

λ_1 A D

0

0 X_1 X_2 x

(b)

Fig. 3P.21

100

3.21. The magnetic field transducer illustrated schematically in Fig. 3P.21a has a movable plunger that is constrained to move only in the x-direction. The coupling field is conservative and electrically linear and has the electrical equation of state

$$\lambda = \frac{L_0 i}{1 + x/a}$$

where L_0 and a are positive constants (see Example 2.1.1).

(a) For any flux linkage λ and position x find the external force f (see Fig. 3P.21a), which must be applied to hold the plunger in static equilibrium.

We now constrain the electrical terminal pair with a voltage source v and the movable plunger by a position source x in such a way that the system slowly traverses the closed cycle in the λ-x plane illustrated in Fig. 3P.21b.

(b) Sketch and label current i as a function of flux linkage λ for the closed cycle of Fig. 3P.21b.

(c) Sketch and label the force f applied by the position source as a function of x for closed cycle of Fig. 3P.21b.

(d) Find the energy converted between electrical and mechanical forms for one traversal of the cycle of Fig. 3P.21b. Specify the direction of flow.

3.22. The system shown in Fig. 3P.22 consists of two thin perfectly conducting plates, one of which is free to move. The movable plate slides on a perfectly conducting plane. It has been proposed that energy could be converted from mechanical to electrical form by the following scheme:

The process is started by holding the plate at $x = X_b$ with the switch in position (1). An external mechanical system moves the plate to $x = X_a$ and holds it there. S is then put in

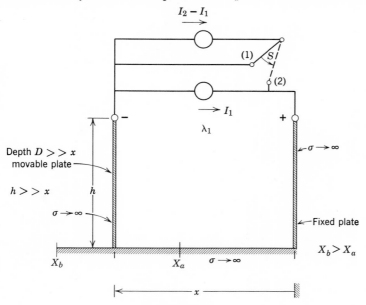

Fig. 3P.22

position (2) and the mechanical system moves the plate back to $x = X_b$ and holds it in place. S is then reset in position (1) and the cycle is repeated several times.

(a) To convert energy *from mechanical to electrical* form during each cycle, how must I_1 and I_2 be related?

(b) Sketch the path of operation in the i-x plane under the conditions of part (a) and compute the amount of energy converted from mechanical to electrical form during one cycle.

(c) Sketch carefully the path of operation for one cycle in the λ-x plane under the conditions of part (a). Compute the amount of energy converted from mechanical to electrical form along each part of the path in the λ-x plane.

Chapter 4

ROTATING MACHINES

4.0 INTRODUCTION

The most numerous and the most widely used electromechanical device in existence is the magnetic field type rotating machine. Rotating machines occur in many different types, depending on the nature of the electrical and mechanical systems to be coupled and on the coupling characteristics desired. The primary purpose of most rotating machines is to convert energy between electrical and mechanical systems, either for electric power generation or for the production of mechanical power to do useful tasks. These machines range in size from motors that consume a fraction of a watt to large generators that produce 10^9 W. In spite of the wide variety of types and sizes and of methods of construction, which vary greatly, most rotating machines fall into two classes defined by their geometrical structures—namely smooth-air-gap and salient-pole. The analysis of the electromechanical coupling systems in rotating machines can thus be reduced to the analysis of two configurations, regardless of the size or type of machine. As is to be expected, some machines do not fit our classification; they are not numerous, however, and their analyses can be performed by making simple changes in the models and techniques presented in this chapter.

After defining the two classes of machine geometry (smooth-air-gap and salient-pole), we establish the conditions necessary for average power conversion and use them as a basis for defining different types of machine. We also derive the equations of motion for the different machine types and solve them in the steady state to describe the machines' principal characteristics. The behavior of machines under transient conditions is covered in Chapter 5.

Before starting the treatment of machines it is important to recognize several significant points. First, as is evident from the treatment, a rotating machine is but one specific embodiment of a more general class of electromechanical devices defined in Chapter 3, and, as such, is conceptually quite simple. In a practical configuration, such as a polyphase machine, the number of terminal pairs is great enough to make the mathematical description seem lengthy. In no case should mathematical complexity be mistaken for conceptual difficulty. The analysis of rotating machines is conceptually simple and mathematically complex. As our treatment unfolds, it will become clear that there are geometrical and mathematical symmetries that imply simplification techniques. These techniques have been developed to a high degree of sophistication and are essential in the analysis of machine systems. Because our interest here is in the basic physical processes, we forego the special techniques and refer the reader to other texts.*

4.1 SMOOTH-AIR-GAP MACHINES

All rotating machines that fit in the smooth-air-gap classification can be represented schematically by a physical structure like that shown in end

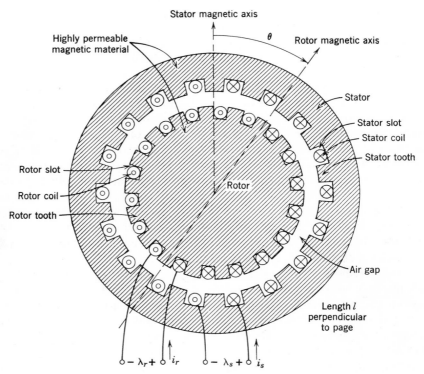

Fig. 4.1.1a Geometry of smooth-air-gap rotating machine showing distributed windings on stator and rotor of a single-phase machine.

* See, for example, D. C. White and H. H. Woodson, *Electromechanical Energy Conversion*, Wiley, New York, 1959, Chapters 4 and 7 to 10.

view in Fig. 4.1.1a. Pictures of a stator and a rotor that fall into this classification are shown in Figs. 4.1.2 and 4.1.3.

In the structure of Fig. 4.1.1a conductors are laid in axial slots that face the air gap. The number of conductors in each slot depends on the type and size of the machine and varies from 1 in large turbo-generators to 10 to 12 in small induction machines. The conductors of one circuit on one member are in series or series-parallel connection at the ends of the machine. (Note the end turns in Figs. 4.1.2 and 4.1.3.) The circuits are arranged so that a current in one winding will produce the antisymmetrical pattern about an axial plane indicated by the dots and crosses in Fig. 4.1.1a. This axial plane is the plane of symmetry of the magnetic field produced by the currents and is therefore called the magnetic axis. The stator and rotor magnetic axes are shown in Fig. 4.1.1.

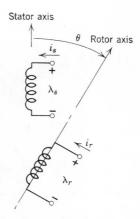

Fig. 4.1.1b Schematic representation of the inductors constituting the rotor and stator windings shown in (a).

The example in Fig. 4.1.1 has only one circuit (winding) on the stator and one circuit on the rotor. Most machines have more than one circuit on each member. In this case a slot will usually contain conductors from different circuits. Nonetheless, the description given fits each circuit on the rotor or stator.

The rotor is free to rotate and its instantaneous angular position θ is, by convention, the displacement of the rotor magnetic axis with respect to the stator magnetic axis.

The structure of Fig. 4.1.1a is called smooth air gap because it can be modeled mathematically with sufficient accuracy by assuming that the magnetic path seen by each circuit is independent of rotor position. Such a model neglects the effects of slots and teeth on magnetic path as the angle is changed. In a real machine (see Figs. 4.1.2 and 4.1.3) the slots and teeth are relatively smaller than those shown in Fig. 4.1.1a. Moreover, special construction techniques, such as skewing the slots of one member slightly with respect to a line parallel to the axis,* minimize these effects. In any case, the essential properties of a machine can be obtained with good accuracy by using a smooth-air-gap model, but slot effects are always present as second-order effects in machine terminal characteristics and as first-order problems to machine designers.

---

* For constructional details of rotating machines see, for example, A. E. Knowlton, ed., *Standard Handbook for Electrical Engineeers*, 9th ed., McGraw-Hill, New York, 1957, Sections 7 and 8. This also includes numerous references to more detailed design treatments.

Fig. 4.1.2 Stator (armature) of an induction motor. This is an example of a smooth-air-gap stator. (Courtesy of Westinghouse Electric Corporation.)

4.1.1 Differential Equations

In terms of the conventions and nomenclature for lumped-parameter systems introduced in Chapter 3, the device in Fig. 4.1.1 has magnetic field electromechanical coupling with two electrical terminal pairs and one rotational mechanical terminal pair. Thus the coupling system can be represented symbolically, as in Fig. 4.1.4.

It is conventional practice in machine analysis to assume electrical linearity (no saturation in stator or rotor magnetic material)*; consequently, the electrical terminal relations can be written in terms of inductances that can be functions of the angle θ (see Section 2.1.1 of Chapter 2). The further assumption of a smooth air gap indicates that because the field produced by

---

* Magnetic saturation in machines is quite important, but it is conventionally treated as a perturbation of the results of an analysis such as we will do. See, for example, White and Woodson, *op. cit.*, pp. 532–535.

$$v = L(\theta)\frac{di}{dt} + i\,\frac{dL}{d\theta}\cdot\frac{d\theta}{dt}$$

Fig. 4.1.3 Rotor of a wound-rotor induction machine. This is an example of a smooth-air-gap rotor. (Courtesy of Westinghouse Electric Corporation.)

each coil is unaffected by rotor position the self-inductances will be independent of rotor position and the mutual inductance will depend on rotor position. Hence the terminal relations for the coupling system of Fig. 4.1.1 as represented symbolically in Fig. 4.1.4 can be written as

$$\lambda_s = L_s i_s + L_{sr}(\theta) i_r, \tag{4.1.1}$$

$$\lambda_r = L_{sr}(\theta) i_s + L_r i_r, \tag{4.1.2}$$

$$T^e = i_s i_r \frac{dL_{sr}(\theta)}{d\theta}, \tag{4.1.3}$$

where L_s and L_r are the constant self-inductances, $L_{sr}(\theta)$ is the angular-dependent mutual inductance, and the variables $(\lambda_s, \lambda_r, i_s, i_r, T^e, \theta)$ are

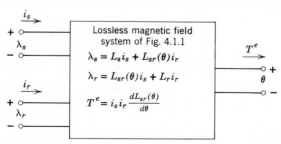

Fig. 4.1.4 Symbolic representation of coupling system in Fig. 4.1.1.

defined in Figs. 4.1.1 and 4.1.4. The torque T^e, given by (4.1.3), was derived by the method of Chapter 3 [(g) in Table 3.1].

From (4.1.1) to (4.1.3) it is clear that we need to know only how the mutual inductance L_{sr} varies with angle to proceed with an analysis of the electromechanical coupling in this machine. A similar configuration with only two slots on the stator and two slots on the rotor was analyzed in Example 2.1.2 of Chapter 2. With reference to that example and to the symmetries of the windings in Fig. 4.1.1a, the mutual inductance can be expressed in the general form

$$L_{sr}(\theta) = M_1 \cos\theta + M_3 \cos 3\theta + M_5 \cos 5\theta + \cdots. \qquad (4.1.4)$$

This is a cosine series containing only odd harmonics. Thus the mutual inductances at θ and at $-\theta$ are the same, the mutual inductance at $(\theta + \pi)$ is the negative of the inductance at θ, and the mutual inductance at $(-\theta - \pi)$ is the negative of the inductance at $-\theta$. This symmetry is justified by considering qualitatively how the flux due to stator current links the rotor winding as the rotor position is varied.

The winding distribution around the periphery of alternating current machines is normally designed to enhance the fundamental component of mutual inductance M_1 and to suppress all higher harmonics. The purpose of this design criterion is to minimize unwanted harmonic current generation in the machine. On the other hand, in the design of dc machines, other criteria are used and several of the harmonics of (4.1.4) are present in appreciable amounts. Nonetheless, it suffices for the purposes here to assume that the mutual inductance is represented by the space fundamental term only. Such an assumption simplifies the analyses, does not eliminate any fundamental properties of machines, and can be used as the basis for a complete analysis, if we assume that all harmonics are present.* Thus for the remainder of this analysis the mutual inductance $L_{sr}(\theta)$ is specified as

$$L_{sr}(\theta) = M \cos\theta. \qquad (4.1.5)$$

and the three terminal relations (4.1.1) to (4.1.3) become

$$\lambda_s = L_s i_s + M i_r \cos\theta, \qquad (4.1.6)$$
$$\lambda_r = M i_s \cos\theta + L_r i_r, \qquad (4.1.7)$$
$$T^e = -i_s i_r M \sin\theta. \qquad (4.1.8)$$

Before beginning a study of the energy conversion properties of the lossless coupling part of the machine in Fig. 4.1.1, it would be worthwhile to inquire into the circuit representation of a machine, including the essential parameters of the machine by itself, which are illustrated in the equivalent circuit of Fig. 4.1.5. On the electrical side the windings have resistances R_s and R_r

---

* For the general analysis see White and Woodson, *op. cit.*, Chapter 11.

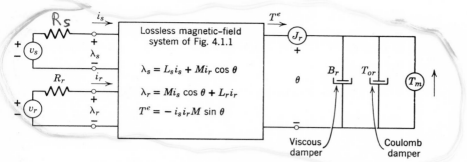

Fig. 4.1.5 Equivalent circuit for machine in Fig. 4.1.1.

which are treated as series resistances external to the lossless coupling system. There are additional losses in the iron (hysteresis and eddy-current losses) which are not included here because they are usually small enough to be treated as a simple perturbation.* On the mechanical side the essential parameters that must be included are the rotor inertia J_r and losses that occur because of friction in bearings and in sliding electrical contacts for exciting the rotor and because of windage losses due to rotation of the rotor in a gas, usually air or hydrogen. It is normally sufficient to represent these mechanical losses as a combination of viscous (B_r) and coulomb (T_{or}) friction, as shown in Fig. 4.1.5. The sources included in Fig. 4.1.5, v_s, v_r, and T_m, are general. Any or all of them may be independently set or they may be dependent on some variable. They may represent passive loads. In addition, they can be replaced by other sources, that is, the electrical terminal pairs can be excited by current sources and the mechanical terminal pair can be excited by a position or velocity source. The point of including the sources is to indicate that, in addition to the essential machine parameters, external circuits must be included before the machine can be made to operate usefully.

Using the equivalent circuit of Fig. 4.1.5, we can write the differential equations that describe the system:

$$v_s = R_s i_s + \frac{d\lambda_s}{dt} \tag{4.1.9}$$

$$v_r = R_r i_r + \frac{d\lambda_r}{dt} \tag{4.1.10}$$

$$T_m + T^e = J_r \frac{d^2\theta}{dt^2} + B_r \frac{d\theta}{dt} + T_{or} \frac{d\theta/dt}{|d\theta/dt|}. \tag{4.1.11}$$

* See, for example, A. E. Fitzgerald and C. Kingsley, Jr., *Electric Machinery*, 2nd ed., McGraw-Hill, New York, 1961, Chapter 7. Although electrical losses can be treated as perturbations when analyzing the behavior of a machine, these losses are vitally important in determining the machine's rating because it is set by thermal limitations in transferring heat generated by losses out of the machine.

Once the sources (or loads) v_s, v_r, and T_m are defined, these three equations with the terminal relations (4.1.6) to (4.1.8) form a complete description of the dynamics of the system, including the machine and the electric and mechanical circuits connected to it.

4.1.2 Conditions for Conversion of Average Power

We next consider the problem of finding the conditions under which the electromechanical coupling system of the machine in Fig. 4.1.1 can convert average power between the electrical and mechanical systems. For this problem a steady-state analysis of the coupling system in Fig. 4.1.4 with ideal sources will suffice. Once the conditions are established, the analysis can be generalized to include nonideal sources and transient conditions.

For this problem the coupling system of Fig. 4.1.4 will be excited by the ideal sources indicated in Fig. 4.1.6. The specific time dependences of these sources are

$$i_s(t) = I_s \sin \omega_s t, \tag{4.1.12}$$

$$i_r(t) = I_r \sin \omega_r t, \tag{4.1.13}$$

$$\theta(t) = \omega_m t + \gamma, \tag{4.1.14}$$

where I_s, I_r, ω_s, ω_r, ω_m, and γ are positive constants and t is the time.

We now ask for the conditions under which the machine with the steady-state excitations of (4.1.12) to (4.1.14) can convert average power between the electrical and mechanical systems. To find these conditions we evaluate the instantaneous power p_m flowing from the coupling system into the position source

$$p_m = T^e \frac{d\theta}{dt} = T^e \omega_m. \tag{4.1.15}$$

Then substitution from (4.1.12) and (4.1.13) into (4.1.8) and of that result into (4.1.15) yield

$$p_m = -\omega_m I_s I_r M \sin \omega_s t \sin \omega_r t \sin (\omega_m t + \gamma). \tag{4.1.16}$$

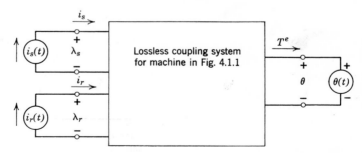

Fig. 4.1.6 Excitations used in derivation of conditions for average power conversion.

To ascertain under what conditions this power can have an average value, trigonometric identities* are used to put (4.1.16) in the form

$$p_m = -\frac{\omega_m I_s I_r M}{4}\{\sin[(\omega_m + \omega_s - \omega_r)t + \gamma] + \sin[(\omega_m - \omega_s + \omega_r)t + \gamma]$$
$$- \sin[(\omega_m + \omega_s + \omega_r)t + \gamma] - \sin[(\omega_m - \omega_s - \omega_r)t + \gamma]\}. \quad (4.1.17)$$

Because a sinusoidal function of time has no average value, (4.1.17) can have a time-average value only when one of the coefficients of t is zero. These four conditions, which cannot in general be satisfied simultaneously, can be written in the compact form

$$\omega_m = \pm\omega_s \pm \omega_r; \quad (4.1.18)$$

for example, when

$$\omega_m = -\omega_s + \omega_r,$$

$$p_{m(av)} = -\frac{\omega_m I_s I_r M}{4}\sin\gamma,$$

and, when

$$\omega_m = \omega_s + \omega_r,$$

$$p_{m(av)} = \frac{\omega_m I_s I_r M}{4}\sin\gamma.$$

It is evident from these expressions that a necessary condition for average power conversion is the frequency condition of (4.1.18). Sufficient conditions for average power conversion are (4.1.18) and $\sin\gamma \neq 0$.

As a result of this analysis, we can state that the whole field of machine theory for smooth-air-gap machines is concerned with how to satisfy the frequency condition of (4.1.18) with the available electrical and/or mechanical sources to obtain the machine characteristics needed for a particular application. It is just this process that has led to the several different machine types presently used. The frequency relations provide the starting point in the invention of new machine types for unusual applications.

4.1.3 Two-Phase Machine

Before describing the different standard machine types, how they are excited to satisfy (4.1.18), and what their essential characteristics are, the smooth-air-gap model of Fig. 4.1.1 will be modified to allow a more realistic portrayal of the energy conversion properties of rotating machines.

It is evident by examination of (4.1.17) that when one of the four possible conditions of (4.1.18) is satisfied, the corresponding term in (4.1.17) becomes a constant, but the other three terms are still sinusoidal time functions

* $\sin x \sin y = \frac{1}{2}[\cos(x-y) - \cos(x+y)]$; $\sin x \cos y = \frac{1}{2}[\sin(x-y) + \sin(x+y)]$.

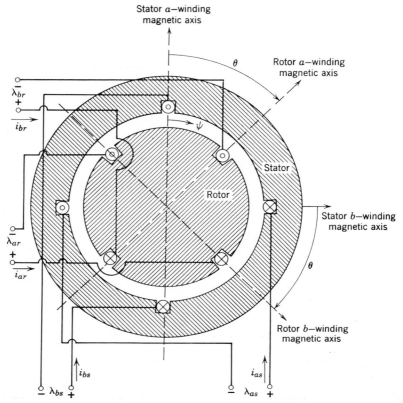

Fig. 4.1.7a Cross-sectional view of a two-phase machine with distributed windings represented by single-turn coils.

and each term represents an alternating power flow. These alternating power flows have no average values and can cause pulsations in speed and vibrations that are detrimental to machine operation and life. The alternating flow can be eliminated by adding one additional winding to both rotor and stator, as illustrated in Fig. 4.1.7a. The windings of Fig. 4.1.7a are represented as being concentrated in single slots for simplicity of illustration. In actual machines the windings are distributed like those of Fig. 4.1.1a. and a single slot can carry conductors from both windings. In Fig. 4.1.7 windings a on rotor and stator represent the original windings of Fig. 4.1.1. Windings b on rotor and stator are identical to the windings a in every respect, except that they are displaced mechanically 90° in the positive θ-direction.

The two additional windings in Fig. 4.1.7a require two additional electrical terminal pairs and, using the assumptions of constant self-inductances and

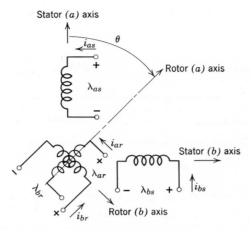

Fig. 4.1.7b Schematic representation of balanced two-phase machine in (a) showing relative orientations of magnetic axes.

sinusoidally varying mutual inductances discussed before, the terminal relations are now written as

$$\lambda_{as} = L_s i_{as} + M i_{ar} \cos\theta - M i_{br} \sin\theta, \tag{4.1.19}$$

$$\lambda_{bs} = L_s i_{bs} + M i_{ar} \sin\theta + M i_{br} \cos\theta, \tag{4.1.20}$$

$$\lambda_{ar} = L_r i_{ar} + M i_{as} \cos\theta + M i_{bs} \sin\theta, \tag{4.1.21}$$

$$\lambda_{br} = L_r i_{br} - M i_{as} \sin\theta + M i_{bs} \cos\theta, \tag{4.1.22}$$

$$T^e = M[(i_{ar}i_{bs} - i_{br}i_{as})\cos\theta - (i_{ar}i_{as} + i_{br}i_{bs})\sin\theta]. \tag{4.1.23}$$

Study of the relative winding geometry in Fig. 4.1.7a verifies the correctness of the mutual inductance terms in the electrical terminal relations. Once again, the torque T^e has been found by using the techniques of Chapter 3 [see (g) in Table 3.1].

The windings of Fig. 4.1.7 are called _balanced two-phase windings_* because excitation with balanced two-phase currents will result in constant power conversion with no alternating components. To show this the terminal variables of the machine are constrained by the _balanced, two-phase,_ current sources

$$i_{as} = I_s \cos\omega_s t, \tag{4.1.24}$$

$$i_{bs} = I_s \sin\omega_s t, \tag{4.1.25}$$

$$i_{ar} = I_r \cos\omega_r t, \tag{4.1.26}$$

$$i_{br} = I_r \sin\omega_r t \tag{4.1.27}$$

* More is said about phases in Section 4.1.7.

and by the angular position source

$$\theta = \omega_m t + \gamma. \tag{4.1.28}$$

The use of these terminal constraints with the instantaneous power given by (4.1.15) and the torque T^e given by (4.1.23) yields, after some trigonometric manipulation,*

$$p_m = -\omega_m M I_s I_r \sin [(\omega_m - \omega_s + \omega_r)t + \gamma]. \tag{4.1.29}$$

This power can have an average value only when the coefficient of t is zero, that is, when

$$\omega_m = \omega_s - \omega_r \tag{4.1.30}$$

for which condition (4.1.29) reduces to

$$p_m = -\omega_m M I_s I_r \sin \gamma. \tag{4.1.31}$$

This is still the instantaneous power out of the machine, but it is now constant in spite of the ac electrical excitation. Note further that (4.1.30) is one of the four conditions of (4.1.18). Thus the additional windings with proper excitation have produced only a single frequency condition (4.1.30) for average power conversion, and when this condition is satisfied the instantaneous power is constant and equal to the average value.

The other three conditions of (4.1.18) can be achieved individually in the machine of Fig. 4.1.7 with the excitations of (4.1.24) to (4.1.28) by changing the time phase of one stator current and/or one rotor current by 180°.

When the two stator currents or the two rotor currents are unbalanced in amplitude or the phase difference is changed from 90°, the pulsating power flow will again occur even when one of the conditions of (4.1.18) is satisfied. The analysis of these situations is straightforward trigonometry and is not carried out here.

4.1.4 Air-Gap Magnetic Fields

It is helpful for qualitative physical reasoning and for a more thorough understanding of the coupling mechanism occurring in rotating machines to think in terms of the magnetic fields that exist in the air gap. To develop these ideas consider again the machine in Fig. 4.1.7a but with only the stator excited by current sources. The assumption that rotor-to-stator mutual inductance varies sinusoidally with rotor position implies that the flux density produced in the air gap by a current in a winding varies sinusoidally with angular position; that is, a current in stator winding a will produce an air-gap flux density whose radial component is maximum along the magnetic axis (positive in one direction, negative in the other) and varies sinusoidally

* $\sin (x - y) = \sin x \cos y - \cos x \sin y$, $\cos (x + y) = \cos x \cos y - \sin x \sin y$.

between these extremes. We now assume that the stator windings of Fig. 4.1.7a are excited by the two-phase current sources of (4.1.24) and (4.1.25) and look at the space distribution of radial air-gap flux density produced by these currents at different instants of time. For this we use the angle ψ defined in Fig. 4.1.7a to indicate position in the air gap and we recognize that the air-gap flux density produced by current in a winding is proportional to the current producing it. Consequently, with reference to Fig. 4.1.7a, we can write for the instantaneous radial flux density due to current in stator winding a

$$B_{ra} = B_{rm} \cos \omega_s t \cos \psi \qquad (4.1.32)$$

and for stator winding b

$$B_{rb} = B_{rm} \sin \omega_s t \sin \psi, \qquad (4.1.33)$$

where B_{rm} is a constant related to the current amplitude I_s. These component flux densities and the resultant air-gap flux density are sketched for five values of time in Fig. 4.1.8. For the interval shown the resultant flux density (B_r) is sinusoidally distributed in space, has a constant amplitude (B_{rm}), and moves in the positive ψ-direction as time progresses. An extension of this process would show that these facts remain true for all time and that the resultant flux density makes one revolution in $(2\pi/\omega_s)$ sec or it rotates with an angular speed ω_s.

A similar argument for the rotor of Fig. 4.1.7a with the excitation of (4.1.26) and (4.1.27) shows that these rotor currents produce a flux density in the air gap that is sinusoidally distributed around the periphery, has constant amplitude, and has an angular velocity ω_r with respect to the rotor.

It is to be expected from simple considerations of the tendency of two magnets to align themselves, that a steady torque and therefore constant power conversion will occur when the rotor and stator fields are fixed in space relative to each other and the rotor is turning at constant angular velocity. To accomplish this a mechanical speed given by (4.1.30) is required. Thus the condition for average power conversion can be interpreted as establishing the condition under which the stator and rotor fields, both of which rotate with respect to the members carrying the excitation currents, are fixed in space relative to each other. Furthermore, we expect the torque (and average power) to be a function of the constant angle of separation of the axes of symmetry of the two fields. This variation with angle is indicated by the sin γ term in (4.1.31). Examination of (4.1.24) to (4.1.28) with the ideas introduced in Fig. 4.1.8 shows that γ is the angle by which the rotor magnetic field axis precedes the stator magnetic field axis around the air gap in the positive θ-direction. Thus the torque [or power in (4.1.31)] is proportional to $(-\sin \gamma)$.

It must be recognized that this analysis of air-gap magnetic fields is idealized. With excitation provided by finite-size coils in finite-size slots and

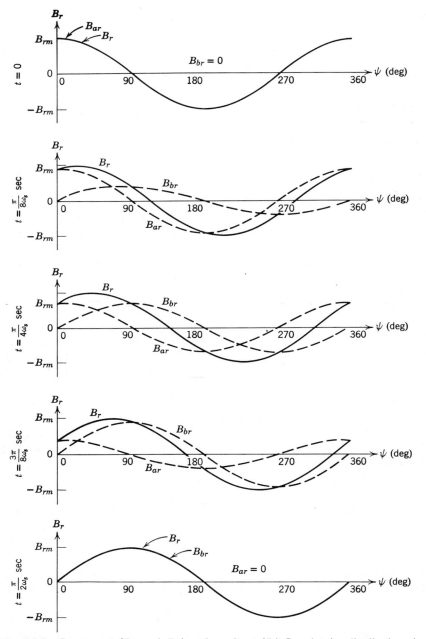

Fig. 4.1.8 Component (B_{ar} and B_{br}) and resultant (B_r) flux density distributions in a balanced two-phase machine due to balanced two-phase stator currents.

usually with equal numbers of turns in all slots, the air-gap flux density will not be exactly sinusoidal. Nonetheless, the simple picture presented is a design objective with ac machines and it yields remarkably accurate results for practical machines. (See part (c) of Prob. 4.4.)

We now reconsider the machine of Fig. 4.1.1 with the excitations of (4.1.12) to (4.1.14) and apply the rotating field ideas. Because the rotor-stator mutual inductance is a sinusoidal function of space, the air-gap flux density will still have a sinusoidal space distribution around the air gap. But now each field, rotor and stator, being excited by a sinusoidal current in a single coil keeps a fixed sinusoidal space distribution with respect to its exciting coil and varies periodically in amplitude. Such an alternating field can be represented by two constant-amplitude fields (B_{r+} and B_{r-}) rotating in opposite directions, as illustrated for one quarter cycle of the stator excitation in Fig. 4.1.9. Thus the stator excitation produces two such fields rotating with angular velocity $\pm\omega_s$ with respect to the stator. Similarly, the rotor excitation produces two fields rotating with angular velocity $\pm\omega_r$ *with respect to the rotor.* Thus each of the four conditions of (4.1.18) represents the situation in which the mechanical speed is adjusted to the proper value to make one component of rotor field fixed in space relative to one component of stator field. When one of these conditions is satisfied, the other three conditions are not, and the interactions of these other field components give rise to alternating torque and alternating power flow. As a consequence, the addition of the second set of windings in Fig. 4.1.7 can be interpreted as being for the purpose of eliminating those field components that do not produce average power conversion.

4.1.5 Discussion

Although these analyses have been made for special cases, the method is quite general; for instance, the analytical techniques are the same when the restriction of a space fundamental mutual inductance variation is removed and the more general form of (4.1.4) is used. Furthermore, the windings added to the machine of Fig. 4.1.1 to obtain the machine of Fig. 4.1.7 need not be identical to the original windings, nor must they be exactly in space quadrature with them. The only requirement for a correct analysis of the coupling mechanisms is that the electrical terminal relations be accurate representations of the physical system under study. The particular restrictions chosen here are representative of design objectives for practical rotating machines and of techniques used in their analysis.

The assumption has been made that stator circuits are excited by currents of the single frequency ω_s and rotor circuits are excited by currents of the single frequency ω_r. This analysis is easily generalized to any number of

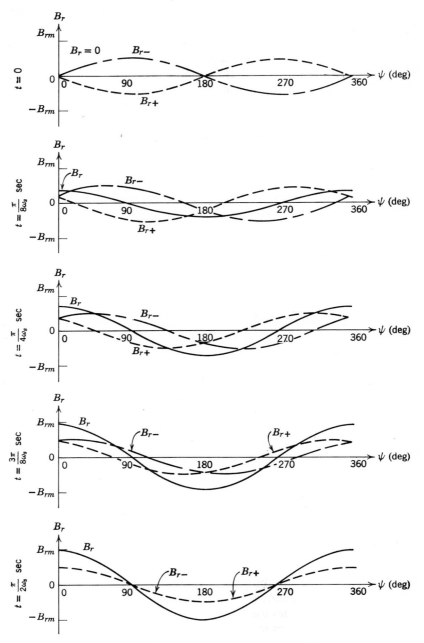

Fig. 4.1.9 Component (B_{r+} and B_{r-}) and resultant (B_r) flux density distributions in a single-phase machine with sinusoidal excitation current on the stator.

118

frequencies on each member (rotor and stator). The result is that for a component of current at a particular frequency to participate in the average power conversion process there must be a current on the other member whose frequency combines with the mechanical velocity and the other electrical frequency to satisfy one of the four conditions of (4.1.18).

The analyses have been done by assuming a steady-state problem with electrical current sources and a mechanical position source. The results are still valid when the sources are changed to voltage and torque sources or to dependent sources of any type. Moreover, transient problems can be analyzed by writing the complete differential equations for the machine and the electrical and mechanical circuits to which it is connected and using the techniques of Chapter 5. The steady-state analysis is representative of the final conditions usually reached in machine operation. Transients of interest include the one necessary to reach steady-state conditions (e.g., starting transient) and those that occur when something forces the operation away from steady-state conditions (e.g., a sudden change in load torque on a motor).

The discussion of air-gap magnetic fields was based on the simple model of a sinusoidal distribution of flux density in space and a sinusoidal variation of flux density with time. When the space distributions and time variations are not sinusoidal they can often be represented by Fourier series. Consequently, our discussion of air-gap magnetic fields can be applied to individual Fourier components to obtain insight into the interactions occurring in the machine.

In summary, our look at the smooth-air-gap machine in terms of simple models has a lot more generality than we at first might suspect. These simple models are building blocks with which we can build understanding of the behavior of complex machines.

4.1.6 Classification of Machine Types

The results of the steady-state analysis expressed as (4.1.18) for the configuration of Fig. 4.1.1 and as (4.1.30) for the machine of Fig. 4.1.7 are used to define conventional machine types. From one viewpoint rotating-machine theory boils down to the practical ways of satisfying the frequency conditions for average power conversion, given the available electrical and mechanical sources and loads and the desired machine characteristics.

In the following sections we indicate how the frequency condition is met and what the steady-state characteristics are for several conventional machine types.

4.1.6a Synchronous Machines

Consider the two-phase machine of Fig. 4.1.7 with direct current applied to the rotor ($\omega_r = 0$) and balanced, two-phase currents of frequency ω_s

applied to the stator. The condition of (4.1.30) indicates that the machine can convert average power only when the rotor is turning with the single value of speed

$$\omega_m = \omega_s. \qquad (4.1.34)$$

These constraints yield a *synchronous* machine, so named because it can convert average power only at one mechanical speed—the synchronous speed ω_s determined by the stator excitation frequency.

In a similar way we can also make a synchronous machine by applying direct current to the stator and alternating current to the rotor. In this case the synchronous speed is determined by the frequency of the rotor currents.

The most common application of a smooth-air-gap, synchronous machine is as the generator, called alternator or turboalternator, that is driven by a steam turbine to generate power. In this machine the ac or *armature* windings are on the stator and the dc or *field* winding is on the rotor. The direct current for the field winding is usually fed through carbon or metal-graphite brushes that make contact with slip rings on the rotor. A large turboalternator with the end bell removed is shown in Fig. 4.1.10.

Fig. 4.1.10 Turboalternator partly assembled for test. This is a 3600-rpm, 192,000-kVA machine showing rotor in place with the upper half of the bearing and the end shield removed. The slip rings (or collector rings) for supplying current to the rotor (field) winding are in the foreground. (Courtesy of General Electric Company.)

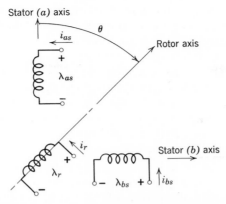

Fig. 4.1.11 Schematic representation of smooth-air-gap synchronous machine with field (dc) winding on the rotor and a balanced two-phase stator (armature) winding.

Some of the principal steady-state characteristics of synchronous machines can be illustrated by considering the machine shown schematically in Fig. 4.1.11. The electrical and mechanical terminal relations are

$$\lambda_{as} = L_s i_{as} + M i_r \cos \theta, \tag{4.1.35}$$

$$\lambda_{bs} = L_s i_{bs} + M i_r \sin \theta, \tag{4.1.36}$$

$$\lambda_r = L_r i_r + M(i_{as} \cos \theta + i_{bs} \sin \theta), \tag{4.1.37}$$

$$T^e = M i_r(i_{bs} \cos \theta - i_{as} \sin \theta). \tag{4.1.38}$$

[These are (4.1.19) to (4.1.21) and (4.1.23) with $i_{br} = 0$ and λ_{ar} and i_{ar} replaced by λ_r and i_r, respectively.]

Synchronous machines are normally operated with the stator windings excited by voltage sources. We express our results in these terms. We find it convenient, however, to constrain the stator winding currents analytically with the balanced, two-phase set

$$i_{as} = I_s \cos \omega t, \tag{4.1.39}$$

$$i_{bs} = I_s \sin \omega t, \tag{4.1.40}$$

and to consider I_s as an unknown in the analysis. We constrain the rotor current to be constant

$$i_r = I_r \tag{4.1.41}$$

and the angle θ with the position source

$$\theta = \omega t + \gamma. \tag{4.1.42}$$

We see that the condition for average power conversion (4.1.30) is automatically satisfied.

It can be verified by direct substitution of (4.1.39) to (4.1.42) into (4.1.37) that the rotor flux linkage λ_r is constant. Thus, under steady-state conditions, there is no voltage induced in the rotor circuit, and we could have applied a constant-voltage source, as we normally do in practice. In such a case the rotor current is constant and determined only by the applied voltage and rotor circuit resistance. Consequently, there is no loss in generality by specifying the rotor current as in (4.1.41). For transient conditions there is a difference between voltage and current excitation of the rotor.

Substitution of (4.1.39) to (4.1.42) into (4.1.38), yields for the instantaneous torque produced by the machine

$$T^e = -MI_r I_s \sin \gamma. \tag{4.1.43}$$

For the analysis of the energy conversion properties of large synchronous machines the mechanical (friction) losses are neglected because they are a small fraction of the power converted by the machine. Thus we follow this procedure and assume that the torque expressed by (4.1.43) is applied to the mechanical load (or source) on the shaft [T_m in Fig. 4.1.5].

To find the electrical terminal characteristics we need to evaluate the stator terminal voltages. Substitution of (4.1.39) to (4.1.42) into (4.1.35) and (4.1.36) yields

$$\lambda_{as} = L_s I_s \cos \omega t + MI_r \cos (\omega t + \gamma), \tag{4.1.44}$$
$$\lambda_{bs} = L_s I_s \sin \omega t + MI_r \sin (\omega t + \gamma). \tag{4.1.45}$$

These two flux linkages are sinusoidal functions of time with a single frequency ω. Moreover, λ_{bs} is the same as λ_{as}, except for a shift of 90° in time phase. The currents exciting these two windings are identical in amplitude and different in phase by the same 90°. Consequently, we expect the electrical behavior of the two stator windings to be the same except for this phase shift; thus we analyze only winding a. When considering power into or out of the stator, we multiply the result for one winding by two to account for the second winding.

As is the usual practice in the analysis of the energy conversion properties of large synchronous machines, we neglect winding resistances and express the terminal voltage of stator winding a as

$$v_{as} = \frac{d\lambda_{as}}{dt} = \frac{d}{dt} [L_s I_s \cos \omega t + MI_r \cos (\omega t + \gamma)]. \tag{4.1.46}$$

Because this expression involves sinusoidal functions of time with the single frequency ω, it is convenient to express the quantities in terms of complex functions and to use vector diagrams to illustrate electrical properties. Hence we write

$$i_{as} = \text{Re}\,(I_s e^{j\omega t}), \qquad v_{as} = \text{Re}\,(\hat{V}_s e^{j\omega t}), \tag{4.1.47}$$

where I_s is real and $\hat{V}_s$ is complex. We substitute this expression for the voltage into (4.1.46) replace the time functions by their complex equivalents,

$$\cos \omega t = \text{Re} (e^{j\omega t}), \qquad \cos (\omega t + \gamma) = \text{Re} (e^{j\gamma} e^{j\omega t}),$$

drop the Re, and cancel the $e^{j\omega t}$ terms to get

$$\hat{V}_s = j\omega L_s I_s + j\omega M I_r e^{j\gamma}. \tag{4.1.48}$$

The last term in this equation is a voltage source that depends on rotor current I_r and rotor phase angle γ. It is conventionally designated as

$$\hat{E}_f = j\omega M I_r e^{j\gamma}, \tag{4.1.49}$$

the subscript f denoting dependence on field (rotor) current. The use of (4.1.49) in (4.1.48) yields the expression

$$\hat{V}_s = j\omega L_s I_s + \hat{E}_f. \tag{4.1.50}$$

This steady-state stator (armature) terminal voltage is used to construct a simple steady-state equivalent circuit for one phase of a balanced two-phase synchronous machine with balanced excitation, as shown in Fig. 4.1.12.* Note from this figure that because $\hat{E}_f$ is independently adjustable the current I_s can be controlled in magnitude and phase relative to $\hat{V}_s$ and the synchronous machine can act as a motor or generator. The quantity $\omega_s L_s$ is conventionally called the *synchronous reactance* and is simply the reactance of the self-inductance of a stator winding.

The complex quantities in (4.1.50) and the equivalent circuit of Fig. 4.1.12 can be used to interpret the properties of a synchronous machine. To do this we sketch the complex quantities as vectors on the complex plane for two conditions in Fig. 4.1.13. To put our analysis in tune with convention we define the *torque angle* δ as measured *from* $\hat{V}_s$ to $\hat{E}_f$, as shown in Fig. 4.1.13. A simple geometrical construction illustrated in Fig. 4.1.13 shows that

$$\omega L_s I_s \sin \gamma = V_s \sin \delta, \tag{4.1.51}$$

where $V_s = |\hat{V}_s|$. Thus from (4.1.43) and (4.1.49)

$$T^e = - \frac{E_f V_s}{\omega^2 L_s} \sin \delta, \tag{4.1.52}$$

where $E_f = |\hat{E}_f|$. This is the expression for the torque normally used in the analysis of

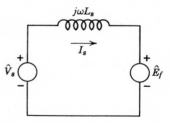

Fig. 4.1.12 Steady-state equivalent circuit for one phase of a balanced two-phase synchronous machine with balanced excitation; $\hat{E}_f$ is defined by (4.1.49).

---

* This same process, which uses an equivalent circuit for one phase, is also applied to machines with more than two phases.

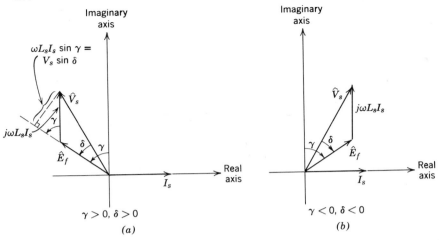

Fig. 4.1.13 Diagrams showing relations among variables in synchronous machine: (a) generator operation in which γ and δ (measured positive in the counterclockwise direction) are positive; (b) motor operation in which γ and δ are negative.

synchronous machines. It is expressed in terms of the magnitude of the stator voltage because this quantity is usually constant, as determined by the source supplying (or absorbing) electrical power.

The instantaneous power into the stator windings is

$$p_e = v_{as}i_{as} + v_{bs}i_{bs}. \tag{4.1.53}$$

It can be verified with some algebra and trigonometry that this power is equal to the mechanical power out of the shaft

$$p_e = p_m = \omega T^e = -\frac{E_f V_s}{\omega L_s}\sin\delta. \tag{4.1.54}$$

Thus the electromechanical power conversion occurs at a constant rate between the stator circuits and the mechanical system connected to the shaft. The rotor (field) circuit does not participate in the conversion process except to control the dependent source E_f. The power required to excite the field winding as a fraction of the stator (armature) power rating varies from 0.5 per cent in large turboalternators to a few per cent in synchronous motors. It is for this reason that the field winding is usually on the rotor, the result being that sliding contacts have to handle less power.

When a synchronous machine is operated with a constant voltage supply (V_s) to the stator and a constant field current (constant E_f), the torque-angle characteristic is the simple sinusoid shown in Fig. 4.1.14. The machine can

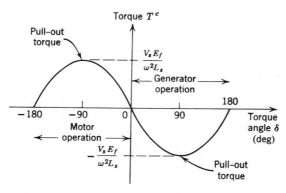

Fig. 4.1.14 Torque versus torque angle for a synchronous machine with constant stator voltage amplitude and constant rotor current.

supply any torque required by the shaft load (or supply) in the range

$$-\frac{V_s E_f}{\omega^2 L_s} < T^e < \frac{V_s E_f}{\omega^2 L_s}$$

and operate as a motor or generator. Any attempt to demand (or supply) a torque outside this range will surpass the ability of the machine and it will no longer run at synchronous speed and produce an average torque. This process of loss of synchronism is called *pulling out of step* and the maximum torque the machine can supply is called the *pull-out torque*.

We shall demonstrate one additional property of synchronous machines, that of adjusting the power factor (phase angle between stator terminal voltage and current) by varying the field (rotor) current. We shall illustrate the property by using motor operation; however, the general features of the analysis also hold for generator operation.

We assume motor operation with constant-amplitude, balanced, two-phase voltages applied to the stator windings of the machine in Fig. 4.1.11. A constant torque load T_m is applied to the machine, and the field (rotor) current I_r can be set to different values. We neglect stator winding resistance and friction losses. We consider three cases illustrated on the torque angle curves of Fig. 4.1.15a, the vector relations among the variables being shown in Figs. 4.1.15b, c, and d. Note two things in studying the vector diagrams of Fig. 4.1.15. First, as the field current I_r is increased from a low value I_{r1} to a high value I_{r3}, the magnitude of the stator current passes through a minimum. Second, for the same variation in I_r the phase angle between stator voltage and current reverses sign. An analysis of this type is used to produce a so-called V-curve like that shown in Fig. 4.1.15e, which is a plot of

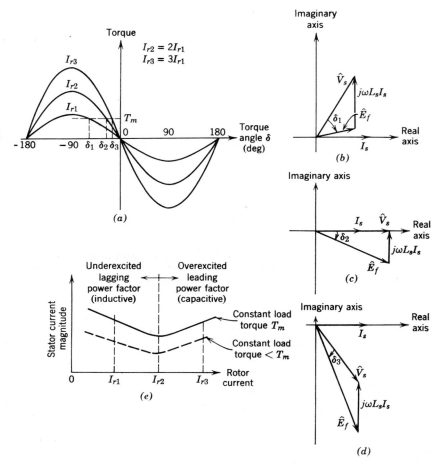

Fig. 4.1.15 Illustration of the performance of a synchronous motor as the field excitation is varied: (a) torque versus torque angle; (b) rotor current I_{r1}; (c) rotor current I_{r2}; (d) rotor current I_{r3}; (e) synchronous motor V-curve.

stator current amplitude as a function of field current with *stator voltage amplitude and load torque held constant.* For small values of field current the machine is said to be underexcited; it appears inductive to the electrical sources and operates with a lagging power factor. For large values of field current the machine is said to be overexcited; it appears capacitive to the electrical sources and operates with a leading power factor.*

* Power factor is defined as $\cos \theta$, where θ is the phase-angle between the current and voltage. A power factor of unity indicates that the load is purely resistive. See, for example, R. M. Kerchner and G. F. Corcoran, *Alternating-Current Circuits*, Wiley, New York, 1955.

In many applications of synchronous motors the machines have adequate field winding capacity for overexcitation and the capacitive characteristics are used for power-factor correction. Special machines, called *synchronous condensers*, are actually synchronous motors that run with no mechanical load and are used as continuously variable capacitors to adjust power factor and regulate voltage on electric power transmission systems.

In this presentation we have discussed only a few of the principal features of synchronous machines. There are many others, depending on the application, and they are studied by the same techniques. Our treatment is intended to be only an introduction to synchronous-machine characteristics. A complete study would fill a book by itself.*

In our analysis we used a two-phase machine as an example. Virtually all synchronous machines manufactured are three-phase because the power supply is usually three-phase. Three-phase synchronous machines have the same energy conversion properties and steady-state characteristics as the two-phase machine of our examples. In fact, a standard procedure in the analysis of a three-phase machine is to transform the electrical variables to obtain the equations for an equivalent two-phase machine. This simplifies the mathematics in the analysis.†

This analysis was made with direct current applied to the rotor (field) winding. The rotor can, and sometimes is, replaced by a permanent-magnet rotor, an arrangement that has the two advantages of requiring no power to maintain the field and no sliding electrical contacts. This also has two primary disadvantages: (a) the amplitude of the magnetic field is fixed by the permanent magnet and cannot be controlled externally during operation, and (b) the magnetic flux densities obtainable with permanent magnet materials are considerably smaller than those obtainable with current-excited, high-permeability iron. As a result of the second disadvantage, permanent magnets are normally used in small synchronous machines.

4.1.6b   Induction Machines

An *induction* machine is conventionally defined as one in which single-frequency alternating currents are fed into the stator circuits and the rotor circuits are all short circuited. Rotor currents are obtained by induction from the stator, hence the name.

To determine that an induction machine can convert average power, consider again the machine of Fig. 4.1.7 with the stator currents constrained by balanced two-phase sources.

$$i_{as} = I_s \cos \omega_s t, \tag{4.1.55}$$

$$i_{bs} = I_s \sin \omega_s t, \tag{4.1.56}$$

---

* See, for example, C. Concordia, *Synchronous Machines*, Wiley, New York, 1951.

† See, for example, White and Woodson, *op. cit.*, Chapter 9.

with the rotor circuits short-circuited

$$v_{ar} = v_{br} = 0, \tag{4.1.57}$$

and with the rotor constrained by the position source

$$\theta = \omega_m t + \gamma. \tag{4.1.58}$$

The terminal relations for the electromechanical coupling system are (4.1.19) to (4.1.23).

In the analysis that follows we neglect the resistance of the stator windings. This is standard practice when analyzing the energy conversion properties of a large induction machine. The primary effect of stator winding resistance is in heating the machine, and it therefore plays a major role in determining the machine's rating. For reasons that will become clear subsequently, we must retain the resistance of the rotor circuits in our analysis.

With the terminal constraints of (4.1.55) to (4.1.58) and with rotor circuit resistance denoted by R_r, we write the differential equations for the two rotor circuits:

$$0 = R_r i_{ar} + L_r \frac{di_{ar}}{dt} + MI_s \frac{d}{dt} [\cos \omega_s t \cos (\omega_m t + \gamma)$$
$$+ \sin \omega_s t \sin (\omega_m t + \gamma)] \tag{4.1.59}$$

$$0 = R_r i_{br} + L_r \frac{di_{br}}{dt} + MI_s \frac{d}{dt} [-\cos \omega_s t \sin (\omega_m t + \gamma)$$
$$+ \sin \omega_s t \cos (\omega_m t + \gamma)]. \tag{4.1.60}$$

The use of appropriate trigonometric identities* allows us to rewrite these equations in the forms

$$MI_s(\omega_s - \omega_m) \sin [(\omega_s - \omega_m)t - \gamma] = L_r \frac{di_{ar}}{dt} + R_r i_{ar}, \tag{4.1.61}$$

$$-MI_s(\omega_s - \omega_m) \cos [(\omega_s - \omega_m)t - \gamma] = L_r \frac{di_{br}}{dt} + R_r i_{br}. \tag{4.1.62}$$

The right sides are identical, linear, first-order differential operators with constant coefficients. The left sides are sinusoidal voltage drives of equal amplitudes, but 90 degrees phase difference (just like the stator currents). Thus we need to consider only one of these equations for a solution.

As indicated by (4.1.61) and (4.1.62), both rotor currents will have frequency $(\omega_s - \omega_m)$ which exactly satisfies the condition of (4.1.30). Thus the induction machine satisfies the condition for average power conversion at all mechanical speeds. With finite rotor resistance an induction machine can

---

* $\cos (x - y) = \cos x \cos y + \sin x \sin y$, $\sin (x - y) = \sin x \cos y - \cos x \sin y$.

Fig. 4.1.16   Cutaway view of a squirrel-cage induction motor. (Courtesy of General Electric Company.)

convert average power at all speeds except synchronous ($\omega_m = \omega_s$), and its mode of operation (motor, generator, or brake) depends on the relative values of ω_m and ω_s, as we shall see subsequently.

An induction motor can also be obtained by exciting the rotor with ac and short-circuiting the stator circuits. This, however, requires that all the power be fed into the machine through sliding electrical contacts (brushes on slip rings), which is impractical in most cases in the light of the simple alternative.

Most induction machines have squirrel-cage rotors in which bare conductors are imbedded in slots in the rotor iron and are then all short-circuited together at the ends by conducting rings. A cutaway view of such a motor is shown in Fig. 4.1.16. The conductor assembly alone looks like a cage, hence the name. Some special-purpose induction machines have rotor circuits wound with insulated conductors with connections to the terminals made through brushes and slip rings. The rotor for a wound rotor induction machine was shown earlier in Fig. 4.1.3. Having access to the rotor circuits allows us to connect different sources, or loads, or to short circuit the rotor circuits externally and thereby obtain a variety of machine characteristics.

For reasons that are stated in Section 4.2.2, all induction machines are smooth-air-gap machines.

We shall now study the steady-state characteristics of induction machines by using the constraints of (4.1.55) to (4.1.58). We first solve (4.1.61) for the steady-state current in rotor circuit $(a)^*$:

$$i_{ar} = \frac{(\omega_s - \omega_m)MI_s}{\sqrt{R_r^2 + (\omega_s - \omega_m)^2 L_r^2}} \cos\left[(\omega_s - \omega_m)t + \alpha\right], \qquad (4.1.63)$$

where

$$\alpha = -\frac{\pi}{2} - \gamma - \beta$$

and

$$\beta = \tan^{-1}\frac{(\omega_s - \omega_m)L_r}{R_r}.$$

The current in rotor circuit b is identical except for a 90° phase shift indicated by (4.1.62) [The cos in (4.1.63) is replaced by sin for i_{br}.]

As usual, we want to know how the machine behaves, as viewed from the electrical input terminals; thus we wish to find the relation between voltage and current. It is helpful at the same time to draw a steady-state electrical equivalent circuit as we did for the synchronous machine.

It can be verified quite easily that for a balanced two-phase machine with balanced two-phase excitation, as we have here, we need to consider only one phase (stator circuit) because the behavior of the other circuit will be identical except for a 90° phase shift.

We use (4.1.19) with the definition of terminal voltage to write

$$v_{as} = \frac{d\lambda_{as}}{dt} = \frac{d}{dt}(L_s i_{as}) + \frac{d}{dt}(M i_{ar} \cos\theta - M i_{br} \sin\theta). \qquad (4.1.64)$$

Substitution from (4.1.55), (4.1.58), and (4.1.63) into this expression yields

$$v_{as} = \frac{d}{dt}(L_s I_s \cos\omega_s t) + \frac{d}{dt}\frac{(\omega_s - \omega_m)M^2 I_s}{\sqrt{R_r^2 + (\omega_s - \omega_m)^2 L_r^2}}$$
$$\times \{\cos\left[(\omega_s - \omega_m)t + \alpha\right]\cos(\omega_m t + \gamma)$$
$$- \sin\left[(\omega_s - \omega_m)t + \alpha\right]\sin(\omega_m t + \gamma)\}. \qquad (4.1.65)$$

A trigonometric identity is used to simplify the second term; thus

$$v_{as} = \frac{d}{dt}(L_s I_s \cos\omega_s t) + \frac{d}{dt}\left[\frac{(\omega_s - \omega_m)M^2 I_s}{\sqrt{R_r^2 + (\omega_s - \omega_m)^2 L_r^2}}\cos\left(\omega_s t - \beta - \frac{\pi}{2}\right)\right].$$
$$(4.1.66)$$

---

* A review of sinusoidal steady-state circuit analysis is given in Section 5.1.

It is now convenient to define the *slip s* as

$$s = \frac{\omega_s - \omega_m}{\omega_s}.$$

(4.1.67)

The slip is a measure of the difference between the actual mechanical speed (ω_m) and the synchronous speed (ω_s) expressed as a fraction of synchronous speed. When the mechanical speed is less than the synchronous speed, the slip is positive.

We now use the definition of slip s to rewrite (4.1.66) in the form

$$v_{as} = \frac{d}{dt}(L_s I_s \cos \omega_s t) + \frac{d}{dt}\left[\frac{\omega_s M^2 I_s}{\sqrt{(R_r/s)^2 + \omega_s^2 L_r^2}} \cos\left(\omega_s t - \beta - \frac{\pi}{2}\right)\right],$$

(4.1.68)

and we rewrite the definition of β in terms of slip s as

$$\beta = \tan^{-1}\frac{\omega_s L_r}{R_r/s}.$$

(4.1.69)

We now use complex notation by defining

$$i_{as} = \text{Re}\,(I_s e^{j\omega_s t}), \qquad \cos\left(\omega_s t - \beta - \frac{\pi}{2}\right) = \text{Re}\,(-je^{j\omega_s t}e^{-j\beta}),$$

$$v_{as} = \text{Re}\,(\hat{V}_s e^{j\omega_s t}),$$

and rewrite (4.1.68) as

$$\hat{V}_s = j\omega_s L_s I_s + \frac{\omega_s^2 M^2 I_s e^{-j\beta}}{\sqrt{(R_r/s)^2 + \omega_s^2 L_r^2}}.$$

(4.1.70)

This equation is conventionally represented by the steady-state equivalent circuit of Fig. 4.1.17 in which we have indicated a complex amplitude $\hat{I}_r$ that can be verified from the circuit to have the value

$$\hat{I}_r = \frac{-j\omega_s M I_s e^{-j\beta}}{\sqrt{(R_r/s)^2 + \omega_s^2 L_r^2}}.$$

(4.1.71)

Thus the second term in (4.1.70) is simply $j\omega_s M \hat{I}_r$ as it should be for the circuit in Fig. 4.1.17.

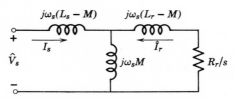

Fig. 4.1.17 Steady-state equivalent circuit for balanced two-phase induction machine with balanced excitation.

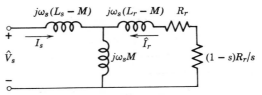

Fig. 4.1.18 Alternative form for steady-state equivalent circuit for balanced two-phase induction machine with balanced excitation. Here the resistance $(1-s)R_r/s$ gives rise to a power dissipation equal to the power converted to mechanical form.

By some simple manipulations it can be verified that the magnitude of $\hat{I}_r$ is the same as the magnitude of i_{ar} found in (4.1.63). The effect of the relative motion has been to change the frequency but not the magnitude of the rotor current as viewed from the stator winding and indicated in (4.1.64) and (4.1.66). Consequently, when the equivalent circuit of Fig. 4.1.17 is redrawn as in Fig. 4.1.18, the power loss calculated in R_r is the actual I^2R loss in one winding of the rotor. The power into the other resistance $(1-s)R_r/s$ represents power converted to mechanical form, as will be demonstrated.

The equivalent circuit of Fig. 4.1.17 or 4.1.18 can be used to study the steady-state electrical behavior of induction machines. Our use of i_{as} as having zero phase angle can be relaxed and I_s can be replaced by a complex amplitude. The equivalent circuit serves the important function of helping to determine the correct relative phase angles.

The b winding on the stator will behave like the a winding except for a 90° phase shift in all variables, as indicated by the excitations (4.1.55) and (4.1.56). This can be verified quite easily and is not done here.

To describe the behavior of the induction machine, as viewed from the mechanical terminal pair, we use (4.1.23) with (4.1.55), (4.1.56), (4.1.63) and the value of i_{br}, obtained by replacing the cosine in (4.1.63) with a sine, and obtain the expression for the torque

$$T^e = \frac{(\omega_s - \omega_m)M^2I_s^2}{\sqrt{R_r^2 + (\omega_s - \omega_m)^2 L_r^2}}$$
$$\times [\{\cos[(\omega_s - \omega_m)t + \alpha]\sin\omega_s t - \sin[(\omega_s - \omega_m)t + \alpha]\cos\omega_s t\}$$
$$\times \cos(\omega_m t + \gamma) - \{\cos[(\omega_s - \omega_m)t + \alpha]\cos\omega_s t$$
$$+ \sin[(\omega_s - \omega_m)t + \alpha]\sin\omega_s t\}\sin(\omega_m t + \gamma)]. \tag{4.1.72}$$

The successive use of trigonometric identities* and the definition of angle β in (4.1.63) lead to the simplified result

$$T^e = \frac{(\omega_s - \omega_m)M^2R_rI_s^2}{R_r^2 + (\omega_s - \omega_m)^2 L_r^2}. \tag{4.1.73}$$

* $\cos(x-y) = \cos x \cos y + \sin x \sin y$, $\sin(x-y) = \sin x \cos y - \cos x \sin y$.

The instantaneous torque T^e is constant. This is to be expected because balanced two-phase currents yield constant-amplitude rotating fields, as discussed in Section 4.1.4, and the interaction of these fields when the condition of (4.1.30) is satisfied produces a steady torque.

The mechanical power output of the machine is

$$p_m = \omega_m T^e = \left[\frac{\omega_s^2 M^2 I_s^2}{(R_r/s)^2 + \omega_s^2 L_r^2} \right] \left(\frac{1-s}{s} \right) R_r \tag{4.1.74}$$

where we have used the definition of slip s in (4.1.67) and manipulated the result to get this form. Note that the term in brackets is the square of the magnitude of $\hat{I}_r$, as given in (4.1.71); thus we have verified that the power absorbed by the resistance $(1-s)R_r/s$ in Fig. 4.1.18 is indeed the power converted to mechanical form when multiplied by two to account for both phases.

The total power input to the stator windings (excluding stator I^2R losses, which we have done) is defined as the *air-gap power* p_g. It is clear from Fig. 4.1.17 that

$$p_g = I_r^2 \frac{R_r}{s}, \tag{4.1.75}$$

where I_r is the magnitude of $\hat{I}_r$ given by (4.1.71) and (4.1.75) is twice the power input to one phase. As already indicated, the rotor I^2R losses p_r are given by

$$p_r = I_r^2 R_r = sp_g. \tag{4.1.76}$$

The power p_m converted to mechanical form is

$$p_m = I_r^2 \left(\frac{1-s}{s} \right) R_r = (1-s)p_g. \tag{4.1.77}$$

Thus the power into the stator equals the sum of rotor losses and converted power

$$p_g = p_r + p_m \tag{4.1.78}$$

and there is no rate of change of total energy stored in the machine. We knew this all the time, because for balanced excitation the air-gap magnetic fields have constant amplitudes.

We now use (4.1.75) to (4.1.78) to identify the three possible modes of operation of an induction machine as illustrated in Fig. 4.1.19. The arrow heads indicate the flow direction of power and the ranges of slip and speed are given in the figure. Note in particular that the rotor power p_r is always greater than zero as it must be because it is an I^2R loss. Note also that brake operation has power coming into the machine from both electrical and mechanical terminal pairs and all of this power is dissipated in the rotor resistance.

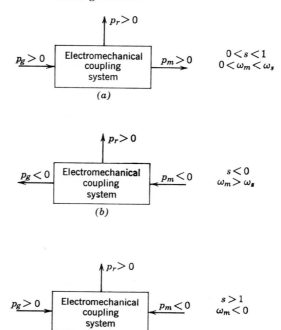

Fig. 4.1.19 The three modes of operation of an induction machine: (*a*) motor operation; (*b*) generator operation; (*c*) brake operation.

When operating as a motor, the machine efficiency η is defined as the mechanical power output divided by the electrical power input to the stator; thus

$$\eta = \frac{p_m}{p_g} = 1 - s. \qquad (4.1.79)$$

As a consequence, large induction machines intended for the efficient production of mechanical power are designed to run at as small a slip (as close to synchronous speed) as possible.

Induction machines are normally excited by almost constant voltage sources. Consequently, the electromechanical coupling properties are of most interest for this condition and we need to express (4.1.73) in terms of the magnitude V_s of the terminal voltage $\hat{V}_s$. We use (4.1.70) to write

$$\hat{V}_s = j\omega_s L_s I_s + \frac{\omega_s^2 M^2 I_s (R_r/s)}{(R_r/s)^2 + \omega_s^2 L_r^2} - j \frac{\omega_s^3 M^2 L_r I_s}{(R_r/s)^2 + \omega_s^2 L_r^2}. \qquad (4.1.80)$$

In obtaining this form we have used the definitions of angle β from (4.1.63) and slip s from (4.1.67). The magnitude squared of $\hat{V}_s$ is then

$$V_s^2 = \left\{ \left[\omega_s L_s - \frac{\omega_s^3 M^2 L_r}{(R_r/s)^2 + \omega_s^2 L_r^2} \right]^2 + \left[\frac{\omega_s^2 M^2 (R_r/s)}{(R_r/s)^2 + \omega_s^2 L_r^2} \right]^2 \right\} I_s^2. \quad (4.1.81)$$

Solution of this equation for I_s^2, substitution of that result in (4.1.73) and simplification lead to the result

$$T^e = \frac{(k^2/\omega_s)(L_r/L_s)(R_r/s) V_s^2}{[\omega_s(1 - k^2)L_r]^2 + (R_r/s)^2}. \quad (4.1.82)$$

We have used the square of the maximum coefficient of coupling

$$k^2 = \frac{M^2}{L_r L_s} \quad (4.1.83)$$

to simplify this expression. Note that this is the coefficient of coupling between the a windings on stator and rotor when rotor position θ is zero.

A curve of electromagnetic torque versus slip (and mechanical speed) typical of large squirrel-cage induction machines is shown in Fig. 4.1.20. The ranges over which the machine operates as a motor, generator, and brake are also indicated.

The torque given by (4.1.82) depends on rotor resistance R_r and slip s only through the ratio R_r/s. By differentiating (4.1.82) with respect to this ratio, setting the derivative equal to zero, and solving for the ratio we can determine that the torque has two maxima that occur when

$$\frac{R_r}{s} = \pm \omega_s(1 - k^2)L_r, \quad (4.1.84)$$

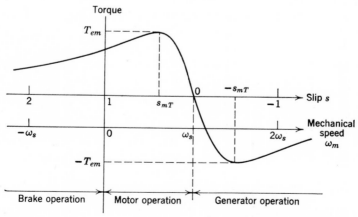

Fig. 4.1.20 Torque-slip curve of a two-phase induction machine with balanced excitation.

from which the slip at which maximum torque occurs is

$$s = \pm s_{mT} = \pm \frac{R_r}{\omega_s(1 - k^2)L_r}. \tag{4.1.85}$$

These two values of slip are indicated in Fig. 4.1.20. Substitution of (4.1.84) into (4.1.82) yields for the maximum torque

$$T^e = \pm T_{em} = \pm \frac{k^2 V_s^2}{2\omega_s^2 L_s(1 - k^2)}. \tag{4.1.86}$$

This maximum torque is indicated in Fig. 4.1.20.

The maximum torque given by (4.1.86) is independent of rotor resistance R_r. Thus for a wound rotor induction motor with which the rotor resistance can be set to any desired value we can get a set of steady-state torque-speed curves as sketched in Fig. 4.1.21. Note that as R_r increases the speed at which maximum torque occurs decreases but the maximum torque stays the same. This fact is often used by introducing external resistance into the rotor circuit to achieve a high starting torque and then short-circuiting the rotor windings for normal running to get a small slip and therefore high efficiency.

The loading of an induction motor normally occurs in the region of negative slope near synchronous speed; for example, the torque-speed curve of an induction motor and a typical load (e.g., a fan) are shown in Fig. 4.1.22. The steady-state operating point of the system is indicated on the curves. If the fan load increases to the dashed curve, the new operating point occurs at a higher torque, lower speed, and higher slip. At the higher slip the motor produces more mechanical power but with less efficiency.

It is worthwhile to understand the reasons for the shape of the torque speed curve of an induction motor. First, in the normal operating range, which is the region of negative slope near synchronous speed in Fig. 4.1.20, the slip is

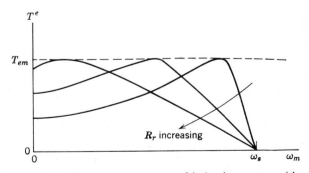

Fig. 4.1.21 Variation of torque-speed curves of induction motor with rotor resistance. Stator voltage held constant.

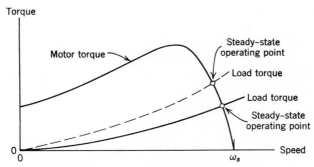

Fig. 4.1.22 Loading of an induction motor.

very small, hence the induced currents in the rotor are at very low frequency [see (4.1.63)]. Under this condition the resistance of the rotor windings has a much greater effect than the inductance. To express this mathematically, the resistive term in the denominator of (4.1.82) dominates such that

$$\left(\frac{R_r}{s}\right)^2 \gg [\omega_s(1 - k^2)L_r]^2$$

and the torque becomes

$$T^e \approx \frac{k^2}{\omega_s} \frac{L_r}{L_s} \frac{s}{R_r} V_s^2. \tag{4.1.87}$$

This torque is a linear function of slip and therefore also of mechanical speed.

When the mechanical speed is far from synchronous speed (the slip is large), the frequency of the rotor currents (4.1.63) is high and inductance predominates over resistance. This region is defined from the denominator of (4.1.82) as the condition

$$[\omega_s(1 - k^2)L_r]^2 \gg \left(\frac{R_r}{s}\right)^2.$$

In this case the torque becomes

$$T^e \approx \frac{k^2}{\omega_s^3(1 - k^2)^2 L_r L_s} \frac{R_r}{s} V_s^2. \tag{4.1.88}$$

This expression varies inversely with slip.

The two asymptotes are sketched in Fig. 4.1.23 for positive slip. These two simplified models are useful for studying the behavior of the machine under particular conditions; for example, for the kind of torque-speed curve shown in Fig. 4.1.23, which is typical of large induction motors, the inductance-dominated model (4.1.88) is sufficient for starting conditions and the resistance-dominated model is adequate for normal running conditions. We have more to say about these kinds of approximations in the next chapter.

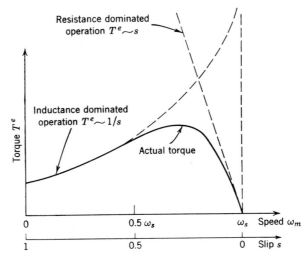

Fig. 4.1.23 Asymptotic behavior of an induction motor.

Our analysis of induction machines has been done with a two-phase model. Most large induction machines are actually excited by three-phase sources. Nonetheless, the standard technique for analysis is to transform a three-phase machine to an equivalent two-phase machine for a study of the energy conversion properties. This is true for any number of phases.* Consequently, our treatment is general and our conclusions are valid for all balanced polyphase machines with balanced polyphase excitation.

We have only highlighted the properties of polyphase induction machines with the idea of trying to establish some insight into the physical processes occurring. The subject of induction machines is complex and extensive enough to be the sole subject of books.†

All of our discussion so far has been relevant to polyphase induction machines. There are also single-phase induction machines which have some unique characteristics. A single-phase induction machine is constructed like the machine illustrated in Fig. 4.1.1. The stator is excited by a single-phase source and the rotor winding is short-circuited. (Actually, the rotor is almost always of squirrel-cage construction and therefore the equivalent of two windings, 90° apart in space.)

As we discovered in Section 4.1.4, single-phase excitation of a symmetrically distributed winding produces two equal-amplitude waves of flux density traveling in opposite directions in the air gap. A squirrel-cage rotor in this

---

* See, for example, White and Woodson, *op. cit.*, Chapter 8.
† See, for example, P. L. Alger, *The Nature of Polyphase Induction Machines*, Wiley, New York, 1951.

environment does not know which way to go and therefore will not start to rotate. Once started, however, the rotor will continue to run in the same direction. The torque-speed curve of a single-phase induction motor can be derived as the superposition of two machines operating with the traveling components of the air-gap flux, as illustrated in Fig. 4.1.24. Thus, with rotation in either direction, the flux wave traveling in that direction dominates and the machine continues to run in that direction. In the normal running range near synchronous speed the single-phase induction motor has properties similar to those of polyphase machines.

In view of the single-phase machine properties illustrated in Fig. 4.1.24, there is a problem in starting the machine. There is a variety of starting methods.* For moderate-size machines ($\frac{1}{10}$ to 5 hp, approximately) of the type installed in refrigerators, air conditioners, washing machines, and the like, an auxiliary winding is used. The auxiliary winding is wound with its magnetic axis displaced 90 degrees from that of the main winding. It is also excited from the single-phase source, but the phase angle of its current is different from that of the main winding, either because of a different L/R ratio or because a capacitor is added in series. This different phase angle of the current in the auxiliary winding causes an unbalance between the two rotating field waves; one of the waves dominates and starts the rotor turning. In most cases the auxiliary winding is disconnected by a centrifugal switch when the rotor reaches a predetermined speed during the acceleration.

For smaller, single-phase induction machines starting torque is provided by shading coils,† which are short-circuited turns on the stator that give the effect of making one flux wave dominate the other.

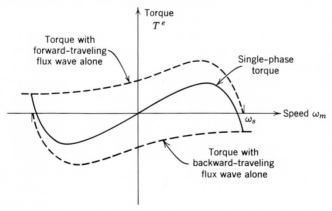

Fig. 4.1.24 The torque-speed curve of a single-phase induction motor.

* See, for example, Fitzgerald and Kingsley, *op. cit.*, Chapter 11.
† See, for example, Fitzgerald and Kingsley, *loc. cit.*

Because of the simple, rugged construction possible with a squirrel-cage rotor, the induction motor is the least expensive and most reliable means of converting electric energy to mechanical energy. As a result, induction motors are more numerous by far than any other type of motor.

Another important class of induction motor is the *two-phase servomotor*, which is essentially a two-phase induction motor with rotor resistance sufficiently high that maximum torque occurs at a slip of around 1.5 (see Fig. 4.1.21). The torque-speed curve then has a negative slope for all positive speeds and can therefore run stably at any speed between zero and synchronous speed. Such a motor is normally operated with full voltage applied to one winding and with variable voltage applied to the other to get smooth control of speed. Such operation is quite inefficient and thus servomotors are made in small sizes, mostly up to 20 W but sometimes up to 1000 W with auxiliary cooling for the rotors. They are, as their name implies, used mostly in servo systems for control applications. The analysis of servomotors is a straightforward application of the techniques we have introduced and is done quite well elsewhere.* Thus we do not discuss them further here.

4.1.6c Commutator Machines

The most widely used machine for control purposes is the *dc machine* which uses (or supplies) electrical power at zero frequency. It is evident from (4.1.18) that with zero-frequency rotor and stator currents it is impossible to satisfy the frequency condition with any nonzero mechanical speed. This problem is circumvented by the use of a *commutator* which can be viewed as a mechanical frequency changer. The stator circuit (field circuit) of the usual dc machine is excited by direct current and the rotor (armature) circuits are fed from direct-current sources through a commutator that provides the currents in the rotor conductors with components at ω_m. This frequency, with the zero stator-current frequency, satisfies the condition in (4.1.18) at all mechanical speeds.

A commutator is a mechanical switch whose state is determined by the rotor position θ. The simplest possible commutator is shown schematically for one rotor coil without the iron in Fig. 4.1.25a. When a constant current I is passed through the external terminals and the rotor carrying the coil and commutator is rotated about its axis with a mechanical velocity ω_m, the waveform of the current in the coil is as shown in Fig. 4.1.25b. It is clear from this waveform that the fundamental frequency of the coil current is ω_m, as stated above.

In practical machines commutators are made with many segments, and the many coils on the rotor are connected to one another and to the commutator

---

* See, for example, G. J. Thaler and M. L. Wilcox, *Electric Machines*, Wiley, New York, 1966, pp. 208–213.

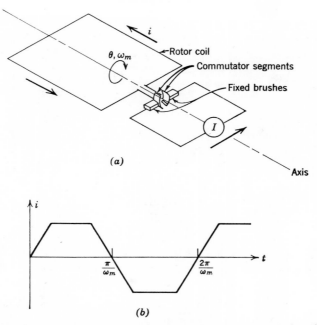

Fig. 4.1.25 Schematic representation of a simple commutator: (a) the physical arrangement; (b) coil current.

in one of two ways to obtain maximum utilization of the copper coils.*
A dc machine rotor is shown in Fig. 4.1.26, and Fig. 4.1.27 illustrates how
brushes are mounted to make contact with the commutator in a dc machine.

In spite of the apparent complications, the commutator can still be viewed
as a mechanical frequency changer that is necessary to satisfy the frequency
condition for average power conversion (4.1.18) when the electrical sources
(or sinks) are at zero frequency (dc).

A variety of dc machine characteristics is possible, depending on whether
the field (stator) circuit and the armature (rotor) circuit are connected in
series, in parallel, or are excited separately (see Section 6.4.1).

The commutator has been described as having dc excitation, but it also
acts as a frequency changer when alternating currents are fed into the
brushes, the change in frequency being equal to the rotational speed of the
commutator. Thus, if currents at frequency ω are fed into the stator circuits
and into the rotor coils through a commutator, the rotor currents will contain
components at frequency $\omega - \omega_m$ and the frequency condition of (4.1.18)
is automatically satisfied at all mechanical speeds. This result gives rise to

* For details see Knowlton, *op. cit.*, Section 8.

Fig. 4.1.26 A dc machine rotor (armature). Note the large number of slots and commutator bars. (Courtesy of Westinghouse Electric Corporation.)

many varieties of *ac commutator* machines*; the most common of which are used to drive vacuum cleaners, hand drills, electric egg beaters, and so forth.

Although we could develop the equations of motion and study the steady-state properties of commutator machines as we have done for synchronous and induction machines, it is more appropriate and meaningful to do so after we have developed some field theory for moving media. Thus we defer this treatment until we reach Chapter 6, Section 6.4.

4.1.7 Polyphase Machines

In our discussions so far machines have been considered with single-phase windings (Fig. 4.1.1) and two-phase windings (Fig. 4.1.7). In this section the definitions and configurations are given for machines with any number of phases, hence the name *polyphase*.

Polyphase electric power is generated and used for several reasons. It is economically optimum to generate and distribute three-phase power; the use

* For more detail see Knowlton, *op. cit.*, Section 7.

of polyphase power allows the operation of rotating machines to produce steady torque, even though the excitation is ac (see Section 4.1.3), and a polyphase machine for a particular application is smaller (and therefore less expensive) than a single-phase machine.

A set of balanced polyphase currents (or voltages) consists of a number of currents (or voltages) equal to the number of phases, each member of the set having the same amplitude and all members of the set being equally spaced in time phase; for example, a balanced set of three-phase currents (labeled by subscripts as phases a, b, and c) is specified as

$$
\begin{aligned}
i_a &= I \cos \omega t, \\
i_b &= I \cos \left(\omega t - \frac{2\pi}{3}\right), \\
i_c &= I \cos \left(\omega t - \frac{4\pi}{3}\right),
\end{aligned}
\tag{4.1.89}
$$

Polyphase Currents (handwritten annotation)

where I is the amplitude and $2\pi/3$ is the phase difference between any two phases.

Fig. 4.1.27 A dc machine. Note how the brush rigging is assembled to hold the brushes in contact with the commutator. Note also the salient poles on the stator. (Courtesy of Westinghouse Electric Corporation.)

It is easy to extend this system to an arbitrary number of phases. Suppose there are n phases. Then a balanced set of voltages is written as

$$v_1 = V \cos \omega t$$
$$v_2 = V \cos \left(\omega t - \frac{2\pi}{n} \right)$$
$$v_3 = V \cos \left(\omega t - \frac{4\pi}{n} \right) \tag{4.1.90}$$
$$\cdot$$
$$\cdot$$
$$\cdot$$
$$v_n = V \cos \left[\omega t - \frac{(n-1)2\pi}{n} \right].$$

In these expressions V is the amplitude and the phase difference between any two adjacent phases is $(2\pi/n)$ rad.

In terms of this general scheme, a two-phase system like that in (4.1.24) and (4.1.25) is the special case of half a four-phase system. A four-phase set of currents is written as

$$i_a = I \cos \omega t,$$
$$i_b = I \cos \left(\omega t - \frac{\pi}{2} \right),$$
$$i_c = I \cos (\omega t - \pi), \tag{4.1.91}$$
$$i_d = I \cos \left(\omega t - \frac{3\pi}{2} \right).$$

A selection of the first two or the last two of this set will yield a set of two-phase currents with the same relative phase ($\pi/2$ rad) as that in (4.1.24) and (4.1.25).

Any set of phases will have a *phase sequence* defined as the order in which the phase variables reach a positive maximum (or any other convenient reference value). Thus the sequence of the three-phase system of (4.1.89) is *a to b to c* which is usually defined as *positive sequence*. A three-phase set with *negative sequence* (*c* to *b* to *a*) is

$$i_a = I \cos \omega t,$$
$$i_b = I \cos \left(\omega t + \frac{2\pi}{3} \right), \tag{4.1.92}$$
$$i_c = I \cos \left(\omega t + \frac{4\pi}{3} \right).$$

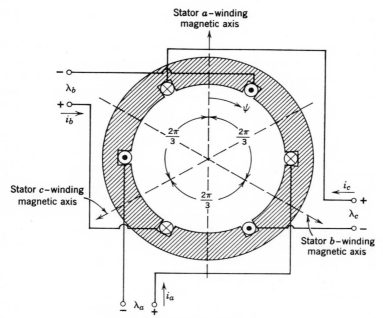

Fig. 4.1.28　A three-phase stator.

Note that the n-phase set of voltages of (4.1.90) and the four-phase set of currents in (4.1.91) are both positive sequence.

Now suppose that a rotating machine is to have its stator wound so that with balanced polyphase currents in its windings the rotating field due to stator currents will have constant amplitude and will rotate at constant speed around the periphery of the air gap. Such a system has already been discussed for a two-phase machine in Section 4.1.4. From that discussion it is clear that the number of windings must equal the number of phases and that the winding magnetic axes must be placed around the periphery in the same relative space positions that the currents are placed in relative time phase.

To illustrate this consider the three-phase windings on the stator of Fig. 4.1.28 in which the rotor is omitted for simplicity and the windings are shown lumped in single slots, although they would be distributed in an actual machine. When the positive-sequence, three-phase currents of (4.1.89) are applied to this machine, a field analysis similar to that of Section 4.1.4 will show that the air-gap flux density distribution will have constant amplitude and will rotate in the positive ψ-direction with the angular speed ω. Excitation of the stator of Fig. 4.1.28 with the negative sequence currents of (4.1.92) yields a constant-amplitude field pattern rotating in the negative ψ-direction with the angular speed ω.

This discussion, in which the example of a stator was used, applies equally well to a rotor. The general case is presented elsewhere.*

A machine can operate successfully with any number of phases on the stator and the same or any other number of phases on the rotor; for instance, a three-phase alternator (a synchronous machine used to generate electric power) usually has a three-phase stator (armature) winding and a single rotor (field) winding.

4.1.8 Number of Poles in a Machine

The number of poles in a machine is defined by the configuration of the magnetic field pattern that occurs; for example, consider the rotor of Fig. 4.1.29a with a single winding. When the instantaneous current is in the direction indicated by the dots and crosses, the resulting **B** field is as sketched in the figure. With the **B** field as shown, the rotor can be viewed as an electro-magnet with north (N) and south (S) poles as indicated. In a trip around its periphery two poles are passed; therefore it is a two-pole rotor.

Consider now the rotor of Fig. 4.1.29b which has four slots carrying coils connected in series with the polarities indicated by dots and crosses. Once again this winding can be single-phase or it can be one phase of a polyphase winding. When the instantaneous winding current has the direction indicated, the resulting **B** field is as sketched in Fig. 4.1.29b and the rotor is effectively a four-pole electromagnet.

These ideas can be generalized to an arbitrary number of poles by stating

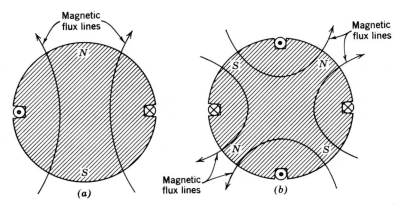

Fig. 4.1.29 Definition of number of poles in a machine: (a) two-pole rotor; (b) four-pole rotor.

* White and Woodson, *op. cit.*, Chapter 10.

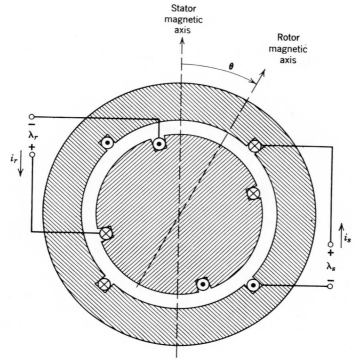

Fig. 4.1.30 Four-pole, single-phase machine.

that with current in one phase the number of poles (north and south) encountered in one turn around the periphery of the air gap defines the number of poles. It is clear that poles occur in pairs.

This discussion of the number of poles on a rotor applies equally well to stators.

Re-examination of the examples of earlier sections shows that they all concern two-pole machines. Some of those ideas are considered here for machines with more than two poles.

Consider the four-pole, single-phase machine illustrated in Fig. 4.1.30. The interconnections are not shown but current i_s is in all the stator coils in the directions shown and current i_r is in all the rotor coils in the directions shown. The slots are assumed to have negligible effects on the self-inductances (this is a smooth-air-gap machine) so that the self-inductances will be independent of rotor position θ. Because of the symmetries involved (see discussion in Section 4.1.1), the mutual inductance can be expressed as

$$L_{sr}(\theta) = M_1 \cos 2\theta + M_3 \cos 6\theta + M_5 \cos 10\theta + \cdots. \quad (4.1.93)$$

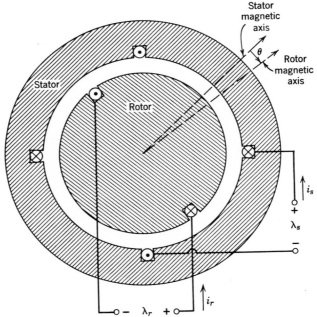

Fig. 4.1.31 Machine with four-pole stator and two-pole rotor. This configuration can produce no torque.

Compare this expression with (4.1.4). It can be generalized immediately by recognizing that for a p-pole-pair machine the mutual inductance between a stator winding and a rotor winding is expressible as

$$L_{sr}(\theta) = M_1 \cos p\theta + M_3 \cos 3p\theta + M_5 \cos 5p\theta + \cdots . \quad (4.1.94)$$

To minimize the generation of harmonics multipole ac machines are designed to accentuate the lowest space harmonic of L_{sr} and to decrease as much as possible the higher space harmonics.

In the two examples in (4.1.93) and (4.1.94) it has been assumed that the rotor and stator have the same number of poles. This is necessary for successful operation of the machine as a power converter. If the rotor and stator had different numbers of poles, the mutual inductance between rotor and stator would be zero and, as evidenced by the terminal relations (4.1.1) to (4.1.3), the electromechanical coupling would disappear. To verify qualitatively that this is so, consider the machine in Fig. 4.1.31 which has a two-pole rotor and a four-pole stator. We can see that if the system has the usual type of symmetry and the stator is excited by direct current the result is that no net flux links the rotor circuit due to stator excitation for any rotor angle θ and the mutual inductance is indeed zero.

By carrying out a process similar to that used in Section 4.1.2, we find that the condition that must be satisfied by the frequencies and mechanical speed (4.1.18) for average power conversion must be generalized for a p-pole-pair machine to

$$\omega_m = \frac{1}{p}(\pm\omega_s \pm \omega_r). \tag{4.1.95}$$

Thus for given electrical frequencies the mechanical speed is reduced as the number of poles is increased; for example, for a synchronous machine operating on 60-Hz power,

$$\omega_s = 2\pi 60 \quad \text{and} \quad \omega_r = 0,$$

the mechanical speed is

$$\omega_m = \frac{2\pi 60}{p};$$

for $p = 1$ $\omega_m = 120\pi$ rad/sec $= 3600$ rpm,

for $p = 2$ $\omega_m = 60\pi$ rad/sec $= 1800$ rpm,

for $p = 15$ $\omega_m = 8\pi$ rad/sec $= 240$ rpm.

For a synchronous machine the maximum obtainable shaft speed is produced by a two-pole machine. The speed can be set at any submultiple of this maximum speed by setting the number of poles.

The freedom to set the number of poles allows for optimum design of systems; for instance, in the generation of electric power at 60 Hz generators for operation with steam turbines have two poles (a few have four) because steam turbines operate best at high speeds. On the other hand, generators for operation with hydraulic turbines (water wheels) usually have many poles, often as many as 40 or more, because hydraulic turbines operate best at low speeds.

Examination of Fig. 4.1.30 shows that the wire in the slots of the four-pole configuration could be reconnected at the end turns to yield a two-pole configuration. Thus a machine can be made to operate at two speeds by changing the number of poles. This is done frequently on induction machines for with a squirrel-cage rotor no rotor reconnections need to be made; for example, induction motors that drive automatic washing machines often operate with four-poles for the washing cycle and are reconnected as two-pole machines to run at approximately twice the speed for the spin-drying cycle.

It is clear from the foregoing analyses and discussions that a rotating machine is conceptually a simple device. It is simply a magnetic field-type, lumped-parameter, electromechanical device whose principal properties can be deduced by the straightforward techniques of Chapters 2 and 3. The many constructional variations (multipole and polyphase) and the wide variety of possible excitations and characteristics lead to long and cumbersome, though necessary, mathematical analysis.* The amount of mathematics required should never be mistaken for conceptual complexity. Moreover, advantage should always be taken of the orderly mathematical procedures made possible by the symmetries that exist in machines.†

4.2 SALIENT-POLE MACHINES

The second geometrical configuration of rotating machines to be considered is that of the two-pole, single-phase, *salient-pole* machine illustrated in Fig. 4.2.1. This machine gets its name from the fact that one member (the rotor in Fig. 4.2.1) has protruding or *salient poles* and thus the air gap is not uniform around the periphery. The stator coil in Fig. 4.2.1 is shown lumped

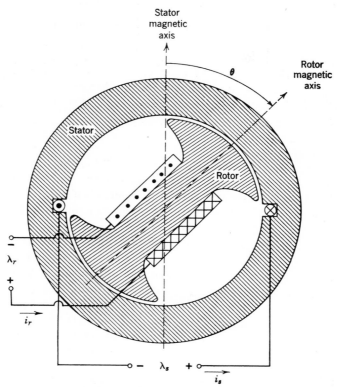

Fig. 4.2.1 Two-pole, single-phase, salient-pole machine with saliency on the rotor.

---

* See, for example, White and Woodson, *op. cit.*, Chapters 3, 4, and 7 to 11.
† White and Woodson, *op. cit.*, Chapter 4.

Fig. 4.2.2 Rotor of a salient-pole, synchronous motor. Note the method in which the coils are wound around the salient poles. (Courtesy of Westinghouse Electric Corporation.)

in two slots for simplicity. In practical machines the stator winding is distributed among several slots. The rotor winding in Fig. 4.2.1 is a fair representation of the method of winding salient rotors in practice, as indicated by the constructional details of the rotor for a salient-pole synchronous motor in Fig. 4.2.2. Another example of a salient-pole synchronous machine is shown in Fig. 4.2.3. This is a multipole generator driven by a hydraulic turbine. An example of a machine with saliency on the stator is the dc device in Fig. 4.1.27.

4.2.1   Differential Equations

Considering the system in Fig. 4.2.1 as an electrically linear, lumped-parameter, magnetic field-type, electromechanical device along the lines of Chapter 3, it is evident that the system is completely described when the inductances (electrical terminal relations) are known. Moreover, power conversion will occur only through inductances that depend on angular position θ; thus to assess the effects of saliency on power conversion properties it is necessary only to investigate the inductances.

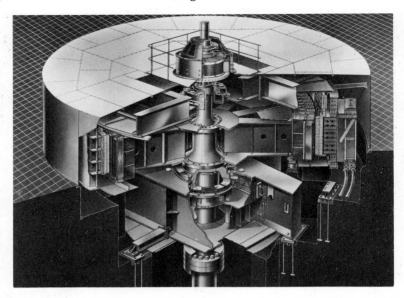

Fig. 4.2.3 Cutaway view of a hydroelectric generator. This is an example of a salient-pole, synchronous machine. (Courtesy of General Electric Company.)

First, when it is assumed that the slots that carry the stator winding in Fig. 4.2.1 cause negligible effects on the air-gap magnetic field, it is apparent that the self-inductance L_r of the rotor winding is independent of angle θ. It is also evident that the mutual inductance and the self-inductance of the stator winding depend on θ. Thus the electrical terminal relations can be written as

$$\lambda_s = L_s(\theta)i_s + L_{sr}(\theta)i_r, \tag{4.2.1}$$

$$\lambda_r = L_{sr}(\theta)i_s + L_r i_r. \tag{4.2.2}$$

Comparison of these expressions with the comparable ones for the smooth-air-gap machine (4.1.1) and (4.1.2) shows that the major difference introduced by saliency is the dependence of the stator self-inductance L_s on angular position θ, although an additional effect can occur in the form of the mutual inductance $L_{sr}(\theta)$.*

Consider first the stator self-inductance L_s. From the symmetry of the rotor structure in Fig. 4.2.1 it should be evident that the lowest space harmonic is the second because turning the rotor π rad in θ brings the inductance to its original value. This inductance is a maximum at $\theta = 0$ because the

---

* In polyphase machines saliency also affects the mutual inductances between windings on the nonsalient member. For an example of this and resulting forms see Section 4.2.2.

magnetic field encounters the smallest reluctance and a minimum at $\theta = \pi/2$ because the magnetic field encounters the maximum reluctance. Thus the stator self-inductance is expressible in general as

$$L_s(\theta) = L_0 + L_2 \cos 2\theta + L_4 \cos 4\theta + \cdots. \tag{4.2.3}$$

In the design of ac salient-pole machines the salient-pole structure is shaped to accentuate the $\cos 2\theta$ term and to minimize all other space harmonics. Consequently, for the remainder of this treatment it is assumed that

$$L_s(\theta) = L_0 + L_2 \cos 2\theta. \tag{4.2.4}$$

This equation for inductance is often interpreted as representing the superposition of a smooth air gap (L_0) and a periodically varying air gap due to saliency ($L_2 \cos 2\theta$).

To ascertain the form of the mutual inductance $L_{sr}(\theta)$ we refer to Fig. 4.2.1 and reason physically. We recognize that reciprocity holds (Section 3.1.2c of Chapter 3) and consider flux linkages with stator windings due to rotor winding excitation by current of the direction indicated in Fig. 4.2.1. At the same time, we remember that the stator winding is actually distributed in many slots around the periphery to form a coil with the magnetic axis shown. Rotor position $\theta = 0$ results in maximum positive flux linking the stator winding, whereas rotor position $\theta = \pi$ yields maximum negative flux linkage. The symmetry indicates that these two maxima are of equal magnitude. As the rotor position θ is varied from 0 to π through positive angles, the flux linkage with the stator varies smoothly from the positive maximum to the negative maximum. Variation of rotor angle from 0 to π through negative angles gives exactly the same variation of flux linkages. Consequently, the mutual inductance is expressible as a Fourier series of odd space harmonics, exactly as it was in the smooth-air-gap machine in (4.1.4),

$$L_{sr}(\theta) = M_1 \cos \theta + M_3 \cos 3\theta + M_5 \cos 5\theta + \cdots. \tag{4.2.5}$$

Although the forms of mutual inductance for the two machine types are the same, it should be clear that for a given frame size the coefficients in (4.1.4) will have different numerical values for the two cases.

For salient-pole ac machines the winding distribution on the member without salient poles (the stator in Fig. 4.2.1) is designed to maximize M_1 and minimize all other terms in (4.2.5), just as is done for smooth-air-gap machines. For the remainder of this treatment it is assumed that this design objective has been met and the mutual inductance is expressed as

$$L_{sr}(\theta) = M \cos \theta. \tag{4.2.6}$$

Substitution of (4.2.4) and (4.2.6) into (4.2.1) and (4.2.2) and calculation of the mechanical torque of electric origin, using the techniques of Chapter 3 [see (g) of Table 3.1], yield

$$\lambda_s = (L_0 + L_2 \cos 2\theta)i_s + Mi_r \cos \theta, \tag{4.2.7}$$

$$\lambda_r = Mi_s \cos \theta + L_r i_r, \tag{4.2.8}$$

$$T^e = -i_s i_r M \sin \theta - i_s^2 L_2 \sin 2\theta. \tag{4.2.9}$$

These terminal relations for the electromechanical coupling system can be used with whatever external electrical and mechanical sources or loads are connected to the machine terminals to write the differential equations for the machine system. For example, if we specify the terminal constraints as those given in Fig. 4.1.5, which include the parameters normally associated with that machine alone, the differential equations derive from Kirchhoff's voltage law and Newton's second law:

$$v_s = R_s i_s + \frac{d\lambda_s}{dt}, \tag{4.2.10}$$

$$v_r = R_r i_r + \frac{d\lambda_r}{dt}, \tag{4.2.11}$$

$$T^e + T_m = J_r \frac{d^2\theta}{dt^2} + B_r \frac{d\theta}{dt} + T_{or} \frac{d\theta/dt}{|d\theta/dt|}, \tag{4.2.12}$$

where (4.2.7) to (4.2.9) are used to express λ_s, λ_r, and T^e. These equations have exactly the same form as (4.1.9) to (4.1.11) for the smooth-air-gap machine, as is to be expected. However, the terminal relations are different for the two machines. Compare (4.2.7) to (4.2.9) for the salient-pole machine with (4.1.6) to (4.1.8) for the smooth-air-gap machine. The sources in (4.2.10) to (4.2.12), v_s, v_r, and T_m, are completely general and can be independent or dependent on some variable.

4.2.2 Conditions for Conversion of Average Power

To establish conditions for average power conversion in a salient-pole machine we assume excitation of the electromechanical coupling system by ideal current and position sources as illustrated in Fig. 4.1.6. The sources are

$$i_s(t) = I_s \sin \omega_s t, \tag{4.2.13}$$

$$i_r(t) = I_r \sin \omega_r t, \tag{4.2.14}$$

$$\theta(t) = \omega_m t + \gamma, \tag{4.2.15}$$

where I_s, I_r, ω_s, ω_r, ω_m, and γ are positive constants. Note that these constraints are the same as those we used with the smooth-air-gap machine (4.1.12) to (4.1.14).

The first term in the torque expressed by (4.2.9) has the same form as (4.1.8) for the smooth-air-gap machine. Consequently, all the discussions of average power conversion in Section 4.1.2 apply equally well to the first term of (4.2.9). In order for the mutual inductance term of the torque in a salient-pole machine to participate in average power conversion, one of the four conditions of (4.1.18), which relates electrical excitation frequencies and mechanical velocity, must be satisfied. This condition is

$$\omega_m = \pm\omega_s \pm \omega_r. \tag{4.2.16}$$

The unique effect of salient poles on the power conversion process is represented by the second term in (4.2.9). With the terminal constraints of (4.2.13) to (4.2.15), the instantaneous mechanical power output of the coupling system due to the second term in (4.2.9) is

$$p_m = -\omega_m I_s^2 L_2 \sin^2 \omega_s t \sin (2\omega_m t + 2\gamma). \tag{4.2.17}$$

The use of trigonometric identities allows us to write this expression in the form

$$p_m = -\frac{\omega_m I_s^2 L_2}{4}\{2 \sin (2\omega_m t + 2\gamma) - \sin [2(\omega_m + \omega_s)t + 2\gamma]$$
$$- \sin [2(\omega_m - \omega_s)t + 2\gamma]\}. \tag{4.2.18}$$

A sinusoidal function of time has an average value only when the coefficient of t in its argument goes to zero. The first term in braces in (4.2.18) has an average value when $\omega_m = 0$, which is uninteresting because for this condition the power conversion is zero. The second term has an average value when

$$\omega_m + \omega_s = 0 \tag{4.2.19}$$

and the third term has an average value when

$$\omega_m - \omega_s = 0. \tag{4.2.20}$$

These two conditions are expressed in the compact form

$$\omega_m = \pm\omega_s, \tag{4.2.21}$$

and when either condition is satisfied the average power converted is

$$p_{m(av)} = \frac{\omega_m I_s^2 L_2}{4} \sin 2\gamma. \tag{4.2.22}$$

Sufficient conditions for nonzero average power conversion are (4.2.21) and $\sin 2\gamma \neq 0$.

It is worthwhile to interpret this result in terms of rotating fields along the lines of Section 4.1.4. Recall that single-phase excitation of the stator winding with a current of frequency ω_s yields two component field patterns rotating in opposite directions with the angular speed ω_s. Thus each of the two conditions of (4.2.21) is interpreted as the condition under which the salient-pole structure is fixed in space with respect to one component of a stator rotating field. As a result, it is reasonable to expect that the use of balanced polyphase windings and balanced polyphase excitation, which produce a constant-amplitude rotating field (see Section 4.1.4), with saliency can produce a constant power conversion with no pulsating terms. Such is the case; in fact, saliency is used in machines (synchronous and direct current) in which such a result occurs. An example that illustrates how saliency affects the steady-state behavior of polyphase synchronous machines is given in Section 4.2.4.

4.2.3   Discussion of Saliency in Different Machine Types

The conditions expressed by (4.2.16) and (4.2.21) are now used to assess the usefulness of saliency in the principal machine types. We must recognize that within the framework of our general treatment there are possibilities for numerous unique machine types and many nonstandard machines are built for special applications. Most of these machines can be analyzed by using the general techniques developed here.

The simplest machine in which saliency is exploited is the *reluctance motor*. In the nomenclature of Fig. 4.2.1 a reluctance motor has a salient-pole rotor, one or two stator windings, but no rotor winding. The stator windings are excited by single-frequency alternating current. The only torque produced by this machine is that due to saliency or the *reluctance* torque given by the second term of (4.2.9) at a mechanical speed defined by (4.2.21). Thus the reluctance motor is a synchronous motor because it converts power at only one speed, ω_s. The steady-state energy conversion properties of a single-phase reluctance motor were studied in Example 3.1.2. Because of poor efficiency and power factor, reluctance motors are made in small sizes for such applications as clocks and phonograph turntables. Like any other synchronous machine, a reluctance motor has no starting torque and is usually started as an induction motor.

Saliency is most often exploited to improve the performance of machines that can operate successfully without it. To determine which machines can be helped by saliency, we must know when (4.2.16) (smooth-air-gap) and (4.2.21) (saliency) can be satisfied simultaneously with the same excitation. In one case we set $\omega_r = 0$ and $\omega_m = \pm\omega_s$, which yields a synchronous machine. We consider this subject in some detail in Section 4.2.4.

Saliency is also useful in dc machines in which the stator excitation is direct current ($\omega_s = 0$) and the commutator produces rotor currents of fundamental frequency $\omega_r = \omega_m$ (see Section 4.1.6c). In this case the saliency is on the stator and (4.2.21) is replaced by

$$\omega_m = \pm\omega_r, \qquad (4.2.23)$$

which is the same form that (4.2.16) assumes with $\omega_s = 0$. Thus saliency on the stator of a dc machine can enhance the power conversion capability. This is also true for commutator machines that operate on alternating current.

Although salient poles are sometimes used in small, single-phase induction motors to simplify the construction and make the machines less expensive, they are never used in large induction machines. As demonstrated in Section 4.1.6b, an induction machine has alternating current on both rotor and stator. Moreover, the machine converts power only when the rotor is *not* in synchronism with the stator-produced rotating field. Consequently, (4.2.16) and (4.2.21) cannot be satisfied simultaneously and saliency in an induction machine will produce only an oscillating power flow with no average value. The attendant noise and vibration make saliency undesirable in an induction machine.

4.2.4 Polyphase, Salient-Pole, Synchronous Machines

Salient poles are used in many synchronous machines; for example, all large synchronous motors, synchronous condensers, and hydro generators have them. It is therefore worthwhile to examine the effects of saliency on steady-state machine performance. The results achieved with saliency are compared with those obtained with a smooth-air-gap machine.

For the analysis we assume the balanced, two-phase, two-pole configuration shown schematically in Fig. 4.2.4. As usual we show the stator coils concentrated in two slots per phase for simplicity, but we realize that in an actual machine the stator windings are distributed in many slots around the periphery while maintaining the same relative symmetries with respect to magnetic axes.

We have already written the electrical terminal relations for a salient-pole machine with a single winding on both the rotor and stator in Section 4.2.1 [(4.2.7) and (4.2.8)]. These equations are still valid, except that saliency adds an angular-dependent mutual coupling term between the two stator windings. In a smooth-air-gap two-phase machine there is no mutual inductance between the two stator windings. [See (4.1.19) and (4.1.20).]

To obtain the form of this mutual inductance between stator windings we reason physically by using the configuration in Fig. 4.2.4. When the rotor magnetic axis is aligned with the magnetic axis of either stator coil $(\theta = 0, \pi/2, \pi, 3\pi/2)$, the flux produced by either coil is symmetrical with respect to its magnetic axis and there is no net flux linking one stator coil

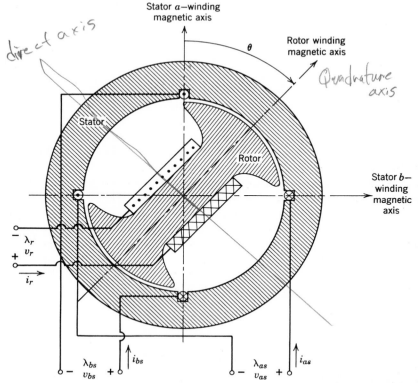

Fig. 4.2.4 Schematic representation of a salient-pole two-pole, balanced two-phase synchronous machine.

due to current in the other. Thus the stator mutual inductance L_{ss} is

$$L_{ss} = 0 \quad \text{for} \quad \theta = n\frac{\pi}{2}, \quad n = 0, \pm 1, \pm 2, \pm 3, \ldots \quad (4.2.24)$$

Now assume a current in stator coil a of the polarity shown. When θ is in the range $(0 < \theta < \pi/2)$, the salient poles distort the flux pattern due to i_{as} and tend to concentrate it at the pole where the air gap is smallest. Thus for $(0 < \theta < \pi/2)$ the flux linkage with winding b on the stator is positive. A similar argument shows that for the range $(-\pi/2 < \theta < 0)$ the flux linkage with winding b is negative. Using these facts, recognizing the machine symmetries, and realizing that reciprocity applies, we write the stator-to-stator mutual inductance as the Fourier series

$$L_{ss}(\theta) = M_{s2} \sin 2\theta + M_{s6} \sin 6\theta + M_{s10} \sin 10\theta + \cdots. \quad (4.2.25)$$

This expression is justified by making use of Fig. 4.2.4 to determine the field patterns as functions of θ.

As discussed in Section 4.2.1, the winding distributions and salient-pole shape are adjusted in ac machine design to accentuate the lowest space harmonic and to minimize higher space harmonics in inductance. This is also true of stator mutual inductance. To be consistent with the assumptions made in Section 4.2.1 that this design objective has been met we simplify (4.2.25) to the form

$$L_{ss} = M_s \sin 2\theta. \qquad (4.2.26)$$

This second harmonic variation in stator mutual inductance results from the same distortion of flux pattern that causes the $\cos 2\theta$ term in stator self-inductance indicated in (4.2.7). Furthermore, both stator windings have the same number of turns and consequently we assume

$$M_s = L_2. \qquad (4.2.27)$$

This assumption is justified by a careful field analysis of the machine* and is borne out in practice.

We now use (4.2.7) and (4.2.8) with (4.2.26) and (4.2.27) to write the electrical terminal relations for the machine in Fig. 4.2.4:

$$\lambda_{as} = (L_0 + L_2 \cos 2\theta)i_{as} + L_2 i_{bs} \sin 2\theta + M i_r \cos \theta, \qquad (4.2.28)$$

$$\lambda_{bs} = L_2 i_{as} \sin 2\theta + (L_0 - L_2 \cos 2\theta)i_{bs} + M i_r \sin \theta, \qquad (4.2.29)$$

$$\lambda_r = M i_{as} \cos \theta + M i_{bs} \sin \theta + L_r i_r. \qquad (4.2.30)$$

In writing (4.2.29) we have replaced θ with $(\theta - \pi/2)$ in (4.2.28) to obtain the self-inductance and stator-to-rotor mutual inductance terms. This change accounts for the angular difference of $\pi/2$ in the positions of the two stator coils. This equation (4.2.29) could have been obtained by reasoning physically with Fig. 4.2.4 and using the assumptions we have for design objectives.

The use of (4.2.28) to (4.2.30) with the techniques of Chapter 3 [see (g) of Table 3.1] leads to the mechanical terminal relation

$$T^e = M i_r(i_{bs} \cos \theta - i_{as} \sin \theta) - L_2(i_{as}^2 - i_{bs}^2) \sin 2\theta$$
$$+ 2L_2 i_{as} i_{bs} \cos 2\theta. \qquad (4.2.31)$$

Equations 4.2.28 to 4.2.31 should be compared with (4.2.7) to (4.2.9) for a single-phase, salient-pole machine to see the effects of adding the second phase and with (4.1.35) to (4.1.38) for a smooth-air-gap, two-phase machine to see the effects of adding saliency.

In our study of the steady-state characteristics of the salient-pole synchronous machine we neglect stator winding resistances and mechanical losses

* White and Woodson, *op. cit.*, pp. 180–190.

and use the same excitations we had in Section 4.1.6a, namely balanced two-phase currents on the stator,

$$i_{as} = I_s \cos \omega t, \tag{4.2.32}$$

$$i_{bs} = I_s \sin \omega t, \tag{4.2.33}$$

direct current on the rotor,

$$i_r = I_r, \tag{4.2.34}$$

and the position source

$$\theta = \omega t + \gamma. \tag{4.2.35}$$

Like the smooth-air-gap machine in Section 4.1.6a, it can be verified by direct substitution that there is constant flux linking the rotor winding, hence no induced voltage. Thus we could have excited the field winding with a constant-voltage source, as is usual in practice. It is convenient analytically, however, to use the constant current of (4.2.34), and there is no loss of generality in the steady-state analysis. For realistic transient analyses a rotor winding voltage source with a series resistance must be used.

Substitution of (4.2.32) to (4.2.35) into (4.2.31) yields for the steady-state instantaneous torque produced by the electromechanical coupling system,

$$T^e = MI_r I_s [\sin \omega t \cos (\omega t + \gamma) - \cos \omega t \sin (\omega t + \gamma)]$$

$$- L_2 I_s^2 [\cos^2 \omega t - \sin^2 \omega t] \sin (2\omega t + 2\gamma)$$

$$+ 2L_2 I_s^2 \cos \omega t \sin \omega t \cos (2\omega t + 2\gamma). \tag{4.2.36}$$

The use of appropriate trigonometric* identities allows the simplification of this expression to the form

$$T^e = -MI_r I_s \sin \gamma - L_2 I_s^2 \sin 2\gamma. \tag{4.2.37}$$

This instantaneous torque is constant because the stator windings with balanced excitation produce a constant amplitude rotating flux wave and the salient-pole rotor is at an instantaneous position fixed with respect to this rotating field.

Comparison of (4.2.37) with (4.1.43) shows that saliency has added a term to the torque expression for a smooth-rotor machine.

Neglecting stator (armature) winding resistance, the terminal voltage of stator winding a is

$$v_{as} = \frac{d\lambda_{as}}{dt}. \tag{4.2.38}$$

---

* $\sin x \cos y - \cos x \sin y = \sin (x - y)$; $\cos 2x = \cos^2 x - \sin^2 x$; $2 \cos x \sin x = \sin 2x$.

Substitution of (4.2.32) to (4.2.35) into (4.2.28) and that result into (4.2.38) yields

$$v_{as} = I_s \frac{d}{dt} \{[L_0 + L_2 \cos(2\omega t + 2\gamma)] \cos \omega t + L_2 \sin \omega t \sin(2\omega t + 2\gamma)\}$$

$$+ MI_r \frac{d}{dt} [\cos(\omega t + \gamma)]. \quad (4.2.39)$$

The use of trigonometric identities reduces this equation to the form

$$v_{as} = \frac{d}{dt} [L_0 I_s \cos \omega t + L_2 I_s \cos(\omega t + 2\gamma) + MI_r \cos(\omega t + \gamma)]. \quad (4.2.40)$$

We define the complex quantities

$$v_{as} = \text{Re}\,(\hat{V}_s e^{j\omega t}), \quad i_{as} = \text{Re}\,(I_s e^{j\omega t}), \quad \cos(\omega t + \alpha) = \text{Re}\,(e^{j\omega t} e^{j\alpha})$$

and use the standard techniques of steady-state ac circuit theory to write

$$\hat{V}_s = j\omega L_0 I_s + j\omega L_2 I_s e^{j2\gamma} + j\omega MI_r e^{j\gamma}. \quad (4.2.41)$$

We define the complex voltage amplitude $\hat{E}_f$ generated by field (rotor) current, as we did for the smooth-air-gap machine in (4.1.19), as

$$\hat{E}_f = j\omega MI_r e^{j\gamma} \quad (4.2.42)$$

and rewrite (4.2.41) as

$$\hat{V}_s = j\omega L_0 I_s + j\omega L_2 I_s e^{j2\gamma} + \hat{E}_f. \quad (4.2.43)$$

This is the same form as (4.1.50) for the smooth-air-gap machine with the addition of the second term due to saliency.

Because of this term, it is not possible to draw a simple equivalent circuit for the salient-pole machine as we did in Fig. 4.1.12 for the smooth-air-gap machine. We can, however, draw vector diagrams to show the relations among variables as we did for the smooth-air-gap machine in Fig. 4.1.13. These diagrams, which illustrate generator and motor operation in the salient-pole machine, appear in Fig. 4.2.5. Note that the additional term due to saliency does not greatly change the over-all nature of the vector diagram.

When analyzing salient-pole synchronous machines with conventional nomenclature, the sum of the two reactance voltages $(j\omega L_0 I_s + j\omega L_2 I_s e^{j2\gamma})$ is normally decomposed into two components, one parallel to $\hat{E}_f$, called the *direct-axis* reactance voltage, and one perpendicular to $\hat{E}_f$, called the *quadrature axis* reactance voltage.*

To complete the description of the steady-state properties of salient-pole machines we need to assume stator excitation from constant-amplitude

---

* See, for example, Fitzgerald and Kingsley, *op. cit.*, Chapter 5.

voltage sources, as is done in practice, and to express the torque T^e in terms of the terminal voltage. It can be established quite easily from the vector diagram in Fig. 4.2.5a or 4.2.5b that

$$\omega(L_0 - L_2)I_s \sin \gamma = V_s \sin \delta \qquad (4.2.44)$$

and

$$\omega(L_0 + L_2)I_s \cos \gamma = V_s \cos \delta - E_f, \qquad (4.2.45)$$

where

$$V_s = |\hat{V}_s|,$$
$$E_f = |\hat{E}_f|;$$

δ is defined in Fig. 4.2.5 and is positive in the counterclockwise direction. The use of (4.2.44) and (4.2.45) to eliminate the angle γ and (4.2.42) for E_f in (4.2.37) lead to the desired form of the torque equation

$$T^e = -\frac{E_f V_s}{\omega^2(L_0 + L_2)} \sin \delta - \frac{L_2 V_s^2}{\omega^2(L_0^2 - L_2^2)} \sin 2\delta. \qquad (4.2.46)$$

When we compare this result with (4.1.52) for the smooth-air-gap machine, we find that the first term of (4.2.46) is the same form as (4.1.52). The second term in (4.2.46) depends solely on the presence of saliency. When saliency is removed, $L_2 = 0$, the second term in (4.2.46) goes to zero, and the first term reduces to (4.1.52) for the smooth-air-gap machine.

The two terms of (4.2.46) are plotted separately with dashed lines and the

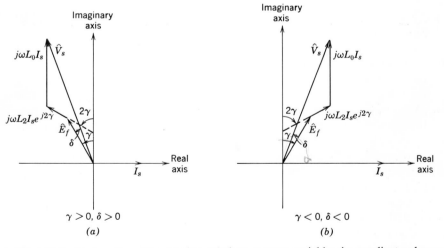

Fig. 4.2.5 Vector diagrams showing relations among variables in a salient-pole synchronous machine. Diagrams drawn for $L_0 = 3L_2$: (a) generator operation; (b) motor operation.

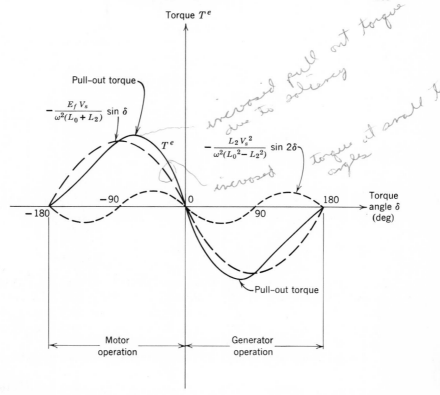

Fig. 4.2.6 Torque versus torque angle for a salient-pole synchronous machine. Curves plotted for $L_0 = 5L_2$ and $E_f = V_s$.

total torque in a solid line in Fig. 4.2.6. These curves are plotted for

$$L_0 = 5L_2,$$

which is typical for water-wheel generators,* and for

$$E_f = V_s.$$

Note from Fig. 4.2.6 that the presence of saliency has increased both the pull-out torque and the torque produced at small angles, which is quite important for transient behavior.

It should be clear from what we have done so far in this section that vector diagrams and V-curves can be drawn for salient-pole machines and that they will be similar to those for the smooth-air-gap machine shown in

---

* See, for example, Fitzgerald and Kingsley, *op. cit.*, Table 5-1, p. 237. In their nomenclature $X_d = \omega(L_0 + L_2)$ and $X_q = \omega(L_0 - L_2)$.

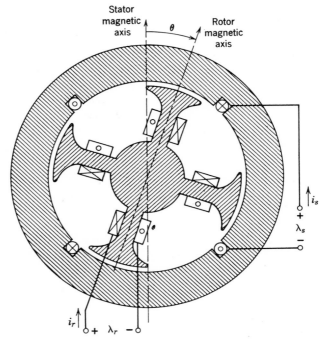

Fig. 4.2.7 Four-pole, single-phase, salient-pole machine with saliency on rotor.

Fig. 4.1.15. The process is straightforward and the interpretation is the same; consequently it is not repeated here.

All of the discussions of polyphase machines and excitations in Section 4.1.7 and of the number of poles in Section 4.1.8 apply equally well to salient pole machines, with the understanding that there is one polar projection per pole in a salient-pole machine; for example, Fig. 4.2.7 is a schematic drawing of a four-pole, single-phase machine.

In our discussions of synchronous machines in this section and in Section 4.1.6a we have made the point that a synchronous machine will produce a time-average torque and convert time-average power only at synchronous speed. Consequently, a synchronous machine alone can produce no starting torque. This is no problem with generators, but it is a problem with motors and synchronous condensers. A few machines are started by auxiliary starting motors, but the vast majority are started as induction machines. Conducting bars are mounted axially in the pole faces and shorted together at the ends to form a squirrel-cage winding, as shown for a motor in Fig. 4.2.2. Such a winding is conventionally called a *damper winding* or *amortisseur winding* because, in addition to acting as an induction motor winding for starting, it also damps out transients in torque angle. Operation as an induction motor brings the speed to near synchronous speed. The torque oscillations resulting from the interaction between the rotor field due to dc excitation and the rotating stator field occur at the slip frequency, which is quite low. This allows the oscillating torque ample time to accelerate the rotor inertia and pull it into step at synchronous speed during one half cycle. In a turbo-generator the solid steel rotor provides enough induction-motor action for adequate damping and no separate damper winding is used (see Fig. 4.1.10).

4.3 DISCUSSION

At this point it is worthwhile to re-emphasize several points made in this chapter.

First, although we have treated two geometrical configurations, the techniques are applicable to other rotating machines by simple extensions and modifications. Thus we should understand the basic concepts that are quite simple physically.

Second, we have considered in some detail the steady-state characteristics of some standard machine types for two purposes: to illustrate how the transition is actually made from basic concepts to practical descriptions of steady-state terminal behavior and to present the characteristics of some of the most important rotating machines.

Next, when the reader thinks back through the material presented in this chapter he will realize that the basic concepts of energy conversion in rotating machines are quite simple, though the mathematics sometimes becomes lengthy. As we indicated earlier, the symmetries that exist in rotating machines have led to orderly mathematical procedures for handling the manipulation. Thus rotating machine theory may appear formidable at first glance, but we, you and the authors, know that this is not so.

Finally, we want to state again that among all electromechanical devices, past, present, and forseeable future, rotating machines occur in the greatest numbers and in the widest variety of sizes and types. Thus they form an important part of any study of electromechanics.

PROBLEMS

4.1. The object of this problem is to analyze a physical configuration that yields the electrical terminal relations of (4.1.6) and (4.1.7) almost exactly. The system of Fig. 4P.1 consists of two concentric cylinders of ferromagnetic material with infinite permeability and zero conductivity. Both cylinders have length l and are separated by the air gap g. As indicated in the figure, the rotor carries a winding of N_r turns distributed sinusoidally and

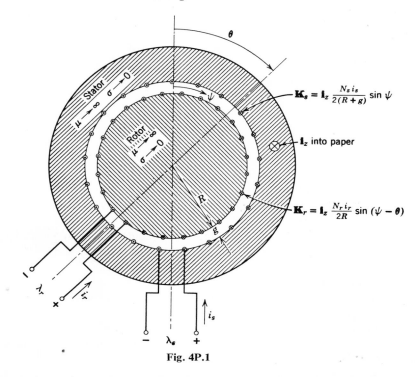

$$\mathbf{K}_s = \mathbf{1}_z \frac{N_s i_s}{2(R+g)} \sin \psi$$

$\mathbf{1}_z$ into paper

$$\mathbf{K}_r = \mathbf{1}_z \frac{N_r i_r}{2R} \sin(\psi - \theta)$$

Fig. 4P.1

having negligible radial thickness. The stator carries a winding of N_s turns distributed sinusoidally and having negligible radial thickness. Current through these windings leads to sinusoidally distributed surface currents as indicated. In the analysis we neglect the effects of end turns and assume $g \ll R$ so that the radial variation of magnetic field can be neglected.

(a) Find the radial component of air-gap flux density due to stator current alone.

(b) Find the radial component of air-gap flux density due to rotor current alone.

(c) Use the flux densities found in parts (a) and (b) to find λ_s and λ_r in the form of (4.1.6) and (4.1.7). In particular, evaluate L_s, L_r, and M in terms of given data.

4.2. Rework Problem 4.1 with the more practical uniform winding distribution representable by surface current densities

$$\mathbf{K}_s = \begin{cases} \mathbf{i}_z \dfrac{N_s i_s}{\pi(R+g)}, & \text{for } 0 < \psi < \pi, \\[3mm] -\mathbf{i}_z \dfrac{N_s i_s}{\pi(R+g)}; & \text{for } \pi < \psi < 2\pi, \end{cases}$$

$$\mathbf{K}_r = \begin{cases} \mathbf{i}_z \dfrac{N_r i_r}{\pi R}, & \text{for } 0 < (\psi - \theta) < \pi, \\[3mm] -\mathbf{i}_z \dfrac{N_r i_r}{\pi R}, & \text{for } \pi < (\psi - \theta) < 2\pi. \end{cases}$$

In part (c) you will find the mutual inductance to be expressed as an infinite series like (4.1.4).

4.3. With reference to Problems 4.1 and 4.2, show that if either the rotor winding or the stator winding is sinusoidally distributed as in Problem 4.1, the mutual inductance contains only a space fundamental term, regardless of the winding distribution on the other member.

4.4. The machine represented schematically in Fig. 4P.4 has uniform winding distributions. As indicated by Problem 4.2, the electrical terminal relations are ideally

$$\lambda_s = L_s i_s + i_r \sum_{n \text{ odd}} \frac{M_o}{n^4} \cos n\theta,$$

$$\lambda_r = L_r i_r + i_s \sum_{n \text{ odd}} \frac{M_o}{n^4} \cos n\theta,$$

where L_s, L_r, and M_o are constants. We now constrain the machine as follows: $i_r = I =$ constant; $\theta = \omega t$, $\omega =$ constant, stator winding open-circuited $i_s = 0$.

(a) Find the instantaneous stator voltage $v_s(t)$.
(b) Find the ratio of the amplitude of the nth harmonic stator voltage to the amplitude of the fundamental component of stator voltage.
(c) Plot one complete cycle of $v_s(t)$ found in (a).

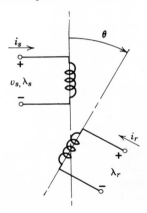

Fig. 4P.4

4.5. Calculate the electromagnetic torque T^e of (4.1.8) by using the electrical terminal relations (4.1.6) and (4.1.7) and the assumption that the coupling system is conservative.

4.6. A schematic representation of a rotating machine is shown in Fig. 4P.6. The rotor winding is superconducting and the rotor has moment of inertia J. The machine is constructed so that the electrical terminal relations are $\lambda_s = L_s i_s + M i_r \cos \theta$, $\lambda_r = M i_s \cos \theta + L_r i_r$. The machine is placed in operation as follows:

(a) With the rotor (r) terminals open-circuited and the rotor position at $\theta = 0$, the current i_s is raised to I_o.
(b) The rotor (r) terminals are short circuited to conserve the flux λ_r, regardless of $\theta(t)$ and $i_s(t)$.
(c) The current i_s is constrained by the independent current source $i(t)$.

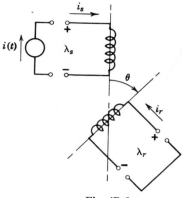

Fig. 4P.6

Write the equation of motion for the shaft with no external mechanical torque applied. Your answer should be one equation involving $\theta(t)$ as the only unknown. Damping may be ignored.

4.7. A smooth-air-gap machine with one winding on the rotor and one on the stator (see Fig. 4.1.1) has the electrical terminal relations of (4.1.1) and (4.1.2).

$$\lambda_s = L_s i_s + L_{sr}(\theta)i_r, \tag{4.1.1}$$

$$\lambda_r = L_{sr}(\theta)i_s + L_r i_r. \tag{4.1.2}$$

The mutual inductance $L_{sr}(\theta)$ contains two spatial harmonics, the fundamental and the third. Thus $L_{sr}(\theta) = M_1 \cos \theta + M_3 \cos 3\theta$, where M_1 and M_3 are constants.

(a) Find the torque of electric origin as a function of i_s, i_r, θ, M_1, and M_3.

(b) Constrain the machine with the current sources $i_s = I_s \sin \omega_s t$, $i_r = I_r \sin \omega_r t$ and the position source $\theta = \omega_m t + \gamma$, where I_s, I_r, ω_s, ω_r and γ are constants. Find the values of ω_m at which the machine can produce an average torque and find an expression for the average torque for each value of ω_m found.

4.8. The smooth-air-gap machine of Fig. 4.1.1 with the terminal relations given by (4.1.6) to (4.1.8) is constrained as follows: single-frequency rotor current, $i_r = I_r \sin \omega_r t$; stator current containing fundamental and third harmonic, $i_s = I_{s1} \sin \omega_s t + I_{s3} \sin 3\omega_s t$; and the position source $\theta = \omega_m t + \gamma$, where I_r, I_{s1}, I_{s3}, ω_r, ω_s, and γ are constants. Find the values of ω_m at which the machine can produce an average torque and give an expression for the average torque for each value of ω_m found.

4.9. Compute the torque T^e of (4.1.23) by using the electrical terminal relations of (4.1.19) to (4.1.22) and the assumption that the coupling system is conservative.

4.10. A smooth-air-gap machine has a two-phase set of stator windings, each with a total of N turns. The windings are distributed sinusoidally and currents in them produce surface current densities as indicated in Fig. 4P.10. When $g \ll R$, the radial flux density produced in the air gap by each winding (see Problem 4.1), is

$$B_{ra} = \frac{\mu_0 N i_a}{2g} \cos \psi,$$

$$B_{rb} = \frac{\mu_0 N i_b}{2g} \sin \psi.$$

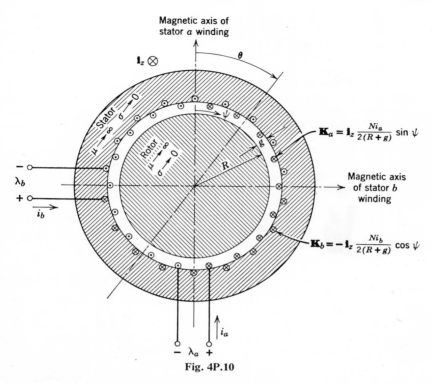

Magnetic axis of stator a winding

$\mathbf{K}_a = \mathbf{1}_z \dfrac{Ni_a}{2(R+g)} \sin \psi$

Magnetic axis of stator b winding

$\mathbf{K}_b = -\mathbf{1}_z \dfrac{Ni_b}{2(R+g)} \cos \psi$

Fig. 4P.10

(a) For the two-phase excitation $i_a = I_a \cos \omega t$, $i_b = I_b \sin \omega t$, which is unbalanced in amplitude, find the total radial flux density.

(b) Express the answer to part (a) as a sum of two traveling waves. Identify the *forward* and *backward* components and show that their respective angular velocities are $\omega_f = \omega$ and $\omega_b = -\omega$.

(c) Evaluate the ratio of the amplitudes of backward and forward waves. Show that the ratio $\to 0$ for a balanced excitation (i.e., consider the limit for $I_b \to I_a$).

(d) Discuss how to achieve a constant amplitude backward wave only. This is the method used to reverse the direction of rotation of an ac machine.

4.11. Rework Problem 4.10 and replace the excitation of part (a) with $i_a = I \cos \omega t$, $i_b = I \sin (\omega t + \beta)$. This is a two-phase set of currents, balanced in amplitude but unbalanced in phase. For part (c) balanced excitation occurs when $\beta \to 0$.

4.12. Use (4.1.53) as the starting point to show that for steady-state operation the electrical power into a two-phase synchronous machine is equal to the mechanical power delivered, as expressed by (4.1.54).

4.13. The two-phase equivalent of a large turbogenerator of the type now being used to generate power is as follows:

2-phase
60 Hz, 2-pole
Rated terminal voltage, 17,000 V rms

Rated terminal current, 21,300 A rms
Rating, 724×10^6 VA
Rated power factor, 0.85
Armature inductance, $L_s = 4.4 \times 10^{-3}$ H
Maximum value of armature-field mutual inductance, $M = 0.030$ H
Rated field current, $I_f = 6100$ A

Calculate and plot a family of V-curves for this generator. The V-curves are plots of armature current versus field current at constant power and constant terminal voltage (see Fig. 4.1.15). Your family of curves should be bounded by rated armature and field current, zero-power-factor, and 90° torque angle. Indicate which of these limits the curves. Also indicate on your plot the 0 and 0.85 power factors, both leading and lagging, and the unity power factor. Plot curves for 0, $\frac{1}{4}$, $\frac{1}{2}$, $\frac{3}{4}$, and full rated load of 615 MW and for rated armature voltage. It will be convenient to normalize armature current to the rated value and field current to that value necessary to produce rated terminal voltage with the armature open-circuited.

4.14. It is customary to define the complex power produced by an alternator as $P + jQ$, where P is real power and Q is reactive power. For a two-phase machine with balanced currents and voltages and a phase angle ϕ

$$v_a = \text{Re}\,(\hat{V}e^{j\omega t}), \qquad i_a = \text{Re}\,(\hat{I}e^{j\omega t}),$$
$$v_b = \text{Re}\,(-j\hat{V}e^{j\omega t}), \qquad i_b = \text{Re}\,(-j\hat{I}e^{j\omega t}),$$

where $\hat{V} = V$ and $\hat{I} = Ie^{-j\phi}$. The complex power supplied by both phases is $P + jQ = \hat{V}\hat{I}^* = VI\cos\phi + jVI\sin\phi$. By convention $Q > 0$ when $\hat{I}$ lags $\hat{V}$ (the load is inductive).

A capability curve for an alternator is a plot of P versus Q for constant armature voltage and for maximum allowable operating conditions defined by rated armature current, rated field current, or steady-state stability (torque angle δ approaching a critical value which we take to be 90°). Plot the capability curve for the alternator described in Problem 4.13 for operation at rated voltage. Indicate on your plot the limit that determines that part of the curve. It is useful to normalize both P and Q to the rating of the alternator:

4.15. An automobile speedometer consists of a permanent magnet mounted on a rotating shaft connected to the automobile transmission. An aluminum "drag cup" with a pointer mounted on it is placed around this rotating magnet. The cup is free to rotate through an angle ψ but is restrained by a torsion spring that provides a torque $T_s = -K\psi$. The angular position of the cup can be used to determine the angular velocity of the shaft connected to the magnet and therefore the speed of the automobile. The model to be used in analyzing the speedometer is illustrated in Fig. 4P.15. The permanent magnet is represented by a coil excited by a constant-current source. The drag cup is simulated by two coils shunted by resistances. These coils are attached to a rotatable frame, which in turn is restrained by the torsion spring. An appropriate electrical model of the coupling field is

$$\lambda_1 = Mi_3\cos(\phi - \psi) + Li_1,$$
$$\lambda_2 = Mi_3\sin(\phi - \psi) + Li_2,$$
$$\lambda_3 = L_3 i_3 + Mi_1\cos(\phi - \psi) + Mi_2\sin(\phi - \psi).$$

Assuming that the rotational velocity of the shaft is constant (i.e., the speed of the car is constant), find the deflection of the rotatable frame (of the speedometer pointer) as a function of the shaft rotational velocity $\dot{\phi}$. You may assume that the device is designed in such a way that

$$\left| L\frac{di}{dt} \right| \ll |Ri|.$$

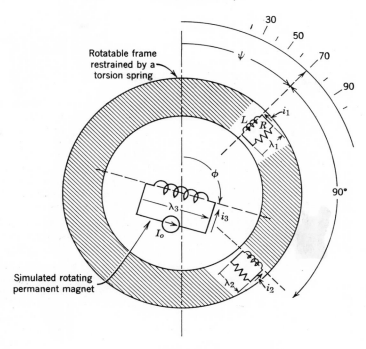

Rotatable frame restrained by a torsion spring

Simulated rotating permanent magnet

Fig. 4P.15

4.16. For nomenclature, refer to Fig. 4.1.17. The two-phase equivalent of a large, two-pole, polyphase, 60-Hz induction motor has the following parameters for operation at 60 Hz: $R_r = 0.100$ ohm, $\omega_s M = 4.50$ ohms, and $\omega_s(L_s - M) = \omega_s(L_r - M) = 0.300$ ohm. Neglect armature resistance. For operation at a constant amplitude of armature voltage $V_s = \sqrt{2}\,500$ V peak, calculate and plot torque, armature current, volt-ampere input, electrical power input, and mechanical power output as functions of mechanical speed for the range $0 < \omega_m < \omega_s = 120\pi$ rad/sec.

4.17. The induction motor of Problem 4.16 is driving a fan load with the torque speed characteristic $T_m = -B\omega_m^3$, where $B = 7.50 \times 10^{-6}$ N-M sec³/rad³. Assume steady-state operation.

(a) For operation with balanced armature voltage of $V_s = \sqrt{2}\,500$ V peak calculate the steady-state slip, mechanical power into the fan, electrical power input, and power factor.

(b) Calculate and plot the quantities of part (a) as functions of armature voltage for a range $\sqrt{2}\,450 < V_s < \sqrt{2}\,550$ V peak.

4.18. This problem is a version of the machine analysis in Problem 4.1 but with a three-phase winding on the stator. The geometry is illustrated in Fig. 4P.18; N_s is the total number of turns on each stator phase and N_r is the total number of turns in the rotor winding. The

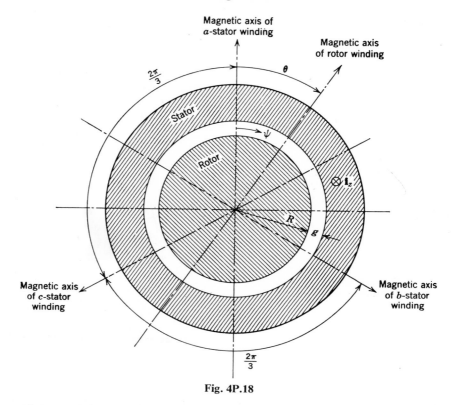

Fig. 4P.18

surface current densities produced by the three armature currents on the surface at $R + g$ are

$$\mathbf{K}_a = \mathbf{i}_z \frac{N_s i_a}{2(R + g)} \sin \psi,$$

$$\mathbf{K}_b = \mathbf{i}_z \frac{N_s i_b}{2(R + g)} \sin \left(\psi - \frac{2\pi}{3} \right),$$

$$\mathbf{K}_c = \mathbf{i}_z \frac{N_s i_c}{2(R + g)} \sin \left(\psi - \frac{4\pi}{3} \right).$$

The surface current density due to rotor current on the surface at R is

$$\mathbf{K}_r = \mathbf{i}_z \frac{N_r i_r}{2R} \sin (\psi - \theta).$$

Assume $g \ll R$ so that there is no appreciable variation in the radial component of magnetic field across the air gap.

   (a) Find the radial flux density due to current in each winding.
   (b) Find the mutual inductance between the a and b windings on the stator.
   (c) Write the electrical terminal relations for the machine.
   (d) Find the torque T^e of electrical origin.

4.19. Consider the machine in Problem 4.18 with the stator excitations

$$i_a = I_a \cos \omega t,$$

$$i_b = I_b \cos \left(\omega t - \frac{2\pi}{3} \right),$$

$$i_c = I_c \cos \left(\omega t - \frac{4\pi}{3} \right).$$

(a) Show that the radial component of air-gap flux density is expressible as a combination of two constant-amplitude waves, one rotating in the positive θ-direction with the speed ω and the other rotating in the negative θ-direction with speed ω.

(b) Show that when $I_a = I_b = I_c$ the amplitude of the wave traveling in the negative θ-direction goes to zero.

4.20. A four-pole smooth-air-gap machine has a two-phase set of stator windings, each with a total of N turns. The windings are distributed sinusoidally and currents in them produce surface current densities as indicated in Fig. 4P.20. When $g \ll R$, the radial flux density produced in the air gap by each winding is (see Problems 4.1 and 4.10)

$$B_{ra} = \frac{\mu_0 N i_a}{2g} \cos 2\psi,$$

$$B_{rb} = \frac{\mu_0 N i_b}{2g} \sin 2\psi.$$

(a) For the two-phase excitation, $i_a = I_a \cos \omega t$, $i_b = I_b \sin \omega t$, which is unbalanced in amplitude, find the total radial flux density.

(b) Express the answer to (a) as a sum of two constant-amplitude traveling waves.

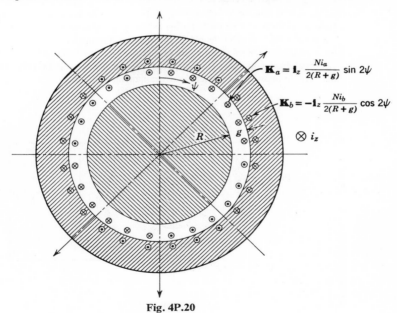

$$\mathbf{K}_a = \mathbf{i}_z \frac{N i_a}{2(R+g)} \sin 2\psi$$

$$\mathbf{K}_b = -\mathbf{i}_z \frac{N i_b}{2(R+g)} \cos 2\psi$$

$\otimes\, i_z$

Fig. 4P.20

Identify the forward and backward components and show that their respective angular velocities are $\omega_f = \omega/2$ and $\omega_b = -\omega/2$.

(c) Show that the amplitude of the backward wave goes to zero when $I_b = I_a$ and that the amplitude of the forward wave goes to zero when $I_b = -I_a$.

4.21. Rework Problem 4.20 for a p-pole-pair machine for which the component radial air-gap flux densities are

$$B_{ra} = \frac{\mu_0 N i_a}{2g} \cos p\psi,$$

$$B_{rb} = \frac{\mu_0 N i_b}{2g} \sin p\psi.$$

Assume the same excitation as in part (a) of Problem 4.20. In part (b) the forward and backward waves have angular velocities $\omega_f = \omega/p$ and $\omega_b = -\omega/p$.

4.22. Derive the electromagnetic torque of (4.2.9), starting with the electrical terminal relations of (4.2.7) and (4.2.8) and the assumption that the coupling system is conservative.

4.23. The salient-pole, synchronous machine of Fig. 4P.23 is electrically linear and lossless and has a terminal inductance expressed as

$$L = \frac{L_o}{(1 - 0.25 \cos 4\theta - 0.25 \cos 8\theta)},$$

where L_o is a positive constant. This is an alternative mathematical representation to the form given by (4.2.3).

(a) Describe briefly why the dependence of this inductance on θ is physically reasonable.

(b) Find the torque of electric origin T^e as a function of flux linkage λ, angle θ, and the constants of the system.

(c) As shown in Fig. 4P.23, the terminals are excited by a sinusoidal voltage source such that the flux λ is given by $\lambda(t) = \Lambda_o \cos \omega t$, where Λ_o and ω are positive constants. The rotor is driven by a constant-angular-velocity source such that $\theta(t) = \Omega t + \delta$, where Ω and δ are constants. Find the values of Ω, in terms of the electrical frequency ω, at which time-average power can be converted by the machine between the electrical and mechanical systems.

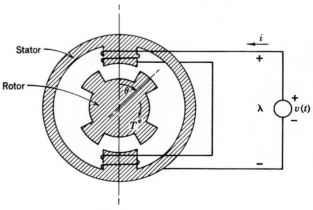

Fig. 4P.23

4.24. The two-phase equivalent of a salient-pole, synchronous motor has the following parameter values and ratings [see (4.2.28) to (4.2.30) for definitions]

2-phase	60 Hz
Rated output power,	6000 hp
Power factor,	0.8 leading
Rated armature voltage,	3000 V rms
Voltage coefficient,	$\omega M = 350$ V/A
Direct axis reactance,	$\omega(L_0 + L_2) = 4$ ohms
Quadrature axis reactance,	$\omega(L_0 - L_2) = 2.2$ ohms

[handwritten: $i_d = \dfrac{\sqrt{2}|V|\sin\delta - E_f}{X_s}$]

[handwritten: $i_q = \dfrac{\sqrt{2}|V|\sin\delta}{X_s}$]

(a) Find the field current necessary to give maximum rated conditions at rated voltage. This is rated field current.

(b) Calculate and plot a family of V-curves for loads of 6000, 3000, and zero hp and rated voltage; V-curves are plots of armature current as a function of field current for constant load power (see Problem 4.13). Indicate the factor that limits the extent of the plot: rated armature current, rated field current, or steady-state stability (pull-out torque is approached).

4.25. As discussed at the end of Section 4.1.6a, synchronous condensers are essentially synchronous machines operating with no shaft torque. They are used for power-factor correction and they are conventionally of the salient-pole type of construction. Start with (4.2.41), assume zero shaft torque [$\gamma = 0$ from (4.2.37)] and operation at constant armature voltage amplitude, and construct vector diagrams to show the machine appearing capacitive and inductive.

4.26. This is a problem that involves the use of a synchronous condenser to correct power factor in a power system. The correction is actually achieved by using the synchronous condenser to regulate voltage. We consider one phase of a balanced two-phase system. In Fig. 4P.26a a power system feeds a steady-state load which has admittance $Ye^{-j\phi}$ as shown.

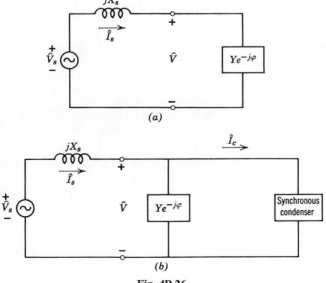

Fig. 4P.26

The Thevenin equivalent circuit of the system, as viewed from the load, is the source $\hat{V}_s$ in series with the inductive reactance jX_s. To fix ideas assume the following parameters and excitations: $V_s = \sqrt{2}\ 100{,}000$ V peak, $X_s = 10$ ohms, $Y = 0.01$ mho.

(a) Find the ratio of the magnitudes of the load voltage V and the source voltage V_s for $\phi = 0$ and $\phi = 45$ degrees.

(b) Now a synchronous condenser is connected across the load as shown in Fig. 4P.26*b* and draws current $\hat{I}_c$. Find the volt-ampere rating required for the synchronous condenser to make the ratio $|\hat{V}|/|\hat{V}_s|$ equal to unity for each case in part (a). Compare each with the real power drawn by the load.

4.27. A two-phase, 60-Hz, salient-pole, 2-pole, synchronous motor has the following ratings and constants:

Rated output power,	1000 hp
Rated armature volts,	$\sqrt{2}\ 1000$ V peak
Rated power factor,	unity
Direct axis reactance,	$\omega(L_0 + L_2) = 3.0$ ohms
Quadrature axis reactance,	$\omega(L_0 - L_2) = 2.0$ ohms
Speed voltage coefficient,	$\omega M = 150$ V/A

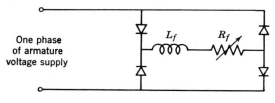

One phase of armature voltage supply

L_f R_f

Fig. 4P.27

(a) The field winding of the motor is supplied from one phase of the supply by a full-wave bridge rectifier as shown in Fig. 4P.27. The field winding inductance is large enough that only the dc component of field voltage need be considered. Calculate the total field circuit resistance R_f necessary to achieve unity-power-factor operation at rated voltage with 1000 hp load.

(b) Calculate and plot the torque angle δ as a function of armature supply voltage from 10 per cent above rating down to the value at which the motor can no longer carry the load.

4.28. The two-phase equivalent of a large, salient-pole, 72-pole, water-wheel generator of the type now being used has the following constants and ratings:

Rating,	200×10^6 V-A
Frequency,	60 Hz
Power factor,	0.85 lagging
Rated terminal voltage,	10,000 V rms
Rated armature current,	10,000 A rms
Armature inductance,	$L_0 = 2.65 \times 10^{-3}$ H
	$L_2 = 0.53 \times 10^{-3}$ H
Maximum armature-field mutual inductance,	$M = 0.125$ H

(a) Calculate the field current necessary to achieve rated conditions of armature voltage, current, and power factor.

(b) Plot a capability curve for this generator. See Problem 4.14 for a description of a capability curve. In this case the stability limit of maximum steady-state torque will occur for $\delta < 90°$ (see Fig. 4.2.6).

4.29. Figure 4P.29 shows a pair of grounded conductors that form the rotor of a proposed rotating device. Two pairs of fixed conductors form the stator; one pair is at the potential

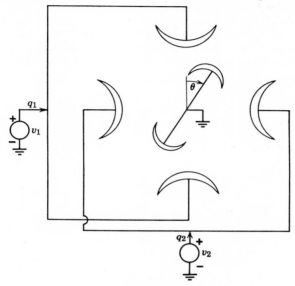

Fig. 4P.29

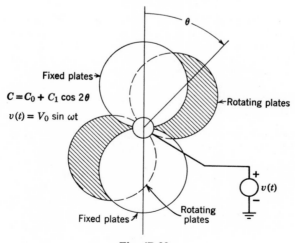

Fig. 4P.30

v_1 and supports a total charge q_1; the other is at the potential v_2 and supports the total charge q_2. Given that $q_1 = C_o(1 + \cos 2\theta)v_1$, $q_2 = C_o(1 + \sin 2\theta)v_2$, where C_o is a given positive constant,

(a) what is the electrical torque exerted on the rotor in the θ direction?

(b) The voltages v_1 and v_2 are now constrained to be $v_1 = V_o \cos \omega t$, $v_2 = V_o \sin \omega t$. Under what condition(s) will the device produce a time-average torque?

(c) Under the condition(s) of (b), what is the time-average torque?

4.30. A pair of capacitor plates is attached to a rotating shaft in such a way that when θ is zero they are directly opposite a pair of fixed plates. It is assumed that the variation in capacitance can be approximately described by the relation $C = C_0 + C_1 \cos 2\theta$. If a potential difference $v(t) = V_o \sin \omega t$ is applied to the plates through a slip ring, what are the shaft rotational velocities at which the device can behave like a motor?

Chapter 5

LUMPED-PARAMETER ELECTROMECHANICAL DYNAMICS

5.0 INTRODUCTION

The representation of lumped-parameter electromechanical systems by means of mathematical models has been the subject of the preceding chapters. Our objective in this chapter is to study their dynamical behavior. Mathematically, we are interested in the solution of differential equations of motion for given initial conditions and with given driving sources. Physically, we are interested in important phenomena that occur in electromechanical systems.

It is clear from previous examples that the differential equations that describe electromechanical systems are in most cases nonlinear. Consequently, it is impossible to develop a concise and complete mathematical theory, as is done for linear circuit theory. We shall find many systems for which we can assume "small-signal" behavior and linearize the differential equations. In these cases we have available to us the complete mathematical analysis developed for linear systems. If exact solutions are required for nonlinear differential equations, each situation must be considered separately. Machine computation is often the only efficient way of obtaining theoretical predictions. Some simple cases however, are amenable to direct integration. The physical aspects of a given problem often motivate simplifications of the mathematical model and lead to meaningful but tractable descriptions. Hence in this chapter we are as much concerned with illustrating approximations that have been found useful as with reviewing and expanding fundamental analytical techniques.

Lumped-parameter systems are described by ordinary differential equations. The partial differential equations of continuous or distributed systems are often solved by a reduction to one or more ordinary differential equations. Hence many concepts used here will prove useful in the chapters that follow.

Similarly, the physical behavior of a distributed system is sometimes most easily understood in terms of lumped parameter concepts. Examples discussed in this chapter are in many cases motivated by the physical background that they provide for more complicated interactions to be considered later.

Because the mathematics of linear systems is comparatively simple, we begin our study of the dynamic behavior of lumped-parameter electromechanical systems by considering the several types of system for which a linear model provides an adequate description. We shall then consider the types of system that are basically nonlinear and for which the differential equations can be integrated directly.

5.1 LINEAR SYSTEMS

We have stated that electromechanical systems are not usually described by linear differential equations. Many devices, however, called incremental-motion transducers, are designed to operate *approximately* as linear systems. Moreover, meaningful descriptions of the basic properties of nonlinear systems can often be obtained by making small-signal linear analyses. In the following sections we develop and illustrate linearization techniques, linearized models, and the dynamical behavior of typical systems.

5.1.1 Linear Differential Equations

First, we should recall the definition of a linear ordinary differential equation.* An nth-order equation has the form

$$\frac{d^n x}{dt^n} + A_1(t)\frac{d^{n-1}x}{dt^{n-1}} + \cdots + A_n(t)x = f(t), \tag{5.1.1}$$

where the order is determined by the highest derivative. Note that the coefficients $A_i(t)$ can in general be functions of the *independent* variable t. If, however, the coefficients were functions of the *dependent* (unknown) variable $x(t)$, the equation would be nonlinear. The "driving function" $f(t)$ is a known function of time.

The "homogeneous" form of (5.1.1) is provided by making $f(t) = 0$. There are n independent solutions $x_n(t)$ to the homogeneous equation. The general solution to (5.1.1) is a linear combination of these homogeneous solutions, plus a particular solution $x_p(t)$ to the complete equation:

$$x(t) = c_1 x_1(t) + \cdots + c_n x_n(t) + x_p(t). \tag{5.1.2}$$

Although (5.1.1) is linear, it has coefficients that are functions of the

---

* A review of differential equations can be found in such texts as L. R. Ford, *Differential Equations*, 2nd Ed., McGraw-Hill, New York, 1955.

independent variable and this can cause complications; for example, if $f(t)$ is a steady-state sinusoid of a given frequency, the solution may contain all harmonics of the driving frequency. Alternatively, if $f(t)$ is an impulse, the response varies with the time at which the impulse is applied. These complications are necessary in some cases; most of our linear systems, however, are described by differential equations with constant coefficients. For now we limit ourselves to the case in which the coefficients $A_i = a_i = $ constant, and (5.1.1) becomes

$$\frac{d^n x(t)}{dt^n} + a_1 \frac{d^{n-1} x(t)}{dt^{n-1}} + \cdots + a_n x(t) = f(t). \tag{5.1.3}$$

The solution to equations having this form is the central theme of circuit theory.* The solutions $x_i(t)$ to the homogeneous equation, when the coefficients are constant, are exponentials e^{st}, where s can in general be complex; that is, if we let

$$x(t) = \sum_{i=1}^{n} c_i e^{s_i t} \tag{5.1.4}$$

and substitute it in the homogeneous equation, we obtain

$$(s_i^n + a_1 s_i^{n-1} + \cdots + a_n) \sum_{i=1}^{n} c_i e^{s_i t} = 0 \tag{5.1.5}$$

and (5.1.4) is a solution, provided that the complex frequencies satisfy the condition

$$s_i^n + a_1 s_i^{n-1} + \cdots + a_n = 0. \tag{5.1.6}$$

Here we have an nth-order polynomial in s, hence a condition that defines the n possible values of s required in (5.1.4). The frequencies s_i that satisfy (5.1.6) are called the *natural frequencies* of the system and (5.1.6) is sometimes called the *characteristic equation*.†

Many commonly used devices are driven in the sinusoidal steady state. In this case the driving function $f(t)$ has the form

$$f(t) = \text{Re} \, [\hat{F} e^{j\omega t}]. \tag{5.1.7}$$

Here $\hat{F}$ is in general complex and determines the phase of the driving signal; for example, if $\hat{F} = 1$, $f(t) = \cos \omega t$, but, if $\hat{F} = -j$, $f(t) = \sin \omega t$. To find

---

* See, for example, F. A. Guillemin, *Theory of Linear Physical Systems*, Wiley, New York, 1963 (especially Chapter 7).
† If the characteristic equation has repeated roots, the solution must be modified slightly, see, for example, M. F. Gardner and J. L. Barnes, *Transients in Linear Systems*, Wiley, New York, 1942, pp. 159–163.

the particular solution with this drive we assume

$$x_p(t) = \text{Re} \, [\hat{X}e^{j\omega t}] \tag{5.1.8}$$

and substitute into (5.1.3) to obtain

$$\text{Re} \, \{e^{j\omega t}[\hat{X}((j\omega)^n + a_1(j\omega)^{n-1} + \cdots + a_n) - \hat{F}]\} = 0. \tag{5.1.9}$$

It follows that (5.1.8) is the particular solution if

$$\hat{X} = \frac{\hat{F}}{(j\omega)^n + a_1(j\omega)^{n-1} + \cdots + a_n}. \tag{5.1.10}$$

Note that the natural frequencies (5.1.6) are the values of $j\omega$ in (5.1.10) which lead to the possibility of a finite response $\hat{X}$ when $\hat{F} = 0$; thus the term natural frequency.

The general solution is the sum of the homogeneous solution and the driven solution (5.1.4) and (5.1.8):

$$x(t) = \sum_{i=1}^{n} c_i e^{s_i t} + \text{Re} \left[\frac{\hat{F}e^{j\omega t}}{(j\omega)^n + a_1(j\omega)^{n-1} + \cdots + a_n} \right]. \tag{5.1.11}$$

Given n initial conditions [e.g., $x(0)$, $(dx/dt)(0)$, . . . , $(d^{n-1}x/dt^{n-1})(0)$], the constants c_i can be evaluated. The first term in (5.1.11) is the transient part of the solution and the second term is the driven or steady-state part. If the system is stable (i.e., if all the s_i have negative real parts), the transient term in (5.1.11) will damp out. After a long enough time the first term will become small enough to be neglected. Then the system is said to be operating in the sinusoidal steady state and the response is given by the second term alone. When we wish to calculate the sinusoidal steady-state response, we find only the particular solution.

5.1.2 Equilibrium, Linearization, and Stability

We have already stated that useful informaton can be obtained about many electromechanical systems by making small-signal linear analyses in the vicinity of equilibrium points. In this section we introduce the concept of equilibrium and illustrate how to obtain small-signal, linear equations. In the process we shall study the nature of the small-signal behavior and define two basic types of instability that can occur in the vicinity of an equilibrium point.

5.1.2a *Static Equilibrium and Static Instability*

In general, the term *equilibrium* is used in connection with a dynamical system to indicate that the motion takes on a particularly simple form; for example, a mass M, constrained to move in the x-direction and subject to a force $f(x)$ will have a position $x(t)$ predicted by the equation [see (2.2.10) of Chapter 2]

$$M \frac{d^2x}{dt^2} = f(x). \tag{5.1.12}$$

We say that the mass is in equilibrium at any point $x = X$ such that $f(X) = 0$. Physically, we simply mean that at the point $x = X$ there is no external force to accelerate the mass, hence it is possible for the mass to retain a static position (or be in equilibrium) at this point.

The word equilibrium is used to refer not only to cases in which the dependent variables (x) take on static values that satisfy the equations of motion but also to situations, such as uniform motion, in which the general (nonlinear) equations of motion are satisfied by the equilibrium solution. Equilibria of this type were of primary interest in Chapter 4, in which the steady-state behavior of rotating magnetic field devices was considered.

Small perturbations from the equilibrium positions are predicted approximately by linearized equations of motion, which are found by assuming that the dependent variables have the form

$$x(t) = X + x'(t), \tag{5.1.13}$$

where X is the equilibrium position and $x'(t)$ is the small perturbation. It is then possible to expand nonlinear terms in a Taylor series* about the equilibrium values; for example, $f(x)$ in (5.1.12) can be expanded in the series

$$f(x) = f(X) + x' \frac{df}{dx}(X) + \tfrac{1}{2}x'^2 \frac{d^2f}{dx^2}(X) + \cdots. \tag{5.1.14}$$

Now, if x' is small enough, it is likely that the first two terms will make the most significant contributions to the series, hence the remaining terms can be ignored. Recall that by definition $f(X) = 0$ and 5.1.12 has the form,

$$\frac{d^2x'}{dt^2} + \omega_o^2 x' = 0, \tag{5.1.15}$$

where

$$\omega_o^2 = - \frac{1}{M} \frac{df}{dx}(X).$$

The resulting equation is linear and can be solved as described in Section 5.1.1. The solution has the form

$$x' = c_1 e^{j\omega_o t} + c_2 e^{-j\omega_o t}. \tag{5.1.16}$$

* F. B. Hildebrand, *Advanced Calculus for Engineers*, Prentice-Hall, New York, 1949, p. 125.

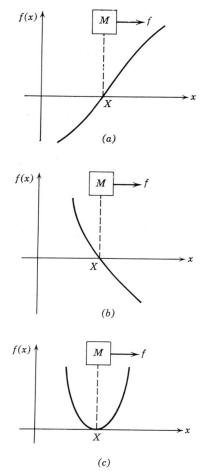

Fig. 5.1.1 Graphical representation of a force $f(x)$ which acts on the mass M with a static equilibrium at $x = X$: (a) unstable; (b) stable; (c) nonlinear.

We see that if $(df/dx)(X)$ is positive ω_o is imaginary and any small displacement of the mass (as will inevitably be supplied by noise) will lead to a motion that is unbounded. In this case we say that the equilibrium position X is unstable, and we call this type of pure exponential instability a *static* instability. We can interpret this situation physically by reference to Fig. 5.1.1a which shows a plot of $f(x)$ with a positive slope at $x = X$. If the mass moves a small distance to the right of the equilibrium point, the force f becomes positive and tends to increase the displacement still further. Thus a static experiment will reveal the presence of the instability. Although our solution cannot be trusted for long after the start of a transient, the small-signal instability provides the essential information that the mass will not remain at the equilibrium point. If df/dx is negative at $x = X$, ω_o is real and the mass will execute a sinusoidal motion about the equilibrium point with the angular frequency ω_o, as can be seen from (5.1.15) and (5.1.16). This result is also easily understood physically. Figure 5.1.1b shows a plot of force f having a negative slope at the equilibrium point. If the mass moves slightly to the right, the force becomes negative and tends to return the mass to $x = X$. When the mass reaches the equilibrium point it has finite velocity and overshoots. In the absence of further external disturbances the mass will oscillate sinusoidally about the equilibrium point with constant amplitude. We call this motion stable because the response is bounded. If there were damping in the system, the amplitude of the oscillation would decay until the mass came to rest at the equilibrium point.

Once a solution has been found to the linearized equations of motion, it is possible to check the accuracy of the prediction by considering the significance of the terms that were dropped in (5.1.14), compared with the second term. An extreme case in which linearized equations would not adequately describe the motion is illustrated in Fig. 5.1.1c, where the slope of $f(x)$ is also zero at the equilibrium point. In this case the lowest order, nonzero term in (5.1.14) must be retained.

Example 5.1.1. To illustrate some of these ideas we consider again the magnetic field transducer shown schematically in Fig. 5.1.2. The electric terminal relations were calculated in Example 2.1.1 and the equations of motion were written in Example 3.2.1.

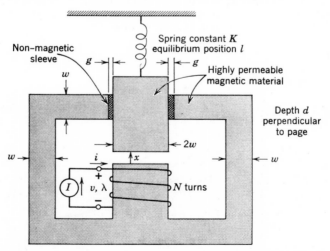

Fig. 5.1.2 Magnetic field transducer used to demonstrate linearization techniques in Example 5.1.1.

The electric terminal relation, as described by (d) and (e) of Example 2.1.1, is

$$\lambda = \frac{L_o i}{1 + x/g} \tag{a}$$

where

$$L_o = \frac{\mu_0 N^2 (2wd)}{g} \tag{b}$$

is the inductance with the air gap closed ($x = 0$). The force of electric origin is given by (d) of Example 3.2.1 and is

$$f^e = - \frac{L_o i^2}{2g(1 + x/g)^2}. \tag{c}$$

Because the electrical excitation is a current source, the equation for the electrical part of the system is not of interest. In the mechanical part we neglect damping; consequently, the equation of motion for the mechanical node (x) is [see (e) of Example 3.2.1]

$$M \frac{d^2 x}{dt^2} = - \frac{L_o I^2}{2g(1 + x/g)^2} - K(x - l). \tag{d}$$

This equation has the form of (5.1.12):

$$f(x) = - \frac{L_o I^2}{2g(1 + x/g)^2} - K(x - l) = f^e(x) + f^s(x). \tag{e}$$

In static equilibrium at $x = X$, (d) becomes

$$f(X) = - \frac{L_o I^2}{2g(1 + X/g)^2} - K(X - l) = 0. \tag{f}$$

This is a cubic equation in X which cannot be solved easily. Its properties, however, can be investigated by sketching the two terms as shown in Fig. 5.1.3. In this figure the negative of f^e has been plotted as a function of X on the same scale as a plot of f^s. Hence the intersections represent solutions to (f); that is, the points X_1 and X_2 are positions at which the

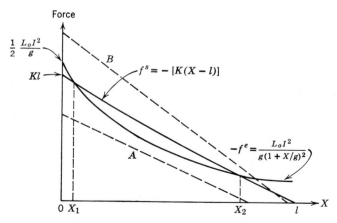

Fig. 5.1.3 Sketch for determining equilibrium points for system of Fig. 5.1.2.

plunger experiences no external forces, hence it can be in static equilibrium. There are, of course, three roots to the cubic equation, but one is not physical, since it requires that X be less than zero or that the plunger extend into the magnetic yoke. The relative values of the parameters can be such that there are no possible equilibrium points, as illustrated by the dashed curve A in Fig. 5.1.3, or there may be only one equilibrium point, as indicated by the dashed curve B. Note that all equilibrium points are such that $X < l$. Physically, this is expected, since the force f^e always tends to pull the plunger into the yoke, hence to extend the length of the spring.

We now assume that the conditions represented by the solid curves of Fig. 5.1.3 have been established and consider the dynamics for small excursions from the equilibrium points; for example, about X_1,

$$x(t) = X_1 + x'(t)$$

and (d) becomes (see 5.1.15)

$$\frac{d^2 x'}{dt^2} + \omega_o^2 x' = 0, \tag{g}$$

where

$$\omega_o^2 = -\frac{1}{M}\frac{df}{dx}(X_1) = \frac{1}{M}\left[K - \frac{L_o I^2}{g^2(1 + X_1/g)^3}\right]. \tag{h}$$

It should be clear from (5.1.15) and (5.1.16), and the associated discussion, that the relative magnitudes of the two terms in brackets determines whether this system is stable at the operating point X_1.

Although we could proceed in a formal mathematical way to study the stability at the equilibrium points, we shall pursue the subject with some qualitative study of the curves in Fig. 5.1.3.

At the point X_1 the magnitude of df^e/dX is larger than the magnitude of df^s/dX. Hence the derivative df/dX at X_1 has the sign of df^e/dX; that is,

$$\frac{df}{dX}(X_1) > 0, \tag{i}$$

and we conclude that this equilibrium point is unstable. We have found mathematically that a small excursion of the mass to the right of $X = X_1$ (Fig. 5.1.3) subjects the plunger to a force dominated by the spring force, which tends to force the plunger further to the right. (Remember that f^s is defined as a force that acts in the $+x$-direction if it is positive.)

Similarly, at X_2 the slope df^s/dX has a larger magnitude than df^e/dX, hence the sign of df/dX is negative at X_2,

$$\frac{df}{dX}(X_2) < 0 \tag{j}$$

and the equilibrium point X_2 is stable.

The process of using the first two terms in a Taylor series expansion to make a linear approximation has been described for the case in which there is a single dependent variable (x). It can be generalized to an arbitrary number of dependent variables. Suppose there are M variables $x_1, x_2, \ldots, x_M$, in terms of which a general function is expressed as $f(x_1, x_2, \ldots, x_M)$. If there is an equilibrium point $(X_1, X_2, X_3, \ldots, X_M)$ about which we wish to obtain a linear approximation to f by using a Taylor series expansion, we express each variable as

$$x_k = X_k + x_k'.$$

Then we write the fixed and linearly varying parts of the Taylor series about the fixed point as

$$f(x_1, x_2, \ldots, x_M) \approx f(X_1, X_2, \ldots, X_M)$$
$$+ \sum_{k=1}^{M} \frac{\partial f}{\partial x_k} (X_1, X_2, \ldots, X_M) x_k'. \quad (5.1.17)$$

The range of x_k' over which this approximation is valid within specified limits of error must be evaluated by using higher order terms in the Taylor series.* In Section 5.2.1 we consider the errors that result from using a linear approximation.

5.1.2b Dynamic or Steady-State Equilibrium

In the preceding section we studied small-signal operation about a static equilibrium. In many cases it is desirable to analyze devices as they are perturbed from a steady-state dynamic condition. This often occurs in rotating devices that are commonly designed to operate with constant angular velocity (as discussed in Chapter 4). Changes in external constraints (excitation or load) produce changes in the angular velocity that can be described as perturbations from the steady-state condition.

The linearization techniques that are the subject of this section are also applicable to many situations containing continuous media. The steady-state equilibrium may involve a moving medium such as a fluid, which has a constant velocity at a given point in space. The dynamics that result from perturbations from this steady flow could be described in a way similar to that developed here and illustrated in Chapter 10.

In the following example a synchronous magnetic field machine is used to illustrate the ideas involved in studying linearized motions about a dynamic equilibrium. The steady-state behavior of this type of device was studied in Section 4.1.6a and the example picks up the equations of motion developed there.

Example 5.1.2. A synchronous machine is modeled by the system of three coils shown schematically in Fig. 5.1.4. The physical arrangement of these coils may be as shown in Fig. 4.1.10.

The magnetic torque on the rotor, as a function of the stator currents i_{as} and i_{bs}, the rotor current i_r, and the rotor angle θ, is (4.1.38)

$$T^e = M i_r (i_{bs} \cos \theta - i_{as} \sin \theta). \quad (a)$$

---

* For a discussion of this expansion see, for example, F. B. Hildebrand, *Advanced Calculus for Engineers*, Prentice-Hall, New York, 1949, p. 353.

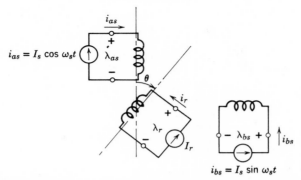

$$i_{bs} = I_s \sin \omega_s t$$

Fig. 5.1.4 Schematic representation of synchronous machine showing two fixed (stator) and one rotatable (rotor) coils.

To obtain steady-state synchronous conditions the stator and rotor terminals are excited by the current sources

$$i_r = I_r, \tag{b}$$

$$i_{as} = I_s \cos \omega_s t, \tag{c}$$

$$i_{bs} = I_s \sin \omega_s t, \tag{d}$$

where it is helpful for purposes of discussion to consider I_r, I_s, and ω_s as positive constants. In addition to the torque T^e, the shaft is subject to an inertial torque, a friction torque, and a load torque. We represent the total moment of inertia about the axis of rotation as J [see (2.2.27)], the friction torque as linear with coefficient B [see (2.2.6)], and the load torque as a driving function $T_m(t)$. Thus we can write the mechanical equation of motion for the angular deflection θ of the rotor as

$$J \frac{d^2\theta}{dt^2} + B \frac{d\theta}{dt} + MI_r I_s(\cos \omega_s t \sin \theta - \sin \omega_s t \cos \theta) = T_m(t). \tag{e}$$

To establish a dynamic equilibrium we assume $T_m = 0$ and constant angular velocity

$$\frac{d\theta}{dt} = \Omega = \text{constant} \tag{f}$$

and write

$$\theta = \Omega t + \gamma_o, \tag{g}$$

where γ_o is a constant to be determined. We substitute (g) into (e) with $T_m = 0$ to obtain the equilibrium equation

$$B\Omega + MI_r I_s[\cos \omega_s t \sin (\Omega t + \gamma_o) - \sin \omega_s t \cos (\Omega t + \gamma_o)] = 0. \tag{h}$$

The use of a trigonometric identity to simplify the term in brackets yields

$$B\Omega = MI_r I_s \sin [(\omega_s - \Omega)t - \gamma_o]. \tag{i}$$

The left side of this equation is constant; consequently, the equation can be satisfied for all t only if

$$\Omega = \omega_s. \tag{j}$$

This is the synchronous speed at which the rotor can run in dynamic equilibrium. Using

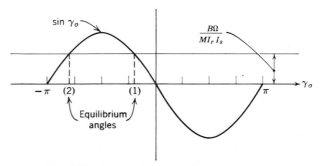

Fig. 5.1.5 The equilibrium values of angle γ_o.

(j) in (i), we obtain an expression for γ_o:

$$\sin \gamma_o = \frac{-B\Omega}{MI_r I_s}. \tag{k}$$

Dynamic equilibrium is defined for the system of Fig. 5.1.4 with the electrical excitations of (b) to (d) by (g), (j), and (k). Note that there is a limited range of parameters over which a dynamic equilibrium is possible because

$$-1 < \sin \gamma_o < 1.$$

Also, for any value of

$$\left| \frac{B\Omega}{MI_r I_s} \right| < 1$$

there are basically two different solutions for γ_o, as indicated in Fig. 5.1.5.

We now assume operation in dynamic equilibrium and describe perturbations from this equilibrium by $\gamma'(t)$; thus

$$\theta(t) = \Omega t + \gamma_o + \gamma'(t). \tag{l}$$

Substitution of this expression into (e), use of appropriate trigonometric identities, and retention of only linear terms yields after some simplification

$$J \frac{d^2\gamma'}{dt^2} + B \frac{d\gamma'}{dt} + K\gamma' = T_m(t), \tag{m}$$

where $K = MI_r I_s \cos \gamma_o$ is the effective spring constant of the magnetic torque. In writing this equation we have subtracted out the equilibrium equation represented by (k).

To study the dynamic behavior we assume that the load torque T_m is a small step occurring at $t = 0$:

$$T_m(t) = Tu_{-1}(t), \tag{n}$$

where T is a constant and $u_{-1}(t)$ is the unit step occurring at $t = 0$.

The method of solution reviewed in Section 5.1.1 can be used here. A particular solution is

$$\gamma' = \frac{T}{K}. \tag{o}$$

The initial conditions are $\gamma'(0) = 0$ and $(d\gamma'/dt)(0) = 0$. The complete solution therefore is

$$\gamma'(t) = \frac{T}{K} \left(1 + \frac{s_2}{s_1 - s_2} e^{s_1 t} + \frac{s_1}{s_2 - s_1} e^{s_2 t} \right), \tag{p}$$

where

$$s_1 = -\frac{B}{2J} + \left[\left(\frac{B}{2J}\right)^2 - \frac{K}{J}\right]^{\frac{1}{2}},$$

$$s_2 = -\frac{B}{2J} - \left[\left(\frac{B}{2J}\right)^2 - \frac{K}{J}\right]^{\frac{1}{2}}$$

are the natural frequencies that satisfy the characteristic equation

$$s^2 + \frac{B}{J}s + \frac{K}{J} = 0. \tag{q}$$

We refer now to the two equilibrium points illustrated in Fig. 5.1.5. At equilibrium point (2) the effective spring constant K is negative because $\cos \gamma_o$ is negative. Consequently, s_1 is positive, the response is unbounded, and the machine has a static instability at equilibrium point (2).

At equilibrium point (1) in Fig. 5.1.5 $\cos \gamma_o$ is positive, K is positive, and the real parts of s_1 and s_2 are both negative. Consequently, this equilibrium point is stable. When we assume the system to be underdamped,

$$\frac{K}{J} > \left(\frac{B}{2J}\right)^2,$$

we can write (p) in the form

$$\gamma'(t) = \frac{T}{K}\left[1 - e^{-\alpha t}\left(\cos \omega t + \frac{\alpha}{\omega}\sin \omega t\right)\right], \tag{r}$$

where

$$\alpha = \frac{B}{2J},$$

$$\omega = \left[\frac{K}{J} - \left(\frac{B}{2J}\right)^2\right]^{\frac{1}{2}}.$$

The response of (r) is plotted as a function of time for two values of α/ω in Fig. 5.1.6. Two

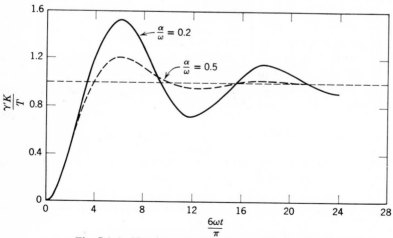

Fig. 5.1.6   Hunting transient of a synchronous machine.

general features of this "hunting" transient should be noted. First the initial parts of both transients are the same because, as (e) indicates, the initial part of the transient is dominated by the angular acceleration term $J(d^2\theta/dt^2)$, which is the same for both cases. Second, the damping retards the phase as indicated by the second term in parentheses in (r). The normalization for the time axis is different in the two cases because ω differs by a small amount.

5.1.2c *Overstability or Dynamic Instability*

In Section 5.1.2a we described a static instability characterized by a pure exponential growth in time. There is a second basic type of instability, called *overstability* or *dynamic instability*, which we now illustrate.

The equilibrium points of the system described by (5.1.12) are not changed if the mass is subject to an additional force proportional to velocity. The equation of motion has the form

$$M \frac{d^2x}{dt^2} + B \frac{dx}{dt} = f(x), \tag{5.1.18}$$

and in static equilibrium the additional term makes no contribution. The linearized equation, however, is

$$\frac{d^2x'}{dt^2} + \frac{B}{M}\frac{dx'}{dt} + \omega_o^2 x' = 0 \tag{5.1.19}$$

and the natural frequencies of the system are

$$s_{\binom{1}{2}} = \frac{-B}{2M} \pm \left(\frac{B^2}{4M^2} - \omega_o^2\right)^{\frac{1}{2}}. \tag{5.1.20}$$

If the term $B(dx/dt)$ is due to viscous damping, B will be positive (see Section 2.2.1b). In this case, if $\omega_o^2 < 0$, one of the natural frequencies will be positive, and the result will be a static instability that can be detected by the static experiment described in Section 5.1.2a. On the other hand, if $\omega_o^2 > 0$, the system will be stable, regardless of the magnitude of ω_o^2.

As we show in Example 5.1.3, feedback can be used to make $B < 0$ in (5.1.18). If $\omega_o^2 < 0$, one of the natural frequencies (5.1.20) will be real and positive and will result in a pure exponential growth that is a static instability detectable with a static experiment. Alternatively, if

$$0 < \omega_o^2 < \frac{B^2}{4M^2}, \qquad B < 0, \tag{5.1.21}$$

the natural frequencies will be real and both will be positive, thus indicating an instability that cannot be detected by our static argument. If

$$0 < \frac{B^2}{4M^2} < \omega_o^2, \qquad B < 0, \tag{5.1.22}$$

the radical in (5.1.20) will be imaginary and the natural frequencies will be complex with positive real parts. In this case the transient is an exponentially growing sinusoid. This is *overstability** or *dynamic instability*.

Note that under conditions of overstability $\omega_o^2 > 0$ and our static experiment of a small displacement will result in a force that tends to return the mass toward the equilibrium point; but this force is reinforced by the negative damping and the system overshoots the equilibrium point and reaches a larger displacement in the opposite direction.

It is clear that the static argument we used in Section 5.1.2a to detect a static instability will not detect overstability and one type of exponential growth. Thus we must regard the static argument as a sufficient, but not a necessary, condition for instability.

We have discussed stability in Section 5.1.2a and in this section in terms of a system describable by a second-order differential equation. Many systems have differential equations of an order higher than 2. Whenever a system goes unstable, however, the instability is usually caused by one or two natural frequencies. Because the instability dominates the dynamical behavior, the system differential equation can sometimes be approximated by a first- or second-order differential equation for studying the instability.

It is worthwhile to establish the physical significance of the three modes of instability. For this purpose, suppose that the mass is given an initial position $x' = x_o$ with no initial velocity. Then the appropriate solution to (5.1.19) is [in terms of the roots s_1 and s_2 defined by (5.1.20)],

$$x'(t) = \frac{x_o}{s_2 - s_1} (s_2 e^{s_1 t} - s_1 e^{s_2 t}). \tag{5.1.23}$$

This solution is shown in Fig. 5.1.7 for the three cases of instability that have been illustrated. Further insight is provided by the following example.

Example 5.1.3. In many situations it is desirable to support an object with a magnetic field; for example, in a wind tunnel effects of the mechanical structure (stinger) supporting the model under study introduce errors in drag and lift measurements. One solution to this problem is to use a magnetic field.† Then, if the fluid is an ordinary nonconducting gas, the magnetic field will not interfere with the flow. To support a large mass it is desirable to use a ferromagnetic core in the model so that magnetic forces will be of a useful magnitude. It is familiar to anyone who has held a piece of magnetic material near a magnet, that any static equilibrium achieved with these forces is unstable. The example undertaken here shows how feedback can be used to stabilize an inherently unstable equilibrium. Without feedback the equilibrium exhibits a static instability. This is obviated by the introduction of feedback, but then dynamic instability comes into play. This second type of instability is removed by additional feedback.

---

* For additional discussion of the terminology we use for describing instabilities see S. Chandrasekhar, *Hydrodynamic and Hydromagnetic Stability*, Oxford University Press, London, 1961, pp. 1–3.

† J. E. Chrisinger et al., "Magnetic Suspension and Balance System for Wind Tunnel Application," *J. Roy. Aeron. Soc.*, **67**, 717–724 (1963).

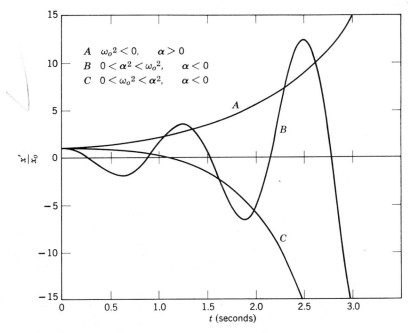

$$A \quad \omega_o^2 < 0, \qquad \alpha > 0$$
$$B \quad 0 < \alpha^2 < \omega_o^2, \qquad \alpha < 0$$
$$C \quad 0 < \omega_o^2 < \alpha^2, \qquad \alpha < 0$$

Fig. 5.1.7 Three modes of instability for a second-order system. The normalized damping α is negative for cases B and C ($\alpha = B/2M$).

The simple example to be considered here is shown schematically in Fig. 5.1.8a and an operating system of this type is illustrated in Fig. 5.1.8b. This system has the basic ingredients of systems constructed to levitate a mass M to be used in gyroscopes and accelerometers. The spherical particle is magnetic and is therefore attracted upward by the magnetic field induced by I. Hence there is a position $x = d$ at which the mass is supported against gravity by the magnetic field. With no feedback ($i' = 0$) the equilibrium is unstable, for, as the ferromagnetic mass approaches the inductor, the upward force increases, whereas the gravitational force remains constant. Feedback is introduced by using the optical system to detect the position of the mass. The photomultipler and amplifier are adjusted to give a current i' as nearly as possible proportional to the deflection x' from the equilibrium position $x = d$. Hence with feedback there is an addition to the magnetic force proportional to the deflection x'. By adjustment of the loop gain it is possible to make the effective spring constant introduced by the feedback large enough so that the equilibrium will appear to be stable on the basis of a static experiment of displacing the sphere from equilibrium and finding a restoring force. The amplifier, however, is not an ideal current source, and the effect of the coil inductance with finite amplifier output impedance causes the equilibrium to be dynamically unstable. A feedback signal proportional to sphere velocity is then added to stabilize the equilibrium completely. This discussion characterizes the design process used with the system shown in Fig. 5.1.8b.*

* The analysis was used in a student laboratory project to achieve the stable suspension of the sphere shown.

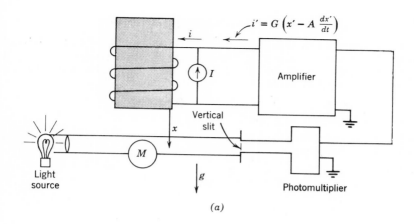

$$i' = G\left(x' - A\frac{dx'}{dt}\right)$$

Amplifier

I

Vertical slit

x

g

Light source

M

Photomultiplier

(a)

(b)

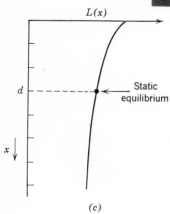

$L(x)$

d --- Static equilibrium

x

(c)

Fig. 5.1.8 (a) Mass M levitated by a magnetic field. The optical system provides a signal that is fed back to stabilize the static equilibrium of the mass at $x = d$; (b) view of laboratory project shown schematically by (a); (c) dependence of coil inductance on the mass displacement.

Measurement of the inductance L as a function of the position of the mass M would produce a curve like that shown in Fig. 5.1.8c. The inductance has its largest value when the ferromagnetic sphere is next to the coil and decreases to a constant as the sphere is removed to $x = \infty$. For the present purposes we take this dependence as

$$L(x) = L_1 + \frac{L_o}{1 + x/a}, \tag{a}$$

where L_1, L_o, and a are positive constants. Then the methods of Chapter 3 provide the force on the mass M; that is, the coenergy (since the electrical terminal relation is linear) is

$$W'(i, x) = \frac{1}{2}\left(L_1 + \frac{L_o}{1 + x/a}\right)i^2 \tag{b}$$

and the force of electrical origin follows as

$$f = \frac{\partial W'}{\partial x} = -\frac{1}{2a}\frac{L_o}{(1 + x/a)^2}i^2. \tag{c}$$

When the sphere is in static equilibrium, the gravitational force is balanced by this force:

$$Mg = \frac{1}{2a}\frac{L_o}{(1 + d/a)^2}I^2. \tag{d}$$

Given the current I, the equilibrium position d is determined. Perturbations x' from the equilibrium lead to a perturbation current i'; that is,

$$\begin{aligned} x &= d + x', \\ i &= I + i'. \end{aligned} \tag{e}$$

To linear terms in the perturbation quantities the force of (c) becomes

$$f = -\frac{L_o}{2a}\left[\frac{I^2}{(1 + d/a)^2} - \frac{2x'I^2}{a(1 + d/a)^3} + \frac{2Ii'}{(1 + d/a)^2}\right]. \tag{f}$$

It follows that the incremental equation of motion is

$$M\frac{d^2x'}{dt^2} - \frac{L_oI^2}{a^2(1 + d/a)^3}x' + \frac{L_oIi'}{a(1 + d/a)^2} = 0, \tag{g}$$

where use has been made of (d) to cancel out the constant part of the force equation.

In the absence of feedback ($i' = 0$) it is clear from (g) that the equilibrium is statically unstable. To consider first the effect of ideal feedback, assume that the output voltage of the photomultiplier is linear with x' and that the amplifier is a perfect current source feeding the coil. In this case

$$i' = Gx', \tag{h}$$

where G is a constant, including the amplifier gain. Substitution of this expression into (g) yields

$$M\frac{d^2x'}{dt^2} + \left[\frac{GL_oI}{a(1 + d/a)^2} - \frac{L_oI^2}{a^2(1 + d/a)^3}\right]x' = 0. \tag{i}$$

This system has natural frequencies determined from [see (5.1.15)]

$$\omega_o{}^2 = \frac{L_oI}{aM(1 + d/a)^2}\left(G - \frac{I}{a + d}\right). \tag{j}$$

Thus the response is bounded and the system is stable when the feedback gain is raised high enough to make

$$G > \frac{I}{a+d}. \tag{k}$$

No amplifier is absolutely ideal; consequently, we consider next the system performance in which the amplifier has a large but finite output impedance. In this case the amplifier produces a voltage proportional to sphere displacement x' and this voltage is applied to the series RL circuit illustrated in Fig. 5.1.9 in which the resistance R includes the internal resistance of the amplifier. The relation between x' and i' is now determined from the equation

$$Gx' = \frac{1}{R}\frac{d(Li')}{dt} + i'. \tag{l}$$

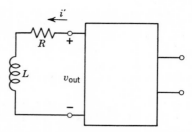

Fig. 5.1.9 The driving current of Fig. 5.1.8a is produced by a voltage amplifier connected in series with a large resistance R. The output voltage is proportional to the displacement x'. The inductance L is the equilibrium inductance of the coil shown in Fig. 5.1.8a.

Expansion of the derivative and retention of only linear terms yields

$$Gx' = \frac{1}{R}\left(L_1 + \frac{L_o}{1+d/a}\right)\frac{di'}{dt} - \frac{L_oI}{Ra(1+d/a)^2}\frac{dx'}{dt} + i'. \tag{m}$$

Using the exponential forms

$$x' = \hat{x}e^{st} \quad \text{and} \quad i' = \hat{i}e^{st}, \tag{n}$$

we rewrite (m) in the form

$$\hat{i} = G\hat{x}\left[\frac{1 + \dfrac{L_oI}{GRa(1+d/a)^2}s}{1 + \dfrac{1}{R}\left(L_1 + \dfrac{L_o}{1+d/a}\right)s}\right]. \tag{o}$$

For relatively high gain G and relatively high amplifier output impedance we assume

$$\frac{L_oI}{GRa(1+d/a)^2}s \ll 1,$$

$$\frac{1}{R}\left(L_1 + \frac{L_o}{1+d/a}\right)s \ll 1,$$

and approximate (o) by the form

$$\hat{i} = G\hat{x}(1 - As), \tag{p}$$

where

$$A = \frac{1}{R}\left[\left(L_1 + \frac{L_o}{1+d/a}\right) - \frac{L_oI}{Ga(1+d/a)^2}\right]. \tag{q}$$

It is evident that when the inequality k is satisfied $A > 0$.

We rewrite (p) in differential form as

$$i' = Gx' - GA \frac{dx'}{dt} \tag{r}$$

and substitute this result in (g) to obtain

$$M \frac{d^2x'}{dt^2} - \frac{GAL_oI}{a(1 + d/a)^2} \frac{dx'}{dt} + \frac{L_oI}{a(1 + d/a)^2} \left(G - \frac{I}{a + d} \right) x' = 0. \tag{s}$$

This has the form of (5.1.19) with $B < 0$; thus the system is overstable or dynamically unstable when the nonideal nature of the amplifier is included. The response of this system to a small disturbance will be like curve B or curve C of Fig. 5.1.7, depending on the relative sizes of the coefficients in (s) [see (5.1.19) to (5.1.22)].

We can interpret the three curves of Fig. 5.1.7 physically with reference to this example. For curve A the electrical force due to the bias current I exceeds the restoring force induced by the feedback. Thus, when the mass is released from rest with a small initial displacement, the displacement increases exponentially. This occurs regardless of whether the damping is negative or positive, the only effect of the damping being to change the *rate* of exponential growth.

Curve B of Fig. 5.1.7 represents the situation in which the feedback force dominates the force due to bias current I to provide a restoring force but the derivative term due to electrical feedback is negative. Also, the relative parameter values are such that the system is oscillatory. When the mass is released from rest with an initial displacement, the feedback force immediately accelerates the mass back toward equilibrium. The negative damping force adds to this feedback force to cause the position to overshoot equilibrium by more than the magnitude of the initial displacement. The process repeats periodically as the amplitude of the oscillation grows exponentially.

Curve C of Fig. 5.1.7 represents the situation in which the feedback force dominates the electrical force due to the bias current I to provide a static restoring force. The negative damping due to the electrical feedback is large enough to make the system's natural frequencies s real. When the mass is released from rest with an initial displacement, the feedback force accelerates the mass back toward equilibrium. As the mass starts moving, however, the negative damping adds a force to accelerate the mass further toward equilibrium. As the mass passes through equilibrium, the negative damping force dominates to accelerate the mass further along a rising exponential in a direction opposite that of the initial displacement.

To stabilize the equilibrium with a nonideal amplifier it is necessary to modify the amplifier signal so that its output current contains a component proportional to (dx'/dt) with the proper sign. This process is called compensation.* The simplest method of compensation is achieved by using the RC circuit of Fig. 5.1.10 between the photomultiplier output and the amplifier input. Implicit in what follows is the assumption that the internal impedance of the photomultiplier is very low and the amplifier input impedance is very high.

In terms of complex exponentials

$$v_2 = \hat{v}_2 e^{st} \quad \text{and} \quad v_1 = \hat{v}_1 e^{st},$$

---

* Compensating networks and their use in automatic control systems are discussed in such texts as J. J. D'Azzo and C. H. Houpis, "Feedback Control System Analysis and Synthesis." McGraw-Hill, New York, 2nd ed., 1966 p. 158.

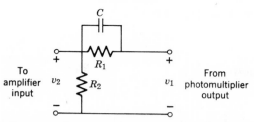

Fig. 5.1.10 Compensating network to provide stabilization of dynamic instability caused by finite amplifier output impedance.

the transfer function of the compensating network is

$$\frac{\hat{v}_2}{\hat{v}_1} = \frac{R_2}{R_1 + R_2} \left[\frac{R_1 Cs + 1}{[R_1 R_2/(R_1 + R_2)]Cs + 1} \right]. \tag{t}$$

For proper operation of the network it is conventional to set $R_2 \ll R_1$; thus

$$\frac{R_1 R_2}{R_1 + R_2} Cs \ll R_1 Cs$$

and for low frequencies we can approximate (t) by the form

$$\hat{v}_2 = \frac{R_2}{R_1 + R_2} (R_1 Cs + 1)\hat{v}_1$$

or in differential form as

$$v_2 = \frac{R_2}{R_1 + R_2} \left(R_1 C \frac{dv_1}{dt} + v_1 \right) \tag{u}$$

Because v_1 is the output voltage of the photomultiplier and is therefore proportional to x', we now rewrite (m) as

$$G_1 x' + G_1 R_1 C \frac{dx'}{dt} = \frac{1}{R} \left(L_1 + \frac{L_o}{1 + d/a} \right) \frac{di'}{dt} - \frac{L_o I}{Ra(1 + d/a)^2} \frac{dx'}{dt} + i', \tag{v}$$

where

$$G_1 = \frac{R_2}{R_1 + R_2} G.$$

Using the exponential forms of (n), we solve for $\hat{i}$ to obtain

$$\hat{i} = G_1 \hat{x} \left[\frac{1 + R_1 Cs + \dfrac{L_o I}{G_1 Ra(1 + d/a)^2} s}{1 + \dfrac{1}{R} \left(L_1 + \dfrac{L_o}{1 + d/a} \right) s} \right] \tag{w}$$

Making the assumption that parameter values and frequency s are such that we need retain only first-order terms in s, (w) becomes

$$i = G_1 \hat{x}[1 + (R_1 C - A)s], \tag{x}$$

where A is defined in (q) and $A > 0$ when inequality k is satisfied. Writing (x) in differential form, we have

$$i' = G_1 x' + G_1 (R_1 C - A) \frac{dx'}{dt} . \tag{y}$$

Substitution of this expression into (g) yields

$$M \frac{d^2 x'}{dt^2} + \frac{L_0 I G_1 (R_1 C - A)}{a(1 + d/a)^2} \frac{dx'}{dt} + \frac{L_0 I}{a(1 + d/a)^2} \left(G_1 - \frac{I}{a + d} \right) x' = 0. \tag{z}$$

It is clear from this equation that the compensation circuit has added positive damping to the system and that the system is completely stable when

$$G_1 > \frac{I}{a + d} \quad \text{and} \quad R_1 C > A.$$

Note that because $G_1 = [R_2/(R_1 + R_2)]G$ and $R_2 \ll R_1$ for proper compensation the amplifier gain must be greater when compensation is used. This is a principal consequence of compensation—that amplifier gain can be traded for a change in dynamic system behavior.

5.1.2d Steady-State Sinusoidal Response

Many incremental-motion transducers, such as speakers, microphones, and electromechanical filters, are designed to operate approximately as linear systems. One of the most important design factors is the driven response. A transducer may be used to convert a mechanical signal (pressure for example) to an electrical form, in which case the electrical signal is the response to a driving force. It may also convert the output of an amplifier to an acoustic signal, and thus the pressure or velocity response to a driving voltage is of interest. The most commonly used and convenient driven response for a linear system with constant coefficients is the sinusoidal steady state. Many systems operate largely in a sinusoidal steady-state condition, but even for those that do not the techniques of Fourier transforms and Fourier series are available. The response to an arbitrary signal can be synthesized from the response to sinusoidal driving signals ranging over the frequency spectrum of interest.*

In this section we show, by means of an example, how the techniques of Section 5.1.1 can be used to find the steady-state response to a sinusoidal excitation. The example also serves to illustrate characteristic dynamical behavior and impedance levels in an electric field system.

* See, for example, S. J. Mason and H. J. Zimmermann, *Electronic Circuits, Signals, and Systems*, Wiley, New York, 1960, Chapter 7.

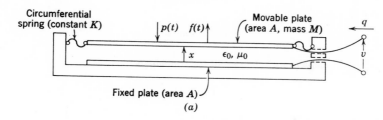

(a)

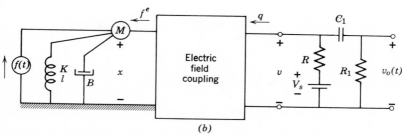

(b)

Fig. 5.1.11 Electric field transducer that can be used as a pressure sensor (microphone) or pressure source (speaker): (a) cross section of device (side view); it would appear circular from above; (b) equivalent electromechanical circuit.

Example 5.1.4. The simple variable capacitor shown schematically in Fig. 5.1.11 illustrates the basic construction of an electric field transducer that can be used as a microphone or as a speaker.* A circular movable plate with a total mass M is mounted on a peripheral bellows spring which has an equivalent constant K. The plate moves against a damping force (primarily caused by the surrounding air), which we assume is linear, with a coefficient B. When the device operates as a microphone, the differential pressure $p(t)$ acting over the area of the moving plate exerts a force $f(t)$ (defined as positive in the positive x-direction) which moves the plate and changes the capacitance, as seen from the electrical terminals. When the electrical terminals are biased with a constant voltage V_s (see Fig. 5.1.11b), a change in capacitance due to the motion induces a current dq/dt in the circuit. This current, at least in part, flows through resistance R_1 and produces a voltage $v_o(t)$ at the output terminals.

In this example we wish to analyze the behavior of the device of Fig. 5.1.11 for steady-state sinusoidal operation as a microphone. We assume that the driving force (pressure) is a sinusoidal function of time with constant amplitude and ask for the steady-state response of the output voltage. In the process we make approximations appropriate for the analysis of devices of this type.

Because the general properties of the coupling network should be described without taking into account the external elements, we begin with the electric field coupling network. We neglect fringing fields at the edges of the plates and describe the capacitance of this

---

* L. L. Beranek, *Acoustic Measurements*, Wiley, New York, 1949, pp. 173–176 and pp. 211–224.

electrically linear system as

$$C(x) = \frac{\epsilon_0 A}{x}. \tag{a}$$

Thus the electrical terminal relation for the coupling network is

$$q(v, x) = C(x)v = \frac{\epsilon_0 A v}{x}. \tag{b}$$

The system is conservative, hence we obtain the force f^e as

$$f^e = \frac{\partial W_e'(v, x)}{\partial x}. \tag{c}$$

Because the system is electrically linear, we express the electric coenergy as

$$W_e' = \tfrac{1}{2}C(x)v^2 = \frac{\epsilon_0 A v^2}{2x}. \tag{d}$$

We use this expression with (c) to evaluate the force

$$f^e = -\frac{\epsilon_0 A v^2}{2x^2}. \tag{e}$$

The equation of motion for the mechanical node (x) is written by referring to the circuit of Fig. 5.1.11b:

$$M\frac{d^2x}{dt^2} + B\frac{dx}{dt} + K(x - l) = f^e + f(t). \tag{f}$$

We use (e) in this expression to rewrite (f) as

$$M\frac{d^2x}{dt^2} + B\frac{dx}{dt} + K(x - l) + \frac{\epsilon_0 A v^2}{2x^2} = f(t). \tag{g}$$

Before equations for the electric circuit shown in Fig. 5.1.11b are written, we shall make some appropriate approximations to simplify the problem. The circuit comprised of capacitance C_1 and resistance R_1 is used to isolate the output terminals from the bias voltage V_s and is not intended to affect the dynamic behavior of the system in normal operation. Consequently, with a driving frequency ω we assume that the values of R_1 and C_1 satisfy the inequalities

$$\frac{1}{\omega C_1} \ll R_1 \quad \text{and} \quad R_1 \gg R \tag{h}$$

over the frequency range of interest. Thus the output voltage $v_o(t)$ is essentially the time-varying component of v and the current through R_1 can be neglected compared with the current through R.

Using the inequality (h) we now write the node equation for the electric circuit as

$$\frac{dq}{dt} = \frac{V_s - v}{R} = \frac{d}{dt}\left(\frac{\epsilon_0 A v}{x}\right) \tag{i}$$

and describe the output voltage as

$$-v_o(t) = R\frac{dq}{dt} = R\frac{d}{dt}\left(\frac{\epsilon_0 A v}{x}\right); \tag{j}$$

(g), (i), and (j) are the general equations from which we can calculate the output voltage $v_o(t)$ once the driving force $f(t)$ is specified. Note that these equations are nonlinear.

This capacitor microphone is representative of a class of devices constructed and operated purposely to behave as linear devices. Nonlinear effects cause distortion and loss of fidelity. Linearization techniques are especially meaningful because they are appropriate under conditions that must be fulfilled in construction and operation to achieve linearity.

We now use the technique presented in Section 5.1.2 to linearize (g), (i), and (j) for small-signal operation about a static equilibrium. We define the static equilibrium by requiring that all time derivatives and $f(t)$ be zero. Thus from (j) the equilibrium value for $v_o(t)$ is zero. Defining the equilibrium values of x and v as X and V, respectively, we find the relations from (g) and (i):

$$K(X - l) + \frac{\epsilon_0 A V^2}{2X^2} = 0, \tag{k}$$

$$V_s - V = 0. \tag{l}$$

It is clear that the equilibrium value of the terminal voltage is the bias voltage V_s and that the equilibrium position X is determined from the cubic equation. This equation and the properties of the equilibria are similar to those studied in Example 5.1.1. For our purposes here it suffices to state that we select the solution of (k) that represents a stable equilibrium position X.

We now assume the two variables x and v to be perturbed from their equilibrium values by small time-dependent functions $x'(t)$ and $v'(t)$. Thus

$$x(t) = X + x'(t),$$

$$v(t) = V_s + v'(t).$$

We substitute these variables into (g), (i), and (j), subtract out equilibrium terms, and retain only linear terms in the perturbation variables to obtain

$$M \frac{d^2 x'}{dt^2} + B \frac{dx'}{dt} + K_o x' + C_o E_o v' = f(t), \tag{m}$$

$$C_o \frac{dv'}{dt} - C_o E_o \frac{dx'}{dt} = -\frac{v'}{R}, \tag{n}$$

$$v_o(t) = v'(t), \tag{o}$$

where we have defined the following constants:

$C_o = \dfrac{\epsilon_0 A}{X}$ is the capacitance at equilibrium,

$E_o = \dfrac{V_s}{X}$ is the magnitude of the electric field intensity between the plates at equilibrium,

$K_o = K - C_o E_o^2$ is the effective (net) spring constant and is positive for the stable equilibrium we are using.

Our interest here is in the steady-state response of the system to a sinusoidal driving force. Thus (see Section 5.1.1 and Fig. 5.1.11) we assume that

$$f(t) = -A \, p(t) = \text{Re} \, (Fe^{j\omega t}) = F \cos \omega t, \tag{p}$$

where F and ω are positive real constants. The system equations are linear with constant coefficients; thus we assume solutions of the form

$$x'(t) = \text{Re } (\hat{X}e^{j\omega t}),$$

$$v_o(t) = v'(t) = \text{Re } (\hat{V}e^{j\omega t}),$$

where $\hat{X}$ and $\hat{V}$ are complex amplitudes. We substitute these forms of the dependent variables into (m) and (n), cancel the $e^{j\omega t}$, and drop the Re to obtain the algebraic equations.

$$[(j\omega)^2M + j\omega B + K_o]\hat{X} + C_oE_o\hat{V} = F, \tag{q}$$

$$\left(j\omega C_o + \frac{1}{R}\right)\hat{V} = j\omega C_oE_o\hat{X}. \tag{r}$$

We solve these two equations to find the complex amplitude of the output voltage $\hat{V}$ as a function of the amplitude of the driving force F:

$$\hat{V} = \left[\frac{j\omega C_oRE_o}{(K_o - \omega^2M + j\omega B)(j\omega C_oR + 1) + j\omega(C_oE_o)^2R}\right]F. \tag{s}$$

This expression could be used to determine the time response $v_o(t)$ for any set of parameters, value of frequency, and amplitude of drive. It is customary, however, to describe the steady-state sinusoidal response by plotting the magnitude (and often the phase) of the complex amplitude as a function of frequency for a constant input amplitude. Such a plot could be made for (s), but the denominator is quite complex and in its general form obscures the fact that different physical phenomena predominate in different frequency ranges.

We plot the amplitude of the transfer function $\hat{V}/F$ as a function of frequency by making approximations to simplify the expression in three frequency ranges. Our approximations are those made to achieve good microphone design.*

We consider first the low frequency behavior of the microphone and set the limit of (s) as $\omega \to 0$ to obtain

$$\left(\frac{\hat{V}}{F}\right)_{\text{lf}} = \frac{j\omega C_oRE_o}{K_o}. \tag{t}$$

The operation at very low frequencies can be interpreted as follows: first, the velocity and acceleration are so small that the inertia and damping forces are much smaller than the spring force in (g) and can be neglected. Next, the perturbation voltage $\hat{V}$ has negligible effect in the force equation and the term $C_oE_o\hat{V}$ can be neglected in (q). These two assumptions lead to the result in (t) if we recognize that the first term is small compared to the second on the left hand side of (r).

The fact that we can neglect the $\hat{V}$ term in (q) indicates that from a mechanical viewpoint the microphone capacitance is constrained to constant voltage. Thus the spring constant K_o includes the electrical spring constant due to the constant (bias) voltage [see (m)].

In summary, in the low-frequency limit the microphone capacitance operates at constant voltage and the mechanical system behaves as a spring, which includes electrical "spring" effects.

The low-frequency approximation breaks down when the frequency becomes large enough that

$$\omega C_oR \approx 1.$$

* *Ibid.*, pp. 211–218 and especially Fig. 5.30a.

This occurs in conventional microphones around a frequency of 10 Hz.* In the region of transition between the low-frequency and the mid-frequency ranges the transfer function is

$$\frac{\hat{V}}{F} = \frac{j\omega C_o R E_o}{K_o(j\omega C_o R + 1) + j\omega (C_o E_o)^2 R}.$$ (u)

We next define the mid-frequency range as starting at a frequency such that

$$\omega \gg \frac{1}{RC_o}$$

and continuing until inertia and damping forces become appreciable. This results in a mid-frequency transfer function

$$\left(\frac{\hat{V}}{F}\right)_{mf} = \frac{E_o}{K}.$$ (v)

Note that the denominator is the spring constant K alone, without the electrical spring force [see (m)]. This is an indication that the microphone capacitance is operating at constant charge because a parallel plate capacitor with negligible fringing fields and constant charge will have a force that is independent of plate spacing. The constraint of constant charge results because the resistance R is so large ($R \gg 1/\omega C_o$) that appreciable charge cannot flow on or off the plates. We can obtain this mid-frequency solution by neglecting the $1/R$ term in (r) and using that result to eliminate the term involving $\hat{V}$ in (q).

The mid-frequency range is the normal operating range of the microphone. The amplitude and phase of the transfer function are constant over this range; thus the output voltage is an exact replica of the input force and high fidelity is obtained.

The approximate transfer function for the mid-frequency range (v) breaks down when inertia and damping forces become appreciable. In practice, the mechanical system is lightly damped and a resonance occurs. In fact, elaborate means are used to provide additional mechanical damping to reduce the size of the resonance peak.† With a resonance, the mid-frequency transfer function breaks down when the frequency becomes high enough so that

$$\omega^2 M \approx K.$$

The frequency corresponding to this transition is usually around 10,000 Hz.‡

In the transition between the mid-frequency and high-frequency ranges the transfer function is

$$\frac{\hat{V}}{F} = \frac{E_o}{K - \omega^2 M + j\omega B}.$$ (w)

Note that in this region the microphone capacitance is still operating at constant charge, as evidenced by the presence of only the mechanical spring constant K in the denominator.

The high-frequency range is defined by the condition

$$\omega^2 M \gg K \quad \text{and} \quad \omega^2 M \gg \omega B.$$

Thus the high-frequency transfer function is

$$\left(\frac{\hat{V}}{F}\right)_{hf} = -\frac{E_o}{\omega^2 M}.$$ (x)

* *Ibid.*
† *Ibid.*, pp. 217 and 220.
‡ *Ibid.*, p. 220.

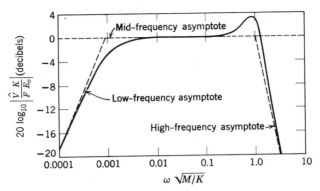

Fig. 5.1.12   Frequency response of capacitor microphone.

In this case the microphone capacitance is still operating at constant charge and the mechanical dynamics are determined completely by the mass M.

The amplitude of the transfer function $\hat{V}/F$ is plotted as a function of frequency in Fig. 5.1.12. The approximate solutions, commonly called asymptotes, given by (t), (v), and (x) are shown as dashed lines. The more exact solutions in the transition regions (u) and (w) are shown as solid lines. The curves are plotted for the following relations among parameters:

$$\frac{B}{\sqrt{MK}} = 0.7; \qquad \frac{K_o}{K} = 0.9; \qquad C_o R\left(\frac{K}{M}\right)^{\frac{1}{2}} = 1000.$$

Note that in Fig. 5.1.12 both the amplitude and frequency scales are logarithmic. This is a Bode plot, used for plotting frequency-response data.*

5.1.3   Physical Approximations

There are two indices by which the usefulness of an engineering model can be measured. First, there is the degree to which it represents the essential features of the physical situation. Second, there is the amount of effort required to use it for an analytical study. Obviously, these two considerations are in conflict and the choice of a model represents a compromise.

The selection of an appropriate model demands an awareness of the interplay between physical approximations and mathematical techniques; for example, if dissipation mechanisms are not significant in a given situation, it may be a simple matter to describe the nonlinear dynamics. In the opposite extreme, if dissipation dominates the dynamics, it may also be possible to include nonlinear effects. In the intermediate case of moderate damping nonlinear effects may be included only with a great deal of effort.

In this section a simple example is used to illustrate how the mathematical model can be simplified by recognizing the important physical effects at the

* F. E. Nixon, *Principles of Automatic Controls*, Prentice-Hall, Englewood Cliffs, N.J., 1953, pp. 165–174.

outset. This is often done in circuit theory. Suppose that the voltage v in the LR circuit of Fig. 5.1.13 is given and the current i is to be computed. We can, of course, solve this problem with little trouble. This allows us to see that if interest is confined to the current at very low frequencies

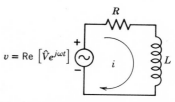

Fig. 5.1.13 L-R circuit to illustrate appropriate electrical approximations when the period of excitation is extreme compared with the time constant L/R.

$$v \simeq iR; \qquad (5.1.24)$$

that is at low frequencies virtually all of the voltage drop is across the resistance. By contrast, at high frequencies the inductive reactance greatly exceeds the resistance and virtually all the voltage drop is across the inductance. In this limit

$$v \simeq L\frac{di}{dt}. \qquad (5.1.25)$$

The frequency is considered to be low or high, depending on the relationship between the period of excitation $2\pi/\omega$ and the time constant L/R of the circuit. This is normally expressed as a ratio of inductive reactance and resistance. Thus, when $\omega L/R \ll 1$, (5.1.24) can be used; and, when $\omega L/R \gg 1$, (5.1.25) can be used. When $\omega L/R \approx 1$, neither approximation is appropriate.

By contrast with the circuit of Fig. 5.1.13, most electromechanical problems are represented by nonlinear equations unless the dynamics are limited to incremental motions. In these situations approximations analogous to those represented by (5.1.24) and (5.1.25) are useful. The electromechanical approximation, however, is more subtle because the frequency or characteristic time constant of the system is often not known until after the problem has been solved. In Fig. 5.1.13 we knew at the outset that the current i had the same frequency as the driving voltage. With the circuit coupled to a mechanical system and natural or free motions of the system under consideration (not the sinusoidal steady state resulting from a given driving function), the temporal behavior of the system is at least in part determined by mechanical effects. Hence the characteristic frequencies of the response to initial conditions can be low or high, compared with the natural frequencies of the electrical system.

The pair of coils shown in Fig. 5.1.14 provides a concrete example of the physical consequences of making electrical approximations in a magnetic field system. A pair of fixed coils is driven by the constant current $i_2 = I$ and arranged to give a uniform magnetic flux density B_o in the region of a pivoted coil with the angular deflection θ. The rotatable coil is short-circuited but has a

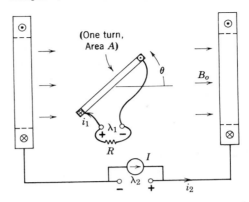

Fig. 5.1.14 A pivoted coil is free to rotate with the angular deflection θ in a uniform magnetic field produced by i_2.

resistance R, which is represented by a resistance connected to the terminals. We wish to study the mechanical response of the coil when it is given an initial angular velocity $d\theta/dt = \Omega$ at the angular position $\theta = 0$.

The equations of motion are found by first writing the electrical terminal relations as

$$\lambda_1 = L_1 i_1 + M i_2 \sin \theta, \tag{5.1.26}$$

$$\lambda_2 = M i_1 \sin \theta + L_2 i_2, \tag{5.1.27}$$

where L_1, M, and L_2 are constants. The dependence of the mutual inductance on θ should be evident from Fig. 5.1.14, and in the absence of magnetic materials the self-inductances are independent of θ. For this electrically linear system the coenergy follows from (5.1.26) and (5.1.27) as

$$W' = \tfrac{1}{2} L_1 i_1^2 + M i_1 i_2 \sin \theta + \tfrac{1}{2} L_2 i_2^2. \tag{5.1.28}$$

Hence the electrical torque is

$$T^e = \frac{\partial W'}{\partial \theta} = M i_1 i_2 \cos \theta. \tag{5.1.29}$$

The rotatable coil has a moment of inertia J, so that if mechanical damping is ignored the mechanical equation of motion is ($i_2 M = IM = AB_o$).

$$J \frac{d^2\theta}{dt^2} = AB_o i_1 \cos \theta. \tag{5.1.30}$$

The electrical equation requires that $-i_1 R = d\lambda_1/dt$, which, in view of (5.1.26) and the fact that $Mi_2 = AB_o$, is

$$-i_1 R - L_1 \frac{di_1}{dt} = AB_o \cos \theta \frac{d\theta}{dt}. \tag{5.1.31}$$

The voltage on the right-hand side of this equation is induced by the motion of the coil through the magnetic induction B_o. The equation expresses the fact that this "speed voltage" is absorbed by the self-inductance of the coil and by the resistance R. Note that the relative magnitudes of these terms on the left are determined by the same considerations discussed in connection with Fig. 5.1.13. Now, however, the current i_1 has a temporal behavior that depends on the mechanical deflection of the coil. From (5.1.31) it is clear that the moment of inertia plays a part in determining whether the inductive reactance or the resistance (or both) are significant.

We approach the problem here by assuming at the outset that one or the other of the terms on the left in (5.1.31) dominates, investigating the analytical consequences, and returning to check the validity of the initial assumption by using the predicted response. Suppose first that

$$|i_1R| \gg L_1 \left| \frac{di_1}{dt} \right|. \tag{5.1.32}$$

Then, i_1 can be found explicitly from (5.1.31) and substituted into (5.1.30). The result, after some trigonometric manipulation, has the form

$$\frac{d}{dt}\left[J\frac{d\theta}{dt} + \frac{(AB_o)^2}{2R}(\cos\theta\sin\theta + \theta) \right] = 0. \tag{5.1.33}$$

Here one derivative has been factored to show that the quantity in brackets is constant. The initial conditions that $d\theta/dt = \Omega$ when $\theta = 0$ fix this constant so that (5.1.33) can be integrated.

$$J\frac{d\theta}{dt} + \frac{(AB_o)^2}{2R}(\cos\theta\sin\theta + \theta) = J\Omega. \tag{5.1.34}$$

This first-order equation can be integrated to find $\theta(t)$ without approximations concerning the amplitude of the angular deflection θ. This approach to nonlinear dynamics is the subject of Section 5.2.2. It serves our purpose here to establish the physical significance of the approximation by limiting consideration to small amplitude (linearized) deflections about $\theta = 0$, in which case (5.1.34) is approximated by

$$\frac{d\theta}{dt} + \frac{\theta}{\tau_o} = \Omega, \tag{5.1.35}$$

where

$$\tau_o = \frac{RJ}{(AB_o)^2}.$$

In view of the initial conditions, this linear equation has the solution

$$\theta = \Omega\tau_o(1 - e^{-t/\tau_o}), \tag{5.1.36}$$

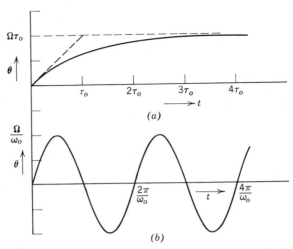

Fig. 5.1.15 Response in angular deflection of the rotatable coil of Fig. 5.1.14 to an initial angular velocity Ω at $\theta = 0$: (a) motion dominated by electrical resistance $(\tau_o \gg L_1/R)$; (b) flux λ_1 conserved at zero $(2\pi/\omega_o \ll L_1/R)$ as it would be if the resistance R were very small.

which is sketched in Fig. 5.1.15a. Remember that this expression is valid only if the inequality of (5.1.32) is satisfied. Use of (5.1.36) shows that the inequality requires

$$\tau_o \gg \frac{L_1}{R} . \tag{5.1.37}$$

Note that the electromechanical time constant τ_o is proportional to the moment of inertia J. When τ_o is large enough to satisfy (5.1.37), it simply means that the inertial effect slows the motion to the point at which the inductive reactance (which depends on the rate of change of i_1) is of negligible influence.

This approximation is typical of those used in the analysis of large, magnetic-field type devices such as rotating machines. Mechanical and electromechanical time constants are so long compared with electrical time constants that mechanical and electromechanical transients are assumed to occur with the electrical system always operating in the steady state $[L_1(di_1/dt)$ neglected in the example just completed]. Conversely, electrical transients are so fast that they are assumed to occur with the mechanical system operating at constant speed.

It is important to see that an equation of motion in the form of (5.1.35) would be obtained if the magnetic induction B_o were absent but the coil rotated in a viscous fluid. In the limit in which the reactance of the coil can be ignored the magnetic field and short-circuited coil combine to act as a mechanical damper. This is the limit used in synchronous machines when short-circuited damper windings are added to the rotor to assist in damping electromechanical oscillations (see Section 4.1.6a and Example 5.1.2).

It is evident from the solution (5.1.36) that there are no oscillations (as would be expected from "springlike" torques). The reactance represents the contribution of self-currents to the total magnetic field. When $L_1 di_1/dt$ is ignored in (5.1.31), it means that we are ignoring the magnetic field induced by the current i_1. This kind of physical approximation is useful in dealing with continuum interactions (see Chapter 10). We shall also find that in the limit in which electrical dissipation dominates, media tend to "ooze" rather than "bounce."

In both lumped parameter and continuum electromechanics it is often meaningful to model a conducting medium as "perfectly" conducting. This model is illustrated here by taking an extreme (to that so far considered) in which characteristic times of the electromechanical system are short enough to warrant neglecting the drop across the resistance compared with that across the reactance; that is, the first term in (5.1.31) is ignored compared with the second. That expression can then be integrated to give

$$i_1 = -\frac{AB_o}{L_1} \sin \theta. \tag{5.1.38}$$

Here, we assume that when the motion is initiated at $t = 0$, not only do $\theta = 0$ and $d\theta/dt = \Omega$ but $i_1 = 0$. Note that (5.1.38) requires that the flux λ_1 linking the rotatable coil be conserved. The initial conditions require that this flux be conserved at $\lambda_1 = 0$.

It follows from (5.1.38) and (5.1.30) that the equation of motion is

$$J \frac{d^2\theta}{dt^2} = -\frac{(AB_o)^2}{L_1} \sin \theta \cos \theta. \tag{5.1.39}$$

This nonlinear expression can be integrated without further approximations. For now, we delay this nonlinear problem until Section 5.2.1 and illustrate the physical consequences of the approximation by considering small amplitude deflections about $\theta = 0$. Then (5.1.39) becomes

$$\frac{d^2\theta}{dt^2} + \omega_o{}^2\theta = 0, \tag{5.1.40}$$

where

$$\omega_o = \frac{AB_o}{\sqrt{JL_1}}.$$

The solution to this equation, which satisfies the initial conditions, is

$$\theta = \frac{\Omega}{\omega_o} \sin \omega_o t. \tag{5.1.41}$$

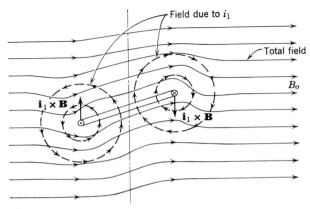

Fig. 5.1.16 Distortion of the initially uniform magnetic field caused by angular deflection of coil shown in Fig 5.1.14. The flux of the moveable coil is constrained to be zero.

This expression is plotted in Fig. 5.1.15b, where it can be compared with the loss-dominated case.

When the electrical dissipation can be ignored, the magnetic torque has the same effect on the motion as a torsional spring (in the nonlinear case, a nonlinear torsional spring). The reason for this can be seen physically with the help of Fig. 5.1.16. Remember that in this limit the total flux λ_1 through the rotatable coil is constrained to be zero. With the angular deflection shown in Fig. 5.1.16, the flux density B_o links the coil, thus contributing to λ_1. This flux must be canceled by a flux induced by the current i_1. The deflection shown in Fig. 5.1.16 is accompanied by the currents, as indicated, which induce a flux that cancels that from B_o. The total magnetic field is distorted to remain tangential to the plane of the coil. Note that the magnetic force $\mathbf{i_1} \times \mathbf{B}$ tends to restore the coil to the angle $\theta = 0$. Because the induced current is proportional to the angular deflection (and not to its rate of change), the magnetic torque is similar to that of a spring.

The assumption that the inductive reactance is of primary importance to the dynamics is equivalent to recognizing that the effect of the magnetic field induced by the motion is on the same order as that of the imposed magnetic field. More is said on this point in Section 7.0, in which the same physical arguments appear in the context of a distributed interaction. In the context of lumped parameters perfectly conducting media (in a magnetic field system) behave in a "springlike" or "bouncing" fashion. In continuous media (e.g., a "perfectly" conducting fluid) the same approximation leads to the possibility of wavelike motions, as illustrated in Section 12.2.3.

Our remarks in this section have been limited to electrical approximations that are appropriate in magnetic field systems. We could further illustrate the role of electrical dissipation in electric field systems. This was done implicitly however, in Example 5.1.4, in which it was shown that the electrical variables of a capacitor microphone were essentially constrained to constant potential and constant charge in the low and high-frequency ranges, respectively; that is, if the capacitor plate in Fig. 5.1.11 responded at a low frequency, the $R\,dq/dt$ drop across the resistance R could be ignored and the potential on the plate taken as the constant V_s. In the opposite extreme rapid variations in the capacitance of the microphone meant that there was little chance of charge leaking off through the resistance R. The result was an essentially constant charge on the movable plate. The critical parameter that determined which approximation was valid was ωRC_o or again essentially the ratio of the electrical time constant and the period of the mechanical response. The simplifying feature of Example 5.1.4 was the known response frequency ω. We could, however, easily envision a situation like the one considered in this section, in which the characteristic dynamic time would not be known until after the problem had been solved.

5.2 NONLINEAR SYSTEMS

As we have seen, most lumped-parameter electromechanical devices are described in general by nonlinear differential equations. Section 5.1 was devoted to showing that for many purposes these equations can be approximated by linearized equations. There are cases in which the nonlinear dynamics are essential, and indeed nonlinear interactions represent possibilities for engineering applications that are not available within the framework of linear systems. Unfortunately, there is no general mathematical theory to cover the solution of all types of nonlinear differential equation. This is not surprising, since nonlinear equations include all types that are not linear, as defined in Section 5.1.1.

The most direct way of obtaining numerical answers to nonlinear problems is to use machine computation, either analog or digital. In some simple cases it is possible to integrate the equations of motion. In the following two sections we illustrate two classes of these simple systems and the analytical techniques that are useful in obtaining solutions. Our objective is not only to study techniques for describing nonlinear systems but to gain a deeper physical insight into electromechanical dynamics.

5.2.1 Conservative Systems

In mechanics, if the energy remains constant throughout the motion of a system, the system is said to be conservative; that is, although the velocity and position of a mass change with time, the total energy is conserved at its

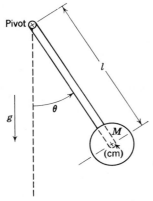

Fig. 5.2.1 Simple pendulum with an angular deflection $\theta(t)$ in the gravitational field g.

initial value. As we show in this section, this provides a basis for finding the motions of many electromechanical systems.

A simple mechanical system that illustrates the approach while allowing considerable physical insight is the simple pendulum of Fig. 5.2.1. It consists of a mass M whose center of mass is connected by a rigid, weightless rod of length l to a frictionless pivot. We consider the motion in which there is no externally applied torque except that due to gravity, which acts downward as shown.

The torque equation is therefore

$$J \frac{d^2\theta}{dt^2} = T_g, \qquad (5.2.1)$$

where the moment of inertia $J = Ml^2$ and T_g, the torque due to gravity, can be written as

$$T_g = -\frac{\partial V}{\partial \theta}; \qquad V = -Mgl \cos \theta. \qquad (5.2.2)$$

It is useful to write the torque as the derivative of the potential V because (5.2.1) can then be written as

$$\frac{d}{dt}\left[\frac{J}{2}\left(\frac{d\theta}{dt}\right)^2 + V \right] = 0. \qquad (5.2.3)$$

The best way to see that this is true is to take the first time derivative in (5.2.3) and see that (5.2.1) is recovered. It follows from (5.2.3) that the quantity in brackets is constant, or conserved. If we call this constant E,

$$\frac{J}{2}\left(\frac{d\theta}{dt}\right)^2 = E - V(\theta). \qquad (5.2.4)$$

To understand the physical significance of this equation it is helpful to think in terms of the potential plot shown in Fig. 5.2.2. The constant E, which is the sum of the kinetic and potential energies, is independent of θ. According to (5.2.4), the kinetic energy, hence the square of the angular velocity, is proportional to the difference between E and $V(\theta)$. This is shown graphically in Fig. 5.2.2. It is apparent from the diagram that at points (a) and (b), at which $|\theta| = \theta_m$, the angular velocity is zero, whereas at $\theta = 0$ the magnitude of the angular velocity has its largest value. The kinetic energy $J(d\theta/dt)^2/2$ is always positive. Hence, given the value of E, we can picture the angular

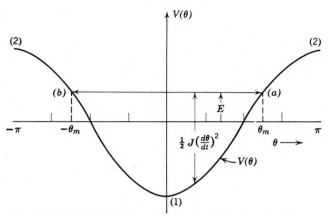

Fig. 5.2.2 Potential well $V(\theta)$ for the pendulum of Fig. 5.2.1 and for the rotatable coil of Fig. 5.2.4. If the pendulum is released from a stationary state at $\theta = \theta_m$, it will have an excursion between the points (a) and (b). The square of the angular velocity at any given position is proportional to the vertical distance between the constant E line and the potential $V(\theta)$.

deflection as limited to those regions of the potential plot in which the constant E line is above the potential $V(\theta)$. For the value of E shown in Fig. 5.2.2 the pendulum oscillates between the angles $\theta = \theta_m$ and $\theta = -\theta_m$.

The invariant E is established by the initial conditions. Suppose that at $t = 0$, $\theta = \theta_m$ and $d\theta/dt = 0$; that is, the pendulum is released from an initial static deflection $\theta = \theta_m$. Then from (5.2.4) $E = V(\theta_m)$ and

$$\frac{J}{2}\left(\frac{d\theta}{dt}\right)^2 = V(\theta_m) - V(\theta). \tag{5.2.5}$$

Similarly, the pendulum could be given an initial velocity $(d\theta/dt)_m$ at $\theta = 0$, and it follows from (5.2.4) that $E = (J/2)(d\theta/dt)_m^2 + V(0)$. If the initial kinetic energy exceeds $V(\pi) - V(0)$, the line of constant E in Fig. 5.2.2 never intersects the potential curve and the pendulum deflection increases monotonically. This simply means that, given a large enough initial energy, the pendulum rotates continuously on its pivot, moving rapidly at $\theta = 0$, 2π, 4π, . . . and slowing down at $\theta = \pi$, 3π, ...

Note that at the angles $\theta = 0$, π, . . . the pendulum can be in static equilibrium, for at these points $\partial V/\partial\theta = 0$ $(T_g = 0)$. The question whether these equilibria are stable can be answered in terms of the potential plot. Suppose that the pendulum is given an initial static position $\theta = 0$. This establishes the constant E line in Fig. 5.2.2 as passing through point (1). To see if the equilibrium is stable, the pendulum is given a slight kinetic energy, which raises the constant E line just above point (1) and shows that small amplitude oscillations result. In the sense defined in Section 5.1.2a we say that this equilibrium is stable. Similarly, if the pendulum is placed in static equilibrium at (2), the constant E line just grazes the peaks of the potential curve. To test for stability the pendulum is given a slight additional kinetic energy (greater E). It is clear that the pendulum does not tend to return to position (2), which is a point of unstable static equilibrium. This is not surprising to someone who has tried to balance a broom on his finger. The pendulum is upside down at $\theta = \pi$.

As a consequence of our deductions concerning Fig. 5.2.2, we can interpret the system behavior as if the moment of inertia were a particle that slides without friction on a physical "hill" with the shape $V(\theta)$. Motions within a *potential well* are bounded and therefore stable.

It is worthwhile to place the linear stability theory of Section 5.1.2a in perspective by relating it to the potential well. The torque T_g can be expanded about a point of static equilibrium $\theta = \Theta$:

$$T_g = -\frac{\partial V}{\partial \theta}(\Theta) - (\theta - \Theta)\frac{\partial^2 V}{\partial \theta^2}(\Theta). \tag{5.2.6}$$

Because the equilibrium is static, the first term on the right is zero. Hence (5.2.1) has been linearized and is

$$J\frac{d^2\theta}{dt^2} + \left[\frac{\partial^2 V}{\partial \theta^2}(\Theta)\right](\theta - \Theta) = 0. \tag{5.2.7}$$

From this constant coefficient linear equation it follows that the solutions will be oscillatory, hence stable, at points of zero slope on the potential plot at which

$$\frac{\partial^2 V}{\partial \theta^2} > 0. \tag{5.2.8}$$

Our linearized techniques of Section 5.1.2a tell us that small perturbations about a point in the bottom of a potential well (1) are stable, whereas those from the peaks (2) are unstable. We shall see in the examples that follow cases in which even though small amplitude deflections are unstable large deflections remain bounded.

We return to this example of the mechanical pendulum to show how (5.2.4) can be integrated to determine the detailed temporal behavior. Before doing so, however, it would be more to the point to see how these ideas can be extended into the context of electromechanics.

In Fig. 5.2.3 an electromechanical system is represented schematically by a mechanical system connected to an electromechanical coupling network.

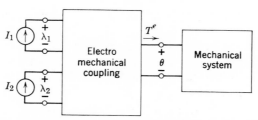

Fig. 5.2.3 Electromechanical system in which conservation of an energy function can be used to determine the dynamics. The mechanical system is composed of lossless elements and one of each of the electrical terminal variables is held constant.

This network, as defined in Chapter 3, does not contain elements that dissipate energy, but, of course, it in turn couples to an electrical system that does contain such elements. If, however, the electrical terminals are constrained so that a variable at each of the terminal pairs is held fixed, we expect to find a constant of the motion for the total electromechanical system. This is true because any additions to the total electromechanical energy of the system must be made through the electrical terminals. If a terminal variable is fixed, there is either no flow of energy or no flow of coenergy through that terminal pair; for example, in the case shown in Fig. 5.2.3 an increment of coenergy at the (i_1, λ_1) terminal pair is $\lambda_1 \, di_1$, which is constrained to zero as long as $I_1 = $ constant. Now we know from Chapter 3 that the torque of electrical origin T^e can be found as the derivative of an "energy function" written as a function of θ and one of each of the electrical terminal variables (the "independent" variables): for example, in Fig. 5.2.4

$$T^e = \frac{\partial W'}{\partial \theta}(i_1, i_2, \theta), \qquad (5.2.9)$$

where W' is the coenergy function (see, for example, Section 3.1.2b). If i_1 and i_2 are constrained to be constant, then T^e is the derivative of a known function of θ:

$$T^e = \frac{\partial W'}{\partial \theta}(I_1, I_2, \theta). \qquad (5.2.10)$$

Because the mechanical system is composed of elements that do not dissipate energy, the mechanical torque can also be written as the derivative with respect to θ of an

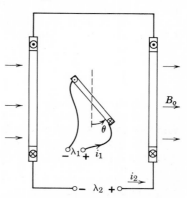

Fig. 5.2.4 A pair of fixed coils is excited in series by the current i_2. A pivoted coil has the angular deflection θ and the electrical terminal variables (i_1, λ_1). When both coils are driven by constant current sources, the potential well is as shown in Fig. 5.2.2.

energy function, which we might call $U(\theta)$

$$T^m = -\frac{\partial U}{\partial \theta}. \tag{5.2.11}$$

It follows that the torque equation can be written as

$$J\frac{d^2\theta}{dt^2} + \frac{\partial V}{\partial \theta} = 0, \tag{5.2.12}$$

where

$$V(\theta) = U(\theta) - W'(I_1, I_2, \theta), \tag{5.2.13}$$

which now takes on the same form as (5.2.3).

Example 5.2.1 is based on this generalization of the potential well to include the electromechanical energy function.

Example 5.2.1. The electromechanical system shown in Fig. 5.2.4 has the schematic description of Fig. 5.2.3. The pivoted coil has the terminal variables (i_1, λ_1), whereas the fixed coils are connected in series, with the terminal variables (i_2, λ_2). There is no magnetic material in the problem, so that self-inductances remain constant and the electrical terminal relations can be written as

$$\lambda_1 = L_1 i_1 + M(\theta)i_2, \tag{a}$$
$$\lambda_2 = M(\theta)i_1 + L_2 i_2, \tag{b}$$

where for this particular case $M(\theta) = M_o \cos \theta$, L_1, L_2, and M_o are constants. From the terminal relations the coenergy $W'(i_1, i_2, \theta)$ follows as

$$W' = \tfrac{1}{2}L_1 i_1^2 + \tfrac{1}{2}L_2 i_2^2 + M(\theta)i_1 i_2. \tag{c}$$

The first two terms in this expression are constant and can be absorbed in the constant of the motion E. Hence from (5.2.13) we have

$$V = -I_1 I_2 M(\theta). \tag{d}$$

For the particular case of Fig. 5.2.4

$$V = -I_1 I_2 M_o \cos \theta. \tag{e}$$

This potential has the same form as the mechanical pendulum of Fig. 5.2.1; hence the developments relevant to dynamics of the pendulum are equally applicable here. For quantitative purposes Mgl is replaced by $I_1 I_2 M_o$.

Note that the state of stable static equilibrium at (1) in Fig. 5.2.2 now corresponds to the situation in which the magnetic field generated by i_1 at the center of the pivoted coil is aligned with the field produced by i_2. If either I_1 or I_2 is made negative, the potential well in Fig. 5.2.2 is inverted, with $\theta = 0$ becoming an unstable static equilibrium and point (2) becoming a stable equilibrium.

Now that we have discussed the basic considerations involved in using potential-well techniques for describing electromechanical problems it would be interesting to embark on examples that illustrate characteristic dynamic behavior. It is not often that an engineer is concerned with the detailed temporal behavior of a system. Example 5.2.2 illustrates how a knowledge of the electrical terminal relations can be used to establish the significant features of dynamic behavior under a variety of electrical constraints. This approach is extremely useful because the relevant features of the electrical terminal relations can be found quantitatively by simple measurements or qualitatively by sketching the electric or magnetic fields.

Example 5.2.2. A coil (mass M) is mounted on a massless pendulum of length R, as shown in Fig. 5.2.5, to allow it to swing through the magnetic field generated by a pair of series-connected fixed coils. We wish to study the dynamical consequences of energizing the fixed coils with a current source I_2 and constraining the electrical terminals of the movable coil in two different ways. First, the pendulum motions that result when $i_1 = I_1$ or the current through the moving coil is constant provide us with an opportunity to illustrate how a combination of electrical and mechanical potentials is handled, a situation that can then be contrasted with the second case to be considered in which the terminals (i_1, λ_1) are constrained to zero flux linkage. This is the physical result if the terminals of the moving coil are short-circuited and the resistance of the coil is "small." This limit is discussed in Section 5.1.3, in which it is shown that the flux can be considered essentially constant if the current i_1 is limited by the self-reactance of the coil and not by the resistance. This demands that the characteristic time constant of the motion be short compared with the L/R time constant of the moving coil.

The mutual inductance between the moving and fixed coils is shown in Fig. 5.2.5c. The

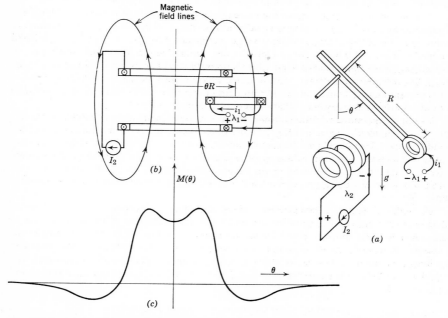

Fig. 5.2.5 (a) A coil is attached to a pendulum in such a way that when $\theta = 0$ it is directly between a pair of fixed coils energized by the current I_2; (b) top view of (a) showing the magnetic field produced by the fixed coils; (c) mutual inductance between the fixed and movable coils of (b).

dependence on θ can be understood qualitatively by considering Fig. 5.2.5b. When θR is very large, it is clear that the magnetic field generated by the fixed coils does not link the movable coil. As the movable coil comes into the vicinity of the fixed coils, it links a magnetic field having the opposite direction to that linked when it is directly between the coils. Hence the mutual inductance first becomes negative and then positive. If the diameter of the fixed coils is large compared with their spacing, the field, which tends to concentrate near the currents, will be smaller at the center ($\theta = 0$) than at off-center angles where the movable coil is adjacent to the fixed windings. Hence the mutual inductance is shown with a dip in the vicinity of $\theta = 0$.

This inductance could be measured by exciting the fixed coil with a sinusoidal current and measuring the induced voltage in the movable coil as a function of position. Therefore we can regard $M(\theta)$ as determined either qualitatively or quantitatively. The electric terminal relations have the form of (a) and (b) in Example 5.2.1.

CONSTANT CURRENT CONSTRAINTS

First, consider the consequences of driving both fixed and movable coils by constant-current sources. The total potential is then the sum of a gravitational potential (5.2.2) and a potential due to the magnetic field [(d) of Example 5.2.1]:

$$V = -Mgl \cos \theta - I_1 I_2 M(\theta). \tag{a}$$

There are two possibilities. Either $I_1 I_2 > 0$, in which case the total potential appears as shown in Fig. 5.2.6a, or $I_1 I_2 < 0$, and $V(\theta)$ is as shown in Fig. 5.2.6b.

Consider first the case in which both currents are positive. If the pendulum holding the coil is released from an initial static position at $\theta = \theta_m$, the line of constant E appears as shown in Fig. 5.2.6a. The pendulum swings completely through the region of the fixed coils. The effect of the negative slope of the mutual inductance is not sufficient to decelerate it as it approaches them. Once the movable coil is between the fixed coils, the $\mathbf{I} \times \mathbf{B}$ force tends to accelerate it toward the center, except very near $\theta = 0$. The effect of the constant current constraints with both currents positive is to make the potential well centered on $\theta = 0$ even deeper than it would be without the field.

A similar experiment with one of the currents reversed results in motions characterized by the constant E line shown in Fig. 5.2.6b. For this case the pendulum released from the initial angle θ_m is reflected by the magnetic interaction with the fixed coil. This is expected, since the $\mathbf{I} \times \mathbf{B}$ force on the moving coil as it nears the origin is now in the direction required to retard the motion. Of course, given enough initial energy, the pendulum will pass on through the interaction region. Note that the pendulum could be trapped in a region near the origin.

A significant feature of the constant current dynamics is its dependence on the sign of the excitation current. If one of the currents is reversed, that part of the potential due to the magnetic field is turned upside down; for example, in Fig. 5.2.6b, in which one of the currents is reversed, the static equilibrium at the origin (a) is stable, and there are two additional points (d and e) at which the pendulum can be in stable static equilibrium. The equilibria (b and c) that were stable in Fig. 5.2.6a are replaced by unstable equilibria (b and c) in Fig. 5.2.6b.

CONSTANT-CURRENT CONSTANT-FLUX CONSTRAINTS

We now embark on describing the motions when the pendulum coil of Fig. 5.2.5 is constrained to constant (zero) flux. As is evident from the development, the electro-mechanical coupling must now be represented by a hybrid energy function, for neither all of the currents nor all of the fluxes are constrained to be constant.

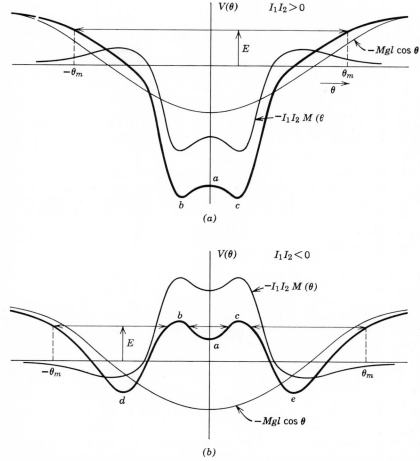

(a)

(b)

Fig. 5.2.6 Potential plots for the system of Fig. 5.2.5 constrained to constant current: (a) both coil currents positive; (b) one coil current positive and one negative.

A schematic representation of the terminal constraints is shown in Fig. 5.2.7. To use the potential techniques, we require a function $W''(\theta)$ from which we can find the electrical torque by taking a derivative:

$$T^e = \frac{\partial W''}{\partial \theta}. \tag{b}$$

This function, with the terminations of Fig. 5.2.3, was simply the coenergy W', since in the coenergy function the currents are used as independent variables. For our present purposes it is helpful to recall that any of the energy functions are derived from a statement of conservation of energy for the electromechanical coupling.

$$i_1 \, d\lambda_1 + i_2 \, d\lambda_2 = dW + T^e \, d\theta; \tag{c}$$

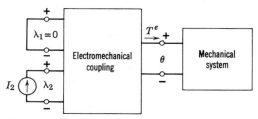

Fig. 5.2.7 Schematic representation of the system shown in Fig. 5.2.5a when the pendulum coil is constrained to zero flux.

for example, in the case in which the currents were held constant it was appropriate to transform this expression to one involving the currents i_1 and i_2 as independent variables (as discussed in Section 3.1.2b). For the present situation λ_1 and i_2 are fixed and therefore should be used as independent variables. Hence the second term in (c) is rewritten as

$$i_2 \, d\lambda_2 = d(i_2\lambda_2) - \lambda_2 \, di_2 \tag{d}$$

so that (c) becomes

$$\lambda_2 \, di_2 - i_1 \, d\lambda_1 = dW'' - T^e \, d\theta, \tag{e}$$

where

$$W'' = i_2\lambda_2 - W.$$

From (e) it follows that the electrical torque is given by (b). As for the energy and coenergy functions, W'' is found by integrating a form of the energy equation, which is now (e). In carrying out this integration, it must be remembered that i_2 and λ_1 are independent variables and must be used to express λ_2 and i_1 in (e). Thus (a) and (b) of Example 5.2.1 are written as

$$i_1 = \frac{\lambda_1}{L_1} - \frac{M(\theta)}{L_1} i_2, \tag{f}$$

$$\lambda_2 = \left(L_2 - \frac{M^2(\theta)}{L_1}\right) i_2 + \frac{M(\theta)}{L_1} \lambda_1. \tag{g}$$

Now, if the integration of (e) is carried out in the usual way (Section 3.1.1), we obtain

$$W'' = \frac{1}{2}\left(L_2 - \frac{M^2}{L_1}\right) i_2{}^2 - \frac{1}{2}\frac{\lambda_1{}^2}{L_1} + \frac{M}{L_1} i_2\lambda_1. \tag{h}$$

The terminal constraints require that $i_2 = I_2$ and that $\lambda_1 = 0$. (The initial conditions determine the constant λ_1 the short-circuited pendulum coil will retain.) For the present purposes we assume that the coil is initially outside the magnetic field, where a short circuit establishes the flux $\lambda_1 = 0$. We have established the function W'' to be used in (b):

$$W'' = \frac{1}{2}\left(L_2 - \frac{M^2}{L_1}\right) I_2{}^2. \tag{i}$$

The potential V, which includes both the effects of the magnetic field and gravity, is [from (5.2.2)]

$$V = -Mgl \cos \theta + \frac{I_2{}^2}{2L_1} M^2(\theta). \tag{j}$$

Here, a constant has been absorbed in the constant of the motion E [which appears in (5.2.4)].

The potential well for the flux-constrained coil is shown in Fig. 5.2.8 as the superposition of the same gravitational potential used before and a magnetic potential that is proportional to the square of $M(\theta)$, as given in Fig. 5.2.5c. At the outset two observations are of physical significance; the potential well is unaltered by reversing the direction of the field due to the fixed coils [I_2 is squared in (j)] and the interaction does not depend on the sign of the mutual inductance. This is by contrast with the current constrained situation in which the potential well could take on the alternative forms shown in Fig. 5.2.6. These observations reflect the fact that the current i_1 is *induced* in a direction that cancels any flux due to i_2 linking the pendulum coil. This type of dynamics is familiar from Section 5.1.3 and is evident here from the potential diagram.

The field generated by the fixed coils represents a magnetic barrier to the pendulum coil; for example, if the pendulum is given the initial velocity required to establish the constant of the motion as E_1 in Fig. 5.2.8, the moving coil will bounce off the potential barrier set up by the magnetic field. In fact, at an energy E_2, the pendulum coil oscillates between a maximum deflection magnitude determined by gravity and a minimum determined by the magnetic interaction.

At an energy E_3 it is possible to trap the coil in a well created solely by the imposed magnetic field. This magnetic trapping is a lumped-parameter illustration of how a magnetic field can be shaped to "bottle up" a highly conducting continuum such as a plasma. We can think of the pendulum coil as replaced by a highly conducting "blob" of material, which in turn can be modeled by many arbitrarily oriented, perfectly conducting loops. Each of these loops tends to behave as described here.

The effects of a finite coil resistance were considered in Section 5.1.3 to place the dynamics as found here in perspective. The zero flux constraint is a meaningful model for the actual

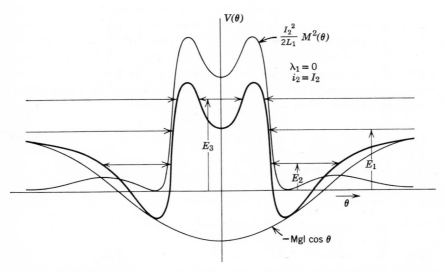

Fig. 5.2.8 Potential well for the system of Fig. 5.2.5a when the pendulum coil is constrained to zero flux. The potential has this shape regardless of the sign of the current I_2.

physical situation only as long as characteristic times for the motion are short compared with the L/R time constant of the pendulum coil.

So far in this discussion of nonlinear conservative systems we have not concerned ourselves with detailed temporal behavior. Sometimes nonlinear periods of oscillation or deflections as a function of time are required and (5.2.4) must be integrated. For this purpose it is written as

$$\frac{d\theta}{dt} = \pm\left\{\frac{2}{J}[E - V(\theta)]\right\}^{1/2}. \tag{5.2.14}$$

The plus and minus signs indicate that the pendulum can be moving in either direction at a given angle θ.

If we specify that when $t = 0$ the angle $\theta = \theta_m$, (5.2.14) can be integrated.

$$t = \pm\int_{\theta_m}^{\theta} \frac{d\theta'}{\left\{\frac{2}{J}[E - V(\theta')]\right\}^{1/2}}. \tag{5.2.15}$$

The parameter θ' is a running variable of integration. Whether (5.2.15) can be integrated analytically depends on the form of $V(\theta)$. In any case, given $V(\theta)$, numerical integration is a straightforward matter.

In the case of the mechanical pendulum of Fig. 5.2.1, $V(\theta)$ is given by (5.2.2) and the integration of (5.2.15) can be carried out. Suppose that the pendulum is released from rest at $\theta = \theta_m$. Then from (5.2.4) $E = V(\theta_m)$ and the integral of (5.2.15) takes the standard form of an elliptic integral* for which solutions are tabulated. One fourth of a cycle of oscillation is shown as a function of time in Fig. 5.2.9, where for (a) the pendulum is released from an initial "small" angle $\theta_m = 20°$ and for (b) the initial amplitude is 90°. For these plots the time is normalized to the frequency $\omega = \sqrt{g/l}$. This is the frequency of oscillation for small amplitudes, as can be seen by combining and linearizing (5.2.1) and (5.2.2) to obtain

$$\frac{d^2\theta}{dt^2} + \omega^2\theta = 0. \tag{5.2.16}$$

For the initial conditions considered in Fig. 5.2.9 the solution to this equation is

$$\theta = \theta_m \cos \omega t. \tag{5.2.17}$$

This response, predicted by the linearized equation of motion, is shown as dashed curves in Fig. 5.2.9. For an amplitude of $\theta = 20°$ the results from the linear and nonlinear models are almost identical, although there is some

* P. Franklin, *Methods of Advanced Calculus*, McGraw-Hill, New York, 1944, Chapter VII.

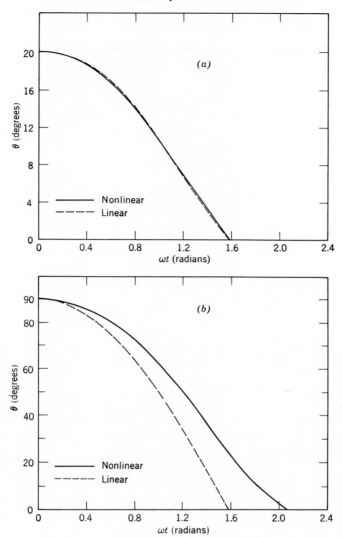

Fig. 5.2.9 Oscillation of a simple pendulum: (*a*) small amplitude; (*b*) large amplitude.

discrepancy between the predictions for $\theta = 90°$. This comparison between the exact and linearized solutions should help to place the methods of Section 5.1 in perspective. Of course, the adequacy of a linearized model will depend greatly on the nature of the nonlinearity. The following example is one in which a linearized model would be difficult to make and would be of doubtful usefulness.

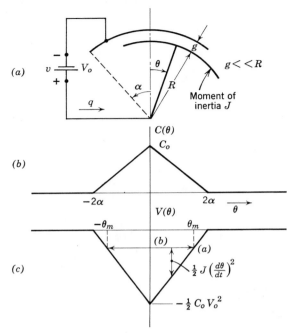

Fig. 5.2.10 (a) Capacitor plates just overlap when $\theta = 0$ and are constrained to constant potential V_o; (b) capacitance as a function of θ; (c) potential for the system of (a).

Example 5.2.3. The electric field system shown in Fig. 5.2.10 illustrates how the period of oscillation, computed from (5.2.15), can have nonlinear behavior. A capacitor is constructed from fixed and rotatable plates with the shape of sections from coaxial cylinders. At $\theta = 0$ the plates are aligned and the capacitance has the maximum value C_o. At $\theta = \pm 2\alpha$ there is no overlap between the plates and the capacitance is essentially zero. Hence $C(\theta)$ depends on θ essentially as shown in Fig. 5.2.10b. With the plates constrained to have the constant potential difference V_o, we expect that the rotatable plate can be at rest at $\theta = 0$, for the induced charges will tend to make the plates attract one another. We wish to determine the period of oscillation that results when the plate is deflected from this equilibrium.

The terminals are constrained to constant potential; hence it is appropriate to write the electric torque in terms of the coenergy $W'(v, \theta)$ (see Section 3.1.2b):

$$T^e = \frac{\partial W'}{\partial \theta} (V_o, \theta). \tag{a}$$

Hence the potential V is [from (5.2.1) and (5.2.2)]

$$V = -W'(V_o, \theta), \tag{b}$$

which for this example is

$$V = -\tfrac{1}{2} V_o^2 C(\theta), \tag{c}$$

with $C(\theta)$ as shown in Fig. 5.2.10b. It follows that the potential produced by the electric field appears as shown in Fig. 5.2.10c. From this diagram it is clear that if the movable plate (with the moment of inertia J but with no effect from gravity) is given a kinetic energy greater than

$$\tfrac{1}{2}J\left(\frac{d\theta}{dt}\right)^2 = \tfrac{1}{2}C_o V_o^{\,2} \tag{d}$$

at $\theta = 0$ the motions will not be oscillatory. Instead, the plate will rotate continuously with constant velocity when the plates do not overlap and with a maximum velocity at $\theta = 0$.

We can compute the period of oscillation T from (5.2.15) when the initial conditions are such that the motions are oscillatory. For this purpose we call the peak deflection θ_m so that the line of constant energy is as shown in Fig. 5.2.10c. In terms of that figure the rotor moves from (a) to (b) in $T/4$ sec. Over this interval the potential can be written as

$$V(\theta) = \frac{C_o}{2\alpha}\,(\theta - 2\alpha)\,\frac{V_o^{\,2}}{2}. \tag{e}$$

For our purposes (5.2.15) becomes

$$\frac{T}{4} = -\int_{\theta_m}^{0} \frac{d\theta'}{\left\{\dfrac{2}{J}\,[V(\theta_m) - V(\theta')]\right\}^{1/2}}, \tag{f}$$

where from (e)

$$V(\theta_m) - V(\theta) = \frac{C_o}{2\alpha}\,(\theta_m - \theta)\,\frac{V_o^{\,2}}{2}. \tag{g}$$

Substitution of (g) into (f), followed by integration, gives the required period of oscillation:

$$T = 8\left(\frac{2J\alpha}{C_o V_o^{\,2}}\right)^{1/2}\sqrt{\theta_m}; \qquad |\theta_m| < 2\alpha. \tag{h}$$

Of course, this result is limited to a range of θ_m in which the plates overlap. Beyond this range the motions are not bounded (oscillatory) and

$$T \to \infty; \qquad |\theta_m| > 2\alpha. \tag{i}$$

The dependence of the oscillation period on θ_m is shown in Fig. 5.2.11. In a linear system the period of oscillation is independent of amplitude. Hence the plot emphasizes the nonlinear character of the motion.

It should be recognized that the approximate function $C(\theta)$ is valid only if the plate spacing g is small compared with deflections θR of interest. In a more exact model the functional dependence of C would be smoothed in the region near $\theta = 0$ and $\theta = \pm 2\alpha$ in Fig. 5.2.10. This is true because the fringing fields would extend beyond the edge of the overlapping plates a distance on the order of g. Hence we cannot expect the period of oscillation given by (h) to be correct unless $\theta_m R \gg g$.

5.2.2 Loss-Dominated Systems

The approach to the analysis of nonlinear problems in Section 5.2.1 took advantage of the small mechanical and electrical energy dissipations. In this section we wish to illustrate how simplifying assumptions can be made valid when there is a *large* effect from damping mechanisms. We can illustrate briefly the notion involved by returning to the example of the pendulum used in Section 5.2.1 (Fig. 5.2.1). If there is viscous damping (with coefficient B),

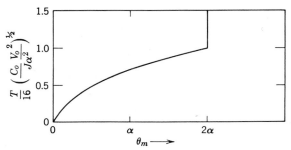

Fig. 5.2.11 Normalized period of oscillation for the electric pendulum of Fig. 5.2.10a as a function of peak amplitude.

(5.2.1) for the deflection of the pendulum is replaced by (see Section 2.2.1b for a discussion of torsional viscous dampers)

$$J \frac{d^2\theta}{dt^2} + B \frac{d\theta}{dt} = -Mgl \sin \theta. \qquad (5.2.18)$$

In the analysis presented in Section 5.2.1 the viscous term was implicitly assumed small compared with the other terms in the equation. In the opposite extreme the viscous damping is so large that the inertial effects of the first term are ignorable. This would be the result of immersing the pendulum in heavy oil. Then we can approximate (5.2.18) by

$$B \frac{d\theta}{dt} = -Mgl \sin \theta, \qquad (5.2.19)$$

which is a simple nonlinear expression to integrate. Rearranging, we have

$$\frac{d\theta}{\sin \theta} = - \frac{Mgl}{B} dt. \qquad (5.2.20)$$

If, when $t = 0$, $\theta = \theta_m$, we can integrate this equation between θ_m and $\theta(t)$

$$\int_{\theta_m}^{\theta(t)} \frac{d\theta}{\sin \theta} = - \frac{Mgl}{B} \int_0^t dt. \qquad (5.2.21)$$

We carry out this integration to obtain*

$$t \left(\frac{Mgl}{B} \right) = -\ln \left[\frac{\tan (\theta/2)}{\tan (\theta_m/2)} \right]. \qquad (5.2.22)$$

This expression for θ is plotted in Fig. 5.2.12.

We now consider an example of a nonlinear, lossy system, for which we can make simplifying assumptions to allow analytical integration of non-linear equations, and analyze a time-delay relay in which the dynamic

* C. D. Hodgman, *Mathematical Tables from Handbook of Chemistry and Physics*, 9th ed., Chemical Rubber Publishing Co., Cleveland, Ohio.

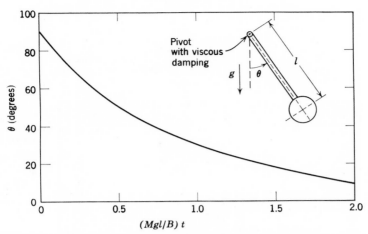

Fig. 5.2.12 Angular deflection θ of a pendulum heavily damped and released from $\theta_m = 90$.

behavior is controlled by mechanical losses. Although we treat a time-delay relay in this example, the approximations and analytical techniques are applicable to many other systems.

Example 5.2.4. In Fig. 5.2.13 we show schematically the basic actuator for a mechanically damped time-delay relay.* The basic operation to be analyzed is as follows: with switch S open, the spring pulls the plunger against a mechanical stop at $x = x_o$; when switch S is closed, current in the coil causes a magnetic force that pulls the plunger against the stop at $x = 0$. This displacement opens or closes relay contacts. The motion of the plunger when driven by the magnetic force is dominated by the mechanical damper. The damper, or dashpot, normally used in this application consists of a piston with a small orifice, moving in a cylinder filled with oil (see Fig. 2.2.10a). As discussed in Section 2.2.1b, a damper of this type is represented quite well by a damping force proportional to the square of the velocity [see (2.2.8)].

The electromechanical coupling of the configuration in Fig. 5.2.13 has been analyzed in Examples 2.1.1, 3.2.1, and 5.1.1. Neglecting fringing fields and assuming infinitely permeable magnetic material, we obtain the electrical and mechanical terminal relations from (a) and (c) of Example 5.1.1.

$$\lambda = \frac{L_o i}{1 + x/g} \tag{a}$$

$$f^e = -\frac{L_o i^2}{2g(1 + x/g)^2}, \tag{b}$$

where

$$L_o = \frac{\mu_0 N^2 (2wd)}{g}.$$

* A. E. Knowlton, ed., *Standard Handbook for Electrical Engineers*, 9th ed., McGraw-Hill, New York, 1957, Section 5–150.

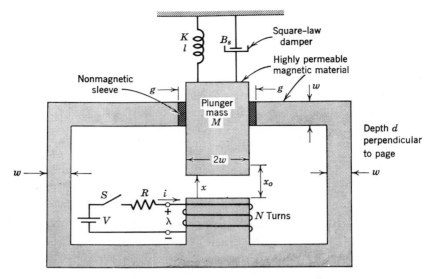

Fig. 5.2.13 Basic configuration of actuator for mechanically damped time-delay relay.

Thus, with switch S closed and the plunger between the stops

$$0 < x < x_o,$$

the equations of motion are

$$V = Ri + \frac{L_o}{1 + x/g}\frac{di}{dt} - \frac{L_o i}{g(1 + x/g)^2}\frac{dx}{dt}, \tag{c}$$

$$M\frac{d^2x}{dt^2} \pm B_s \left(\frac{dx}{dt}\right)^2 + K(x - l) = -\frac{L_o i^2}{2g(1 + x/g)^2}. \tag{d}$$

The $+$ or $-$ sign on the damping force is chosen to make the damping force oppose the motion.

As already stated, we wish to analyze the transient that occurs when the switch S is closed at $t = 0$ with the initial conditions at $t = 0$

$$x = x_o, \qquad i = 0. \tag{e}$$

The mechanical damper dominates the mechanical motion and slows down the motion of the plunger so that the closing time can be of the order of seconds to minutes. Consequently, the speed voltage, the last term in (c), can be neglected throughout the analysis, and the transient in current is complete before the position x changes significantly from the initial position x_o. Thus we find the current from the simplified equation

$$V = Ri + \frac{L_o}{1 + x_o/g}\frac{di}{dt}, \tag{f}$$

which has constant coefficients. The current transient is

$$i = \frac{V}{R}(1 - e^{-t/\tau_e}), \tag{g}$$

where

$$\tau_e = \frac{L_o}{R(1 + x_o/g)}.$$

The time constant τ_e is the electrical time constant with the gap fully open.

With the purely electrical transient completed before the mechanical motion starts and with the neglect of the speed voltage in (c) the mechanical motion occurs with the current essentially constant. Thus from the viewpoint of the mechanical motion the voltage source V and resistance R form an effective current source. This situation, in which electrical time constants are much shorter than mechanical time constants (see Section 5.1.3), occurs often in electromechanical transducers and is the source of significant simplification.

As stated before, the mechanical motion is dominated by the damper. This means that except for the very short time during which the mass initially accelerates, the damping force, the second term on the left of (d), is much greater than the acceleration force and the spring force. Consequently, when our interest is in the time required for the air gap to close, we can simplify (d) to

$$-B_s \left(\frac{dx}{dt}\right)^2 = -\frac{L_o(V/R)^2}{2g(1 + x/g)^2}, \tag{h}$$

where we have chosen the minus sign because $B_s(dx/dt)^2$ must act to retard the motion of the plunger in the $-x$-direction. Solution of this expression for the velocity yields

$$\frac{dx}{dt} = -\frac{\sqrt{L_o/2gB_s}\, V/R}{1 + x/g}. \tag{i}$$

We have specified a minus sign because we know from the initial conditions and the physical nature of the problem that x is decreasing.

With the initial condition as specified by (e), we integrate (i) to find the time t at which the plunger is at position x as

$$\int_{x_o}^{x} \left(1 + \frac{x'}{g}\right) dx' = -\int_{0}^{t} \left(\frac{L_o}{2gB_s}\right)^{1/2} \frac{V}{R}\, dt'. \tag{j}$$

Integration of this expression yields

$$(x_o - x) + \frac{(x_o^2 - x^2)}{2g} = \left(\frac{L_o}{2gB_s}\right)^{1/2} \frac{V}{R}\, t. \tag{k}$$

We find x as a function of time by solving this quadratic equation. The result is

$$x = -g + \left[(g + x_o)^2 - \left(\frac{2L_og}{B_s}\right)^{1/2} \frac{V}{R}\, t\right]^{1/2} \tag{l}$$

Note that this expression satisfies the initial condition that at $t = 0$, $x = x_o$. Because the other root of (h) does not satisfy this condition, it is extraneous.

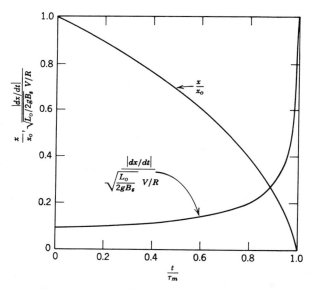

Fig. 5.2.14 Dynamic response of system of Fig. 5.2.13.

Alternatively, if we wish to evaluate the time τ_m necessary for the airgap to close, we set $x = 0$ in (k) and obtain

$$\tau_m = \left(\frac{2gB_s}{L_o}\right)^{1/2} \frac{R}{V} x_o \left(1 + \frac{x_o}{2g}\right). \tag{m}$$

It is clear from this expression how the closing time can be controlled by the damping constant B_s or by the current V/R.

The response of the position as a function of time (l) is plotted in Fig. 5.2.14. For this purpose (l) is normalized in the following way:

$$\frac{x}{x_o} = -\frac{g}{x_o} + \left[\left(\frac{g}{x_o} + 1\right)^2 - \left(\frac{2g}{x_o} + 1\right)\frac{t}{\tau_m}\right]^{1/2}, \tag{n}$$

and we assume the ratio

$$\frac{g}{x_o} = 0.1.$$

Also plotted in Fig. 5.2.14 is the magnitude of the velocity, normalized, by using (i) and (n) in the form

$$\frac{|dx/dt|}{(L_o/2gB_s)^{1/2}V/R} = \left[\left(1 + \frac{x_o}{g}\right)^2 - \frac{x_o}{g}\left(2 + \frac{x_o}{g}\right)\frac{t}{\tau_m}\right]^{-1/2}. \tag{o}$$

We note from the curves of Fig. 5.2.14 that the plunger moves at almost constant velocity over most of the travel and then accelerates markedly. This results because the magnetic force (b) increases rapidly as $x \to 0$. A characteristic of this type is desirable in a time-delay relay to ensure that the contacts will close rapidly to avoid arcing. In any given situation, however, the validity of ignoring the acceleration and speed voltage effects in this last region should be examined.

The curve of velocity in Fig. 5.2.14 indicates that this system behaves much like a linear statically unstable system (see curve A of Fig. 5.1.7). In some cases it may be desirable to approximate the equations of motion by a linear set with a static instability. This is especially true if the nonlinear expressions cannot be integrated analytically.

Although we have confined our attention in this section to discussing examples in which the damping is mechanical in nature, electrical damping can also dominate the dynamics. An example in which this is the case was discussed in Section 5.1.3. There the dynamic behavior of a coil rotating in a magnetic field was discussed in the limit at which the inductive reactance could be ignored [condition of (5.1.32)]. This made it possible to reduce the solution of the nonlinear motions to the problem of integrating (5.1.34), a procedure that is analogous to integrating (5.2.19).

5.3 DISCUSSION

In this chapter there have been two objectives. For the first, important types of dynamical behavior have been illustrated in which attention has been given to the relation of basic electromechanical interactions to mathematical models. For the second objective we have formed a basis on which to build an understanding of continuum interactions. In this regard both the mathematical techniques and physical approximations of this chapter are important in the chapters that follow.

PROBLEMS

5.1. Two parallel, perfectly-conducting plates are constrained as shown in Figure 5P.1 in such a way that the bottom plate is fixed and the top one is free to move only in the x-direction. A field is applied between the plates by the voltage source $v(t)$. When $x = 0$, the spring is in its equilibrium position.

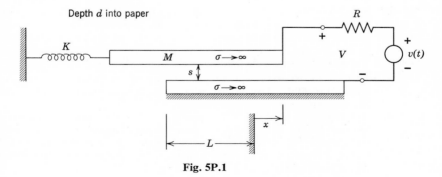

Fig. 5P.1

(a) What is the force of electric origin exerted on the upper plate?

(b) Write the complete equations of motion for this system.

(c) If $R = 0$ and $v(t) = (V_o \sin \omega t)u_{-1}(t)$, where $u_{-1}(t)$ is the unit step function, what is $x(t)$? Assume that the system is in static equilibrium when $t < 0$.

5.2. The system illustrated in Fig. 5P.2 is a schematic model of a differential transformer, which is a device for measuring small changes in mechanical position electrically. The movable core is constrained by bearings (not shown) to move in the x-direction. The two excitation windings, each having N_1 turns, are connected in series with relative polarity such that, when the movable core is centered as shown, there is no coupling between the excitation circuit and the signal winding. When the core moves from the center position in either direction, a voltage is induced in the signal winding. In the analysis neglect fringing fields and assume that the magnetic material is infinitely permeable.

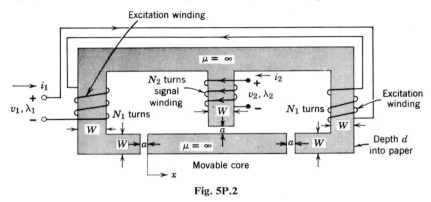

Fig. 5P.2

(a) Calculate the lumped-parameter equations of state, $\lambda_1(i_1, i_2, x)$, $\lambda_2(i_1, i_2, x)$, for this system.

(b) Terminal pair 1 is constrained by a current source $i_1 = I_o \cos \omega t$ and the system operates in the steady state. The open-circuit voltage v_2 is measured. Calculate the amplitude and phase angle of v_2 as a function of displacement x for the range $-a < x < a$.

5.3. A pair of highly conducting plates is mounted on insulating sheets, as shown in Fig. 5P.3a. The bottom sheet is immobile and hinged to the top sheet along the axis A. The top sheet is therefore free to rotate through an angle ψ. A torsion spring tends to make $\psi = \psi_o$ so that there is a spring torque in the $+\psi$-direction $T^s = K(\psi_o - \psi)$. A source of charge $Q(t)$ is shunted by a conductance G and connected by flexible leads between the conducting plates. We wish to describe mathematically the motion of the upper plate [e.g., find $\psi(t)$]. To do this complete the following steps:

(a) Find the static electric field $\mathbf{E}$ between the two flat, perfectly conducting plates shown in Fig. 5P.3b. Assume that each of the plates extends to infinity in the r- and z-directions.

(b) If the angle ψ is small [$\psi a \ll D$, $\psi a \ll (b - a)$] so that fringing fields are not important, the electric field of part (a) can be used to approximate $\mathbf{E}$ between the metal plates of Fig. 5P.3a. Under this assumption find the charge q on the upper metal plate. Your answer should be in the form of $q = q(V, \psi)$ and is the electrical terminal relation for the block diagram of Fig. 5P.3c.

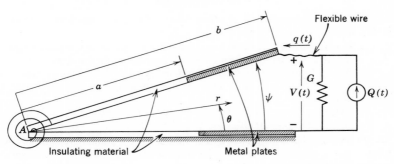

Fig. 5P.3a

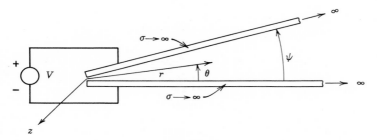

Fig. 5P.3b

Fig. 5P.3c

(c) Use part (b) to find the electrical energy stored between the plates $W = W(q, \psi)$ and, using W, find the torque of electrical origin T^e exerted by the field on the movable plate.

(d) Write two differential equations that, with initial conditions, define the motion of the top plate. These equations should be written in terms of the two dependent variables $\psi(t)$ and $q(t)$. The driving function $Q(t)$ is known and the movable plate has a moment of inertia J.

(e) Use the equations of part (d) to find the sinusoidal steady-state deflection $\psi(t)$ if $G = 0$ and $Q(t) = Q_o \cos \omega t$. You may wish to define ψ as $\psi = \psi_1 + \psi'(t)$, where ψ_1 is a part of the deflection which is independent of time. Identify the steady-state frequency at which the plate vibrates and give a physical reason why this answer would be expected.

5.4. This is a continuation of Problem 3.4, in which the equations of motion for the system shown in Fig. 3P.4 were developed.

    (a) The resistance R is made large enough to be ignorable and the current $I(t) = I_o$, where I_o is a constant. Write the equation of motion for $x(t)$.

    (b) Use a force diagram (as in Example 5.1.1) to determine the position $x = x_o$, where the mass can be in static equilibrium, and show whether this equilibrium is stable.

    (c) With the mass M initially in static equilibrium, $x(0) = x_o$, it is given an initial velocity v_o. Find $x(t)$ for $x \approx x_o$.

5.5. Two small spheres are attached to an insulating rod, and a third sphere is free to slide between them. Each of the outside spheres has a charge Q_1, whereas the inside sphere has a charge Q_o and a mass M. Hence the equation of motion for the inside sphere is

$$M \frac{d^2x}{dt^2} = \frac{Q_o Q_1}{4\pi\epsilon(d + x)^2} - \frac{Q_1 Q_o}{4\pi\epsilon(d - x)^2}.$$

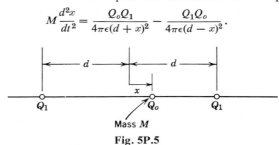

Fig. 5P.5

    (a) For what values of Q_o and Q_1 will the movable sphere have a stable static equilibrium at $x = 0$? Show your reasoning.

    (b) Under the conditions of (a), what will be the response of the sphere to an initial small static deflection $x = x_o$? $x_o \ll d$. (When $t = 0$, $x = x_o$, $dx/dt = 0$.)

5.6. Figure 5P.6 shows a sphere of magnetic material in the magnetic field of a coil. The coenergy of the coil is

$$W'(i, x) = \frac{L_o}{2}\left[1 - \left(\frac{x}{b}\right)^4\right]i^2,$$

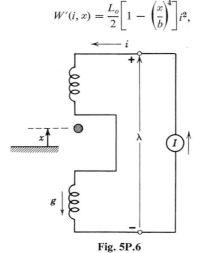

Fig. 5P.6

where L_o is positive. The sphere has a mass M and is subject to a gravitational force Mg (as shown).

(a) Write the differential equation that determines $x(t)$.

(b) Find the equilibrium position(s).

(c) Show whether this (these) equilibrium position(s) is (are) stable.

5.7. In Problem 3.15 we developed the equation of motion for a magnetic wedge, and it was shown that, with a constant current $i = I_o$ applied, the wedge could be in static equilibrium at $\theta = 0$. Under what conditions is this equilibrium stable?

5.8. The system shown in Fig. 5P.8 is one third of a system (governing vertical motion only) for suspending an airfoil or other test vehicle in a wind tunnel without mechanical support. The mass M_o, which represents the airfoil, contains magnetizable material and is constrained by means not shown to move in the vertical direction only. The system is designed so that the main supporting field is generated by current i_1 and the stabilizing field is generated by current i_2. Over the range of positions (x) of interest, the electrical terminal relations may be expressed as:

$$\lambda_1(i_1, i_2, x) = \frac{L_1 i_1}{(1 + x/a)^3} + \frac{M i_2}{(1 + x/a)^3},$$

$$\lambda_2(i_1, i_2, x) = \frac{M i_1}{(1 + x/a)^3} + \frac{L_2 i_2}{(1 + x/a)^3},$$

where a, L_1, L_2, and M are positive constants and $M^2 < L_1 L_2$.

(a) Find the force of electric origin $f^e(i_1, i_2, x)$ acting on mass M_o.

(b) Set $i_1 = I$, a constant current, and set $i_2 = 0$. Find the equilibrium position X_o where f^e is just sufficient to balance the gravitational force on the mass M_o.

(c) With the currents as specified in part (b), write the linear incremental differential equation that describes the motion of mass M_o for small excursions $x'(t)$ from the equilibrium X_o. If an external force $f(t) = I_o u_o(t)$ (an impulse) is applied to the mass in the positive x-direction with the mass initially at rest, find the response $x'(t)$.

(d) For stabilization of the equilibrium at X_o a feedback system, which uses a light source, photoelectric sensor, and amplifiers, supplies a current i_2 such that $i_2(t) = \alpha x'(t)$, where α is a real constant. Keeping $i_1 = I$, write the equation of motion for $x'(t)$. For what range of α is the impulse response $x'(t)$ bounded?

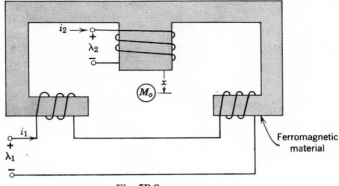

Fig. 5P.8

(e) To make the impulse response tend to zero as $t \to \infty$, the signal from the photo-electric sensors is operated on electronically to produce a current i_2 such that

$$i_2 = \alpha x'(t) + \beta \frac{dx'}{dt},$$

where α and β are real constants. Again, write the equation of motion for $x'(t)$. For what ranges of α and β does the impulse response $x'(t)$ tend to zero as $t \to \infty$?

5.9. A conservative magnetic field transducer for which variables are defined in Fig. 5P.9 has the electrical equation of state $\lambda = Ax^3 i$, for $x > 0$, where A is a positive constant. The system is loaded at its mechanical terminals by a spring, whose spring constant is K

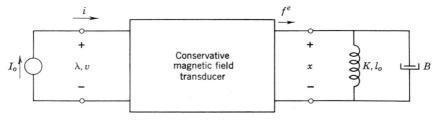

Fig. 5P.9

and whose force is zero when $x = l_o$, and a mechanical damper with the constant B. The electrical terminals are excited by a direct-current source I_o with the value

$$I_o = \left(\frac{K}{8Al_o} \right)^{1/2}.$$

(a) Write the mechanical equation in terms of f^e.
(b) Find f^e in terms of data given above.
(c) Find by *algebraic* techniques the possible equilibrium positions for the system and show whether each equilibrium point is stable.
(d) Check the results of part (c) by using *graphical* techniques to investigate the stability of the equilibrium points.

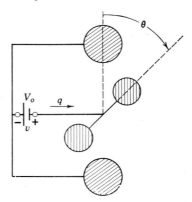

Fig. 5P.10

5.10. An electric field system has a single electrical terminal pair and one mechanical degree of freedom θ (Fig. 5P.10). The electrical terminal variables are related by $q = C_o(1 + \cos 2\theta)v$, where θ is the angular position of a shaft. The only torques acting on this shaft are of electrical origin. The voltage $v = -V_o$, where V_o is a constant.

(a) At what angles θ can the shaft be in static equilibrium?

(b) Which of these cases represents a stable equilibrium? Show your reasoning.

5.11. Figure 5P.11 shows a diagrammatic cross section of a two-phase, salient-pole synchronous machine. The windings in an actual machine are distributed in many slots

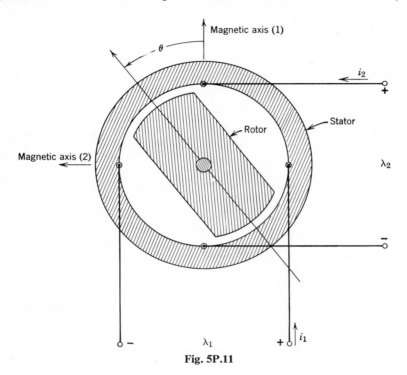

Fig. 5P.11

along the periphery of the stator, rather than as shown. The rotor is made of magnetically soft iron which has no residual permanent magnetism. The electrical terminal relations are given by

$$\lambda_1 = (L_o + M \cos 2\theta)i_1 + M \sin 2\theta\, i_2,$$

$$\lambda_2 = M \sin 2\theta\, i_1 + (L_o - M \cos 2\theta)i_2.$$

(a) Determine the torque of electrical origin $T^e(i_1, i_2, \theta)$.

(b) Assume that the machine is excited by sources such that $i_1 = I \cos \omega_s t$, $i_2 = I \sin \omega_s t$, and the rotor has the constant angular velocity ω_m such that $\theta = \omega_m t + \gamma$. Evaluate the instantaneous torque T^e. Under what conditions is it constant?

(c) The rotor is subjected to a mechanical torque (acting on it in the $+\theta$-direction): $T = T_o + T'(t)$, where T_o is a constant. The time-varying part of the torque perturbs the steady rotation of (b) so that $\theta = \omega_m t + \gamma_o + \gamma'(t)$. Assume that the rotor has a moment of inertia J but that there is no damping. Find the possible equilibrium angles γ_o between the rotor and the stator field. Then write a differential equation for $\gamma'(t)$, with $T'(t)$ as a driving function.

(d) Consider small perturbations of the rotation $\gamma'(t)$, so that the equation of motion found in (c) can be linearized. Find the response to an impulse of torque $T'(t) = I_o u_o(t)$, assuming that before the impulse in torque the rotation velocity is constant.

(e) Which of the equilibrium phase angles γ_o found in (c) is stable?

5.12. An electromechanical model for a magnetic transducer is shown in Fig. 5P.12. A force $f(t)$ is to be transduced into a signal $v_o(t)$ which appears across the resistance R. The

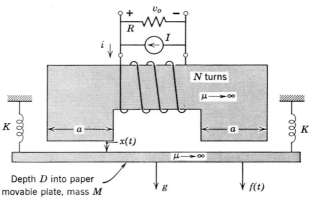

Fig. 5P.12

system is designed to provide linear operation about an equilibrium where the coil is excited by a constant current I. The plate is constrained at each end by springs that exert no force when $x = 0$.

(a) Find the force of electrical origin $f^e(x, i)$ on the plate in the x-direction.

(b) Write the equations of motion for the system. These should be two equations in the dependent variables (i, x).

(c) The static equilibrium is established with $f(t) = 0$, $x = X$, and $i = I$. Write the equilibrium force equation that determines X. Use a graphical sketch to indicate the equilibrium position X at which the system is stable. Assume in the following that the system is perturbed from this stable static equilibrium.

(d) The resistance R is made large enough so that the voltage drop across the resistance is much larger than that across the self-inductance of the coil. Use this fact as the basis for an approximation in the electrical equation of motion. Assume also that perturbations from the equilibrium conditions of (c) are small enough to justify linearization of the equations. Given that $f(t) = \text{Re }[\hat{f}e^{j\omega t}]$, $v_o(t) = \text{Re }[\hat{v}_o e^{j\omega t}]$, solve for the frequency response $\hat{v}_o/\hat{f}$.

5.13. The cross-section of a cylindrical solenoid used to position the valve mechanism of a hydraulic control system is shown in Fig. 5P.13. When the currents i_1 and i_2 are equal, the plunger is centered horizontally ($x = 0$). When the coil currents are unbalanced, the plunger

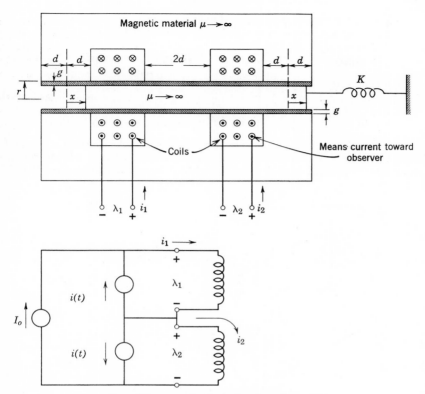

Note. When $x = 0$, the spring force is zero!

Fig. 5P.13

moves a distance x. The nonmagnetic sleeves keep the plunger centered radially. The mass of the plunger is M, the spring constant K, and the viscous friction coefficient is B. The displacement x is limited to the range $-d < x < d$. You are given the terminal conditions

$$\begin{bmatrix} \lambda_1 = L_{11}i_1 + L_{12}i_2 \\ \lambda_2 = L_{12}i_1 + L_{22}i_2 \end{bmatrix}$$

where

$$L_{11} = L_o\left(3 - 2\frac{x}{d} - \frac{x^2}{d^2}\right),$$

$$L_{22} = L_o\left(3 + 2\frac{x}{d} - \frac{x^2}{d^2}\right),$$

$$L_{12} = L_o\left(1 - \frac{x^2}{d^2}\right).$$

(a) Write the mechanical equation of motion.
(b) Assume that the system is excited by the bias current I_o and the two signal current sources $i(t)$ in the circuit of Fig. 5P.13 with the restriction that $|i(t)| \ll I_o$. Linearize the mechanical equation of motion obtained in part (a) for this excitation.
(c) Is the system stable for all values of I_o?
(d) The system is under damped. Find the response $x(t)$ to a step of signal current $i(t) = Iu_{-1}(t)$.
(e) Find the steady-state response $x(t)$ to a signal current $i(t) = I \sin \omega t$.

5.14. A plane rectangular coil of wire can be rotated about its axis as shown in Fig. 5P.14. This coil is excited electrically through sliding contacts and the switch S by the constant-current source I in parallel with the conductance G. A second coil, not shown, produces a

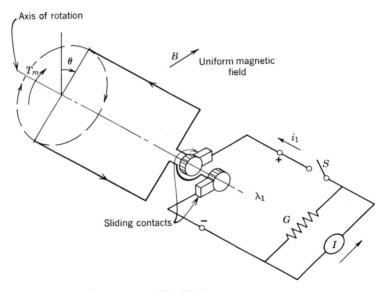

Fig. 5P.14

uniform magnetic field perpendicular to the plane of the rectangular coil when $\theta = 0$. Assume that the terminals of the second coil are described by the variables i_2, λ_2, so that we can write the electrical terminal relations as $\lambda_1 = L_1 i_1 + i_2 M \cos \theta$, $\lambda_2 = i_1 M \cos \theta + L_2 i_2$, where L_1, M, and L_2 (the self- and maximum mutual inductances of the coils) are constants. Concentrate attention on the electrical variables of the rotating coil by assuming that $i_2 = I_2 = $ constant. This is the excitation that provides the uniform constant magnetic field. In addition, assume that the mechanical position is constrained by the source $\theta = \Omega t$.

(a) Write the electrical equation for the coil. This equation, together with initial conditions, should determine $i_1(t)$.

(b) Assume that the switch S is closed at $t = 0$; that is, the initial conditions are, when $t = 0$, $\theta = 0$ and $i_1 = 0$. Find the current $i_1(t)$.

(c) Find the flux $\lambda_1(t)$ that links the rotating coil.

(d) Consider the limiting case of (b) and (c) in which the current i_1 can be considered as constrained by the current source.

$$\Omega GL_1 \ll 1 \quad \text{and} \quad \Omega GL_1 \ll \frac{L_1 I}{M I_2}.$$

Sketch $i_1(t)$ and $\lambda_1(t)$.

(e) Consider the limiting case in which the electrical terminals can be considered to be constrained to constant flux $\Omega GL_1 \gg 1$ and sketch $i_1(t)$ and $\lambda_1(t)$.

(f) Compute the instantaneous torque of electrical origin on the rotating coil.

(g) Find the average power required to rotate the coil. Sketch this power as a function of the normalized conductance ΩGL_1. For what value of ΩGL_1 does G absorb the maximum power?

5.15. In the system illustrated in Fig. 5P.15 the lower capacitor plate is fixed and the upper plate is constrained to move only in the x-direction. The spring force is zero when $x = l$, and the damping with coefficient B is so large that we can neglect the mass of the movable

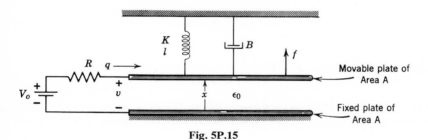

Fig. 5P.15

plate. The capacitor plates are excited by a constant voltage source in series with a resistance R. Neglect fringing fields. The voltage V_o is adjusted so that a stable, static equilibrium occurs at $X_o = 0.7l$. With the system at rest at this equilibrium position, a small step of mechanical force f is applied: $f = Fu_{-1}(t)$. In all of your analyses assume that the perturbations from equilibrium are small enough to allow use of linear incremental differential equations.

(a) Calculate the resulting transient in position x.

(b) Specify the condition that must be satisfied by the parameters in order that the mechanical transient may occur essentially at constant voltage. Sketch and label the transient under this condition.

(c) Specify the condition that must be satisfied by the parameters in order that the initial part of the mechanical transient may occur essentially at constant charge. Sketch and label the transient under this condition.

5.16. A mass M has the position $x(t)$. It is subjected to forces f_1 and f_2 which have the dependence on x shown in Fig. 5P.16. The mass is released at $x = 0$ with the velocity v_o. In terms of F_o and K, what is the largest value of v_o that will lead to bounded displacements of M?

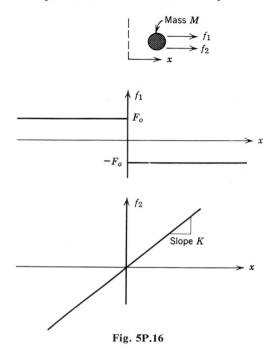

Fig. 5P.16

5.17. The electric field transducer shown in Fig. 5P.17 has two electrical terminal pairs and a single mechanical terminal pair. Both plates and movable elements can be regarded as perfectly conducting.

   (a) Find the electrical terminal relations $q_1 = q_1(v_1, v_2, x)$, $q_2 = q_2(v_1, v_2, x)$.

   (b) Now the terminals are constrained so that $v_2 = V_o = $ constant and $q_1 = 0$. Find the energy function $U(x)$ such that the force of electrical origin acting in the x-direction on the movable element is

$$f^e = -\frac{\partial U}{\partial x}.$$

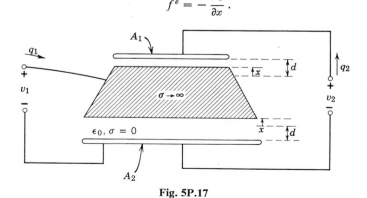

Fig. 5P.17

5.18. The central plate of a three-plate capacitor system (Fig. 5P.18) has one mechanical degree of freedom, x. The springs are relaxed in the equilibrium position $x = 0$ and fringing can be neglected. For a long time the system is maintained with the central plate fixed at $x = 0$ and the switch closed. At $t = 0$ the switch is opened and the center plate is released simultaneously.

(a) Find, in terms of given parameters, a hybrid energy function W'' such that $f^e = -\partial W''/\partial x$ for $t > 0$.

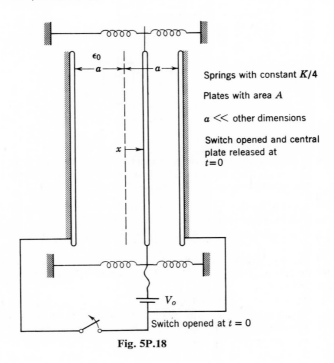

Springs with constant $K/4$

Plates with area A

$a \ll$ other dimensions

Switch opened and central plate released at $t=0$

Fig. 5P.18

(b) Determine the criterion that the central plate be in stable equilibrium at $x = 0$.
(c) In the case in which the criterion of part (b) is satisfied, sketch a potential well diagram for $-a \le x \le a$, indicating all static equilibrium points, and whether they are stable or unstable.

5.19. An electromechanical system with one electrical and one mechanical terminal pair is shown in Fig. 5P.19. The electrical terminal relation is

$$\lambda = \frac{L_o i}{(1 - x/a)^4},$$

where L_o and a are given constants. The system is driven by a voltage $V_o + v(t)$, where V_o is constant. The mass of the plunger can be ignored. Gravity acts on M as shown.

(a) Write the complete equations of motion for the system. There should be two equations in the unknowns i and x.

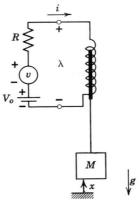

Fig. 5P.19

(b) With $v(t) = 0$, the current produced by V_o holds the mass M in static equilibrium at $x = x_o$. Write the linearized equations of motion for the perturbations from this equilibrium that result because of $v(t)$.

5.20. The upper of the three plane-parallel electrodes shown in the Fig. 5P.20 is free to move in the x-direction. Ignore fringing fields, and find the following:

(a) The electrical terminal relations $q_1(v_1, v_2, x)$ and $q_2(v_1, v_2, x)$.

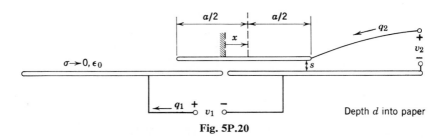

Fig. 5P.20

(b) Now the top plate is insulated from the lower plates after a charge $q_2 = Q$ has been established. Also, the potential difference between the lower plates is constrained by the voltage source $v_1 = V_o$. Find a hybrid energy function $W''(V_o, Q, x)$ such that

$$f^e = \frac{\partial W''(V_o, Q, x)}{\partial x}.$$

5.21. In Problem 3.8 the equation of motion was found for a superconducting coil rotating in the field of a fixed coil excited by a current source. This problem is a continuation of that development in which we consider the dynamics of the coil in a special case. The current I is constrained to be $I_o = $ constant.

(a) Write the equation of motion in the form

$$J\frac{d^2\theta}{dt^2} + \frac{\partial V}{\partial \theta} = 0.$$

(see Section 5.2.1) and sketch the potential well.

(b) Indicate on the potential-well sketch the angular positions at which the rotor can be in stable static equilibrium and in unstable static equilibrium.

(c) With the rotor initially at rest at $\theta = 0$, how much kinetic energy must be imparted to the rotor to make it rotate continuously?

5.22. The system of Fig. 5P.22 contains a simple pendulum with mass M and length l. The pivot has viscous (linear) friction of coefficient B. The mass is made of ferromagnetic material. It causes a variation of coil inductance with angle θ that can be represented

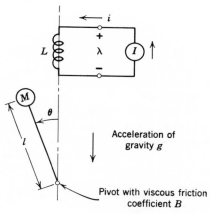

Fig. 5P.22

approximately by the expression $L = L_o(1 + 0.2\cos\theta + 0.05\cos 2\theta)$, where L_o is a positive constant. The coil is excited by a constant-current source I at a value such that $I^2 L_o = 6Mgl$ with no externally applied forces other than gravity g.

(a) Write the mechanical equation of motion for the system.

(b) Find all of the possible static equilibria and show whether or not each one is stable.

5.23. The one-turn inductor shown in Fig. 5P.23 is made from plane parallel plates with a spacing w and depth (into the paper) D. The plates are short-circuited by a sliding plate in the position $x(t)$. This movable plate is constrained by a spring (constant K) and has a mass M.

(a) Find the equation of motion for the plate, assuming that the electrical terminals are constrained to constant flux $\lambda = \Lambda = $ constant.

(b) Find the position(s) $x = X_o$ at which the plate can be in static equilibrium. Determine if each point represents a stable equilibrium. Can you assign an equivalent spring constant to the magnetic field for small-signal (linear) motions?

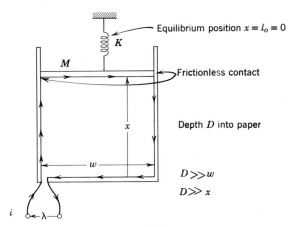

Equilibrium position $x = l_o = 0$

K

M

Frictionless contact

x

Depth D into paper

w

$D \gg w$

$D \gg x$

i

Fig. 5P.23

(c) Use a potential-well argument to describe the nonlinear motions of the plate. Include in your discussion how you would use the initial conditions to establish the constant of the motion E.

(d) Briefly describe the motions of the plate constrained so that $i = I = $ constant.

5.24. The terminals of the device shown in Problem 4.23 are now constrained to a constant value of λ: $\lambda = \Lambda_o = $ constant. The rotor has a moment of inertia J and is free of damping.

    (a) When $\theta = 0$, the angular velocity $d\theta/dt = \Omega$. Find an analytical expression for $d\theta/dt$ at each value of θ. (Given the angle θ, this expression should provide the angular velocity.)

    (b) What is the minimum initial angular velocity required to make the rotor rotate continuously in one direction?

    (c) For what values of θ can the rotor be in static equilibrium? Which of these equilibria is stable?

    (d) Describe quantitatively the angular excursion of the rotor when it is given an initial angular velocity less than that found in (b).

5.25. A mass M_1 attached to a weightless string rotates in a circle of radius r on a fixed frictionless surface as illustrated in Fig. 5P.25. The other end of the string is passed through a frictionless hole in the surface and is attached to a movable capacitor plate of mass M_2. The other capacitor plate is fixed and the capacitor is excited by a voltage source $v(t)$. The necessary dimensions are defined in the figure. The length of the string is such that when $x = 0$, $r = 0$. You may assume that $a \gg x$ and ignore the effects of gravity and electrical resistance. With $v(t) = V_o = $ constant and $r = l$, the mass M_1 is given an angular velocity ω_m necessary for equilibrium.

    (a) Find the force of electromagnetic origin exerted on the capacitor plate.

    (b) Determine the equilibrium value of ω_m.

    (c) Show that the angular momentum $M_1 r^2 \, d\theta/dt$ is constant, even if $r = r(t)$ and $\theta = \theta(t)$. [See Problem 2.8 for writing force equations in (r, θ) coordinates.]

    (d) Use the result of (c) to write the equation of motion for $r(t)$. Write this equation in a form such that potential well arguments can be used to deduce the dyamics.

    (e) Is the equilibrium found in (b) stable?

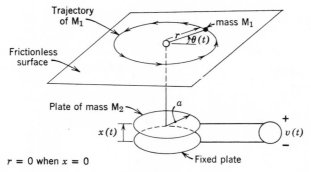

Trajectory of M_1

mass M_1

Frictionless surface

r $\theta(t)$

Plate of mass M_2

a

$x(t)$

$v(t)$

$r = 0$ when $x = 0$

Fixed plate

Fig. 5P.25

5.26. As an example of a lossy nonlinear system, consider the basic actuator for an electrically damped time-delay relay* illustrated in Fig. 5P.26. The transducer is designed to operate as follows. With switch S open, the spring holds the plunger against a mechanical stop at $x = x_o$. When switch S is closed, the magnetic field is excited, but the winding that is short-circuited through resistance R_2 limits the rate of buildup of flux to a low value. As the flux builds up slowly, the magnetic force increases. When the magnetic force equals the spring force, the plunger starts to move and close the air gap. The velocity of the plunger is so low that inertia and friction forces can be neglected; thus, when the plunger is moving, the spring force is at all times balanced by the magnetic force (see Section 5.2.2).

(a) Write the electrical circuit equations. The magnetic flux Φ is defined such that $\lambda_1 = N_1\Phi$ and $\lambda_2 = N_2\Phi$. Use these equations to find a single equation involving (Φ, x) with V as a driving function.

(b) Define two constants: the flux Φ_o linking the coils with the air gap closed ($x = 0$), $\Phi_o = 2\mu_0 w d N_1 V/g R_1$, and the time constant τ_o for flux buildup when the air gap is closed,

$$\tau_o = \frac{2\mu_0 w d}{g}\left(\frac{N_1^2}{R_1} + \frac{N_2^2}{R_2}\right).$$

Show that the result of (a) can be written in the form

$$\Phi_o = \left(1 + \frac{x}{g}\right)\Phi + \tau_o\frac{d\Phi}{dt}.$$

The transient behavior of this device can be divided into three intervals:

1. The switch S is closed with the plunger at $x = x_0$ and with zero initial flux Φ. The flux builds up to a value necessary to provide a magnetic force equal to the spring force that is holding the plunger against the stop at $x = x_0$.

2. The plunger moves from the stop at $x = x_0$ to the stop at $x = 0$. During this motion the spring force is the only appreciable mechanical force and is balanced by the magnetic force.

3. The plunger is held against the stop at $x = 0$ by the magnetic force, whereas the flux Φ continues to build up to Φ_0.

* *Standard Handbook for Electrical Engineers*, 9th ed., McGraw-Hill, New York, 1957, Sections 5-150 and 5-168.

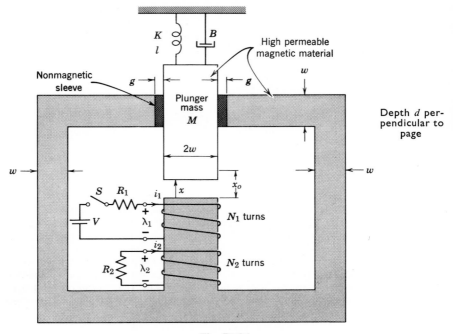

Fig. 5P.26

(c) Determine the transient in Φ during interval (1). Write an equation of force equilibrium for the plunger to determine the flux $\Phi = \Phi_1$ when interval (1) ends.

(d) Write an equation for Φ during interval (2). Assume the parameters

$$\frac{l}{x_o} = 2, \qquad \frac{x_o}{g} = 4, \qquad \frac{\Phi_o}{\Phi_1} = 10$$

and integrate the equation resulting from (c) to find $\Phi(t)$ in interval (2).

(e) Find the transient in Φ during interval (3).

(f) Sketch Φ and x as functions of time throughout the three intervals.

CHAPTER 6

FIELDS AND MOVING MEDIA

6.0 INTRODUCTION

In Chapter 1 we reviewed the basic postulates and definitions of electromagnetic theory. We defined the quasi-static electromagnetic field theory suitable for efficient analysis of low-frequency, low-velocity electromechanical systems. In Chapter 2 we used the quasi-static electromagnetic equations to calculate lumped parameters for important classes of electromechanical systems. The effect of mechanical motion on the electric or magnetic fields was accounted for by allowing the electrical lumped parameters to have a dependence on the mechanical displacements. In Chapter 3 this lumped-parameter model was used to determine the electric or magnetic forces on the mechanical system. We were then prepared for the study in Chapters 4 and 5 of the dynamics of lumped-parameter electromechanical systems.

In this chapter we return to the field description introduced in Chapter 1. This is necessary if we are to extend the class of electromechanical situations with which we can deal beyond the lumped-parameter systems of Chapters 2 to 5. In subsequent chapters we shall be treating continuum systems, that is, those in which both the electrical and mechanical parts of the system are described, at least in part, by partial differential equations. This necessitates a field description of the electromechanical coupling.

Even if we are concerned only with lumped-parameter systems, a field description of the electromechanical interaction provides a useful alternative to the lumped-parameter models of Chapters 2 to 5. In many cases forces of electrical origin can be most easily deduced from the fields themselves, thus bypassing the computation of lumped parameters and an energy function. Similarly, the effects of material motion on the electrical system can be deduced from field considerations. On the other hand, an understanding of lumped-parameter systems, based on the viewpoint of Chapters 2 to 5, provides considerable insight into what is required of a field description that includes effects of moving media. By the time this chapter is completed, the reader should be acquainted with Appendix B, in which the subject of quasi-statics is reviewed.

A simple example explains how the following sections lead to a generalization of electromagnetic theory to include the effects of material motion. A disk of copper is shown in Fig. 6.0.1a as it moves with velocity $\mathbf{v}$ into a region of flux density $\mathbf{B}$ imposed by a magnet. (We could do this experiment by attaching a handle to the disk so that we could wield it through the magnetic field.) Our lumped-parameter model provides a qualitative description of what happens. Suppose we model the disk as a one-turn, perfectly conducting loop shorted through a resistance, as shown in Fig. 6.0.1b. Then, as the loop enters the magnetic field region, it links an increasing flux λ from the imposed magnetic field $\mathbf{B}$, and an induced current i flows in a direction that induces a magnetic field which tends to cancel the flux of the imposed field $\mathbf{B}$. As the loop enters the field, this current i, interacting with $\mathbf{B}$, gives rise to a force tending to retard the motion. As we know from Section 5.1.3, the nature of this force depends on the resistance R of the loop. For a copper disk of reasonable size, as we move it through the magnetic field, it is likely that there would be an impression of passing it through a viscous liquid. The important point is that there is a magnetic force on the disk, hence a current within the disk.

Suppose that we are to analyze this problem in terms of fields. As discussed in Chapter 1, we are concerned with solutions to field equations for a quasi-static magnetic field system (equations summarized in Table 1.2).

$$\nabla \times \mathbf{H} = \mathbf{J}_f, \tag{6.0.1}$$

$$\nabla \cdot \mathbf{B} = 0, \tag{6.0.2}$$

$$\nabla \cdot \mathbf{J}_f = 0, \tag{6.0.3}$$

$$\nabla \times \mathbf{E} = -\frac{\partial \mathbf{B}}{\partial t}, \tag{6.0.4}$$

$$\mathbf{B} = \mu_0(\mathbf{H} + \mathbf{M}) \qquad (\mathbf{M} \simeq 0 \text{ for copper}). \tag{6.0.5}$$

In addition, there are boundary conditions on the surfaces of the disk and magnet. Also, we need the continuum equivalent of Ohm's law, for that was used in the lumped parameter model to explain the experiment. The necessary constituent relation was introduced in Chapter 1 as (1.1.9) and is

$$\mathbf{J}_f = \sigma \mathbf{E} \tag{6.0.6}$$

where σ is the electrical conductivity of the disk material. One approach to solving the obviously difficult problem at hand is to guess a reasonable

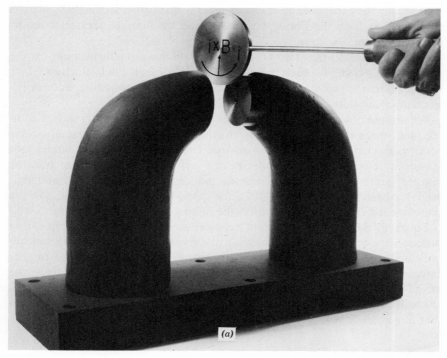

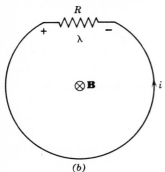

Fig. 6.0.1 (a) As the copper disk moves into the field **B**, there is an induced current i which interacts with **B** to retard the motion; (b) conducting loop equivalent to the disk of copper.

solution and show that it satisfies all of the equations and boundary conditions. In the absence of the moving conductor we have the fields $\mathbf{H} = \mathbf{H}_s$, $\mathbf{E} = 0$, $\mathbf{B} = \mu_0 \mathbf{H}_s$ and $\mathbf{J}_f = 0$, where $\mathbf{H}_s$ is a function of position but is independent of time. By definition this solution satisfies (6.0.1) to (6.0.6). In fact, it satisfies these equations and boundary conditions even as the disk passes through the magnetic field!

What we have found is that our field equations in the form given do not account for the experimental result. If there is no current in the disk, there is no force. Yet both the simple experiment and the lumped parameter model show that there is a force.

We might suspect that (6.0.1) to (6.0.6) could not possibly account for the effect of the moving medium because they do not involve the velocity **v**. This, in fact, is true, but note that the boundary conditions could depend on the mechanical motions.

We are now faced with the question, how do we alter (6.0.1) to (6.0.6) to account for the effects of the moving medium? At least one of these equations is not correct if there is material motion. One possibility is that we left out important effects by approximating the system as quasi-static; but the lumped parameter model explains the induced force on the disk and that model is based on (6.0.1) to (6.0.5), the quasi-static field equations. We are therefore led to the conclusion that the culprit in our description is (6.0.6.)

Equation 6.0.6 is a constituent relation that represents the conduction process in a certain class of materials discussed in Section 1.1.1. Hence not only is it a law deduced from experiments [(6.0.1) to (6.0.6) are in that category] but it is found to hold for certain media in a particular state: the media are at rest. To analyze our experiment we must know what form this law will take when the material is in motion. Suffice it to say at this point that our analysis will be correct when we rewrite (6.0.6) as

$$\mathbf{J}'_f = \sigma \mathbf{E}', \tag{6.0.7}$$

where $\mathbf{J}'_f$ and $\mathbf{E}'$ are the current density and field intensity that would be measured by an observer moving with the material. Of course, we wish to formulate the problem in the laboratory reference frame in which the current density and electric field intensity are $\mathbf{J}_f$ and $\mathbf{E}$, respectively. Hence our first objective is to relate the field variables measured in a frame of reference moving with a constant velocity to the field variables measured in the laboratory frame. We then discuss constituent relations for moving media.

We confine our attention to quasi-static electric and magnetic field systems. As discussed in the following sections, this means that we consider Galilean transformations that are appropriate also for Newtonian mechanics. This approach is the logical extension of a division of electromechanics into electric and magnetic field systems. The relationship of Galilean and Lorentz transformations and the relevance of Einstein relativity are discussed at the appropriate points.

Our treatment of relative motion is based on two postulates: (a) the equations of motion, including Maxwell's equations, are always written for an inertial coordinate system, that is, a coordinate system that is traveling with a velocity of constant magnitude and fixed direction; and (b) the laws of physics (e.g., Newton's laws and Maxwell's equations) are the same in every inertial coordinate system. These postulates are normally associated with Einstein relativity but they are also valid for Galilean systems.*

In Sections 6.3 and 6.4 examples that demonstrate how field transformations, boundary conditions, and constituent relations (the subjects of Sections 6.1 to 6.3) are used in the analysis of practical problems are considered. Emphasis is given to the magnetic field system; Section 6.4 is devoted to a class of rotating machines we were not prepared to discuss in detail in Chapter 4. These commutator-type machines, which are also of considerable practical significance, illustrate the fundamental point of this chapter.

6.1 FIELD TRANSFORMATIONS

In this treatment we are interested in field phenomena that occur in systems with material media in relative motion. The Lorentz force was introduced as the definition of the $\mathbf{E}$ and $\mathbf{B}$ fields in (1.1.28) of Chapter 1:

$$\mathbf{f} = q\mathbf{E} + q\mathbf{v} \times \mathbf{B}. \tag{6.1.1}$$

This expression states that a charge q in motion with velocity $\mathbf{v}$ with respect to an observer will experience the force $\mathbf{f}$ when subjected to the fields $\mathbf{E}$ and $\mathbf{B}$. Because Newton's laws must be the same in all inertial reference systems, another observer in a different reference frame will measure the same force on the charge but the charge will have a different velocity. It should be clear then that the two observers will measure different values of electric field intensity and magnetic flux density. The object of this section is to find the relations between electromagnetic quantities that are measured by two observers in uniform relative motion.

We have already stated that when an observer defines electromagnetic quantities he does so with the understanding that they are defined in his reference frame (coordinate system). Hence they are related by Maxwell's equations written in his coordinate system. It is a postulate of special relativity that physical laws, such as Maxwell's equations, must be the same in all inertial coordinate systems. We use this postulate to determine the relations between electromagnetic quantities measured in different inertial coordinate systems.

We define two inertial coordinate systems $\mathbf{r}$ and $\mathbf{r}'$ which are moving with a constant relative velocity $\mathbf{v}^r$. The times t and t' measured by observers in the two coordinate systems are assumed to be the same

$$t = t'. \tag{6.1.2}$$

* For discussions of the postulates and consequences of the special theory of relativity see, for example, J. D. Jackson, *Classical Electrodynamics*, Wiley, New York, 1962, Chapters 11 and 12; L. Landau and E. Lifshitz, *The Classical Theory of Fields*, Addison-Wesley, Reading, Mass., 1951, Chapters 1 and 2.

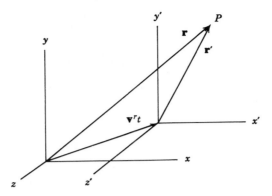

Fig. 6.1.1 Two inertial coordinate systems in relative motion.

We select the origins of the coordinate systems to coincide at $t = 0$. The relative geometry at a time t is illustrated in Fig. 6.1.1, from which we can obtain the relation between $\mathbf{r}$ and $\mathbf{r}'$, the instantaneous position vectors of point P, as measured in the two coordinate systems

$$\mathbf{r}' = \mathbf{r} - \mathbf{v}^r t. \tag{6.1.3}$$

Equations 6.1.2 and 6.1.3 define a *Galilean coordinate transformation* between inertial coordinate systems. We now show that this transformation is consistent with the quasi-static Maxwell equations. An analogous procedure can be used to show that the Galilean transformation is also consistent with all mechanical equations of motion introduced in Chapter 2 or in later chapters.

It is worthwhile to interject at this point that the general form of Maxwell's equations cannot be transformed consistently by means of the Galilean transformation. This, in fact, is the basis for a relativistic treatment, which demands that the transformation be consistent (that the equations be invariant) and results in the Lorentz transformation.* Because the relativistic terms usually make no significant contribution to the electromechanics, it is most convenient to work with the quasi-static equations from the outset, as is done here. This avoids our having to discuss effects that we would end up neglecting in a practical context.

We obtain our transformations for field variables from the differential equations; consequently, before we derive the transformations, we need to consider the differential operators in the two coordinate systems and how they are related. The space differential operator ∇ for cartesian coordinates

* For the relativistic treatment see, for example, J. A. Stratton, *Electromagnetic Theory*, McGraw-Hill, New York, 1941, pp. 59–82.

x, y, z of the unprimed coordinate system $\mathbf{r}$ is

$$\mathbf{\nabla} = \left(\mathbf{i}_x \frac{\partial}{\partial x} + \mathbf{i}_y \frac{\partial}{\partial y} + \mathbf{i}_z \frac{\partial}{\partial z} \right). \tag{6.1.4}$$

The space differential operator $\mathbf{\nabla}'$ for coordinates x', y', z' of the primed coordinate system $\mathbf{r}'$ is

$$\mathbf{\nabla}' = \left(\mathbf{i}_x \frac{\partial}{\partial x'} + \mathbf{i}_y \frac{\partial}{\partial y'} + \mathbf{i}_z \frac{\partial}{\partial z'} \right). \tag{6.1.5}$$

To determine the relation between $\mathbf{\nabla}$ and $\mathbf{\nabla}'$ we first write out the three coordinates of the vector equation (6.1.3).

$$x' = x - v_x^r t, \tag{6.1.6a}$$

$$y' = y - v_y^r t, \tag{6.1.6b}$$

$$z' = z - v_z^r t. \tag{6.1.6c}$$

Consider a function $f'(x, y, z, t)$ which can also be written as $f'(x', y', z', t')$ by making substitutions from (6.1.2) and (6.1.6). The gradient of this function in the primed coordinate system is

$$\mathbf{\nabla}' f' = \mathbf{i}_x \frac{\partial f'}{\partial x'} + \mathbf{i}_y \frac{\partial f'}{\partial y'} + \mathbf{i}_z \frac{\partial f'}{\partial z'}. \tag{6.1.7}$$

The chain rule of differentiation* is used to write

$$\frac{\partial f'}{\partial x} = \frac{\partial f'}{\partial x'} \frac{\partial x'}{\partial x} + \frac{\partial f'}{\partial y'} \frac{\partial y'}{\partial x} + \frac{\partial f'}{\partial z'} \frac{\partial z'}{\partial x} + \frac{\partial f'}{\partial t'} \frac{\partial t'}{\partial x}. \tag{6.1.8}$$

It is evident from (6.1.2) and (6.1.6) that

$$\frac{\partial x'}{\partial x} = 1; \qquad \frac{\partial y'}{\partial x} = \frac{\partial z'}{\partial x} = \frac{\partial t'}{\partial x} = 0, \tag{6.1.9a}$$

$$\frac{\partial y'}{\partial y} = 1; \qquad \frac{\partial x'}{\partial y} = \frac{\partial z'}{\partial y} = \frac{\partial t'}{\partial y} = 0, \tag{6.1.9b}$$

$$\frac{\partial z'}{\partial z} = 1; \qquad \frac{\partial x'}{\partial z} = \frac{\partial y'}{\partial z} = \frac{\partial t'}{\partial z} = 0. \tag{6.1.9c}$$

We now use (6.1.8) and (6.1.9) with (6.1.7) to establish that

$$\mathbf{\nabla}' f' = \mathbf{\nabla} f'. \tag{6.1.10}$$

The scalar function f' may be a component of a vector; therefore we can use

* P. Franklin, *Methods of Advanced Calculus*, McGraw-Hill, New York, 1944, Chapter 2.

this same formalism to establish that for any vector $\mathbf{A}'(x', y', z', t')$ the space derivatives can be written as

$$\mathbf{\nabla}' \cdot \mathbf{A}' = \mathbf{\nabla} \cdot \mathbf{A}', \tag{6.1.11}$$

$$\mathbf{\nabla}' \times \mathbf{A}' = \mathbf{\nabla} \times \mathbf{A}'. \tag{6.1.12}$$

The same mathematical techniques are used to establish the relation between time derivatives. We again assume a function $f'(x', y', z', t')$ and write the time derivative in the unprimed system as

$$\frac{\partial f'}{\partial t} = \frac{\partial f'}{\partial t'}\frac{\partial t'}{\partial t} + \frac{\partial f'}{\partial x'}\frac{\partial x'}{\partial t} + \frac{\partial f'}{\partial y'}\frac{\partial y'}{\partial t} + \frac{\partial f'}{\partial z'}\frac{\partial z'}{\partial t}. \tag{6.1.13}$$

From (6.1.2) and (6.1.6) it follows that

$$\frac{\partial t'}{\partial t} = 1; \qquad \frac{\partial x'}{\partial t} = -v_x^{\,r},$$

$$\frac{\partial y'}{\partial t} = -v_y^{\,r}; \qquad \frac{\partial z'}{\partial t} = -v_z^{\,r}. \tag{6.1.14}$$

Substitution of these results into (6.1.13) yields

$$\frac{\partial f'}{\partial t} = \frac{\partial f'}{\partial t'} - \left(v_x^{\,r}\frac{\partial}{\partial x'} + v_y^{\,r}\frac{\partial}{\partial y'} + v_z^{\,r}\frac{\partial}{\partial z'}\right)f'. \tag{6.1.15}$$

The term in parentheses can be written as $\mathbf{v}^r \cdot \mathbf{\nabla}'$; thus (6.1.15) is written in the form

$$\frac{\partial f'}{\partial t} = \frac{\partial f'}{\partial t'} - (\mathbf{v}^r \cdot \mathbf{\nabla}')f'. \tag{6.1.16}$$

We use (6.1.10) to write this result in the alternative form

$$\frac{\partial f'}{\partial t'} = \frac{\partial f'}{\partial t} + (\mathbf{v}^r \cdot \mathbf{\nabla})f'. \tag{6.1.17}$$

The function f' can be a component of a vector; thus, if we define a vector $\mathbf{A}'(x', y', z', t')$, the same mathematical process leads to

$$\frac{\partial \mathbf{A}'}{\partial t'} = \frac{\partial \mathbf{A}'}{\partial t} + (\mathbf{v}^r \cdot \mathbf{\nabla})\mathbf{A}'. \tag{6.1.18}$$

Suppose that the unprimed frame is the fixed or laboratory frame. Then, from the left-hand side of (6.1.18) it is clear that the right-hand side is *the rate of change with respect to time of* $\mathbf{A}'$ *for an observer moving with velocity* $\mathbf{v}^r$. This derivative, written in terms of the coordinates (x, y, z, t) of the fixed frame, is used not only in this chapter but in many of the chapters that follow. Hence it is designated

$$\frac{D\mathbf{A}'}{Dt} \equiv \frac{\partial \mathbf{A}'}{\partial t} + (\mathbf{v}^r \cdot \nabla)\mathbf{A}' \tag{6.1.19}$$

and is called the *substantial* or *convective derivative*. An example will help to clarify the significance of this derivative.

Example 6.1.1. To illustrate the significance of (6.1.19) consider an example in which $\mathbf{A}'$ is the displacement of a surface from the x-z plane given by

$$\mathbf{A}' = \xi(x, t)\mathbf{i}_y, \tag{a}$$

as shown in Fig. 6.1.2a. The function ξ gives the y-coordinate of the surface. At a given position on the surface this y-coordinate has the same value, no matter whether it is viewed from the fixed frame or from a (primed) frame moving in the x-direction with velocity $\mathbf{v}^r = V\mathbf{i}_x$; that is, $\mathbf{A}' = \mathbf{A}$ and $\xi' = \xi$ *for this particular case*. If we evaluate (6.1.19), using (a), it follows that

$$\frac{D\mathbf{A}'}{Dt} = \left(\frac{\partial \xi}{\partial t} + V\frac{\partial \xi}{\partial x}\right)\mathbf{i}_y. \tag{b}$$

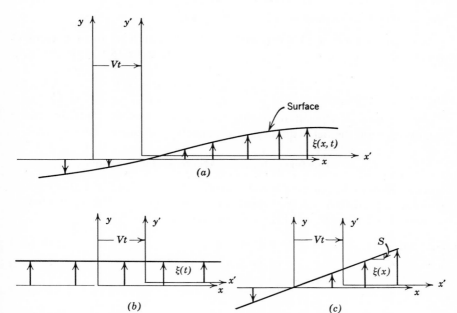

Fig. 6.1.2 (*a*) A surface described by $y = \xi(x, t)$ has an elevation above the x-z plane which is the same whether viewed from the moving (primed) frame or the fixed frame ($\xi' = \xi$); (*b*) ξ is independent of position so that only the first term in (6.1.19) makes a contribution to D/Dt; (*c*) ξ is independent of time and only the second term in (6.1.19) makes a contribution.

The significance of the two terms in this expression can be understood by considering limiting cases in which they, individually, make the sole contribution to the substantial derivative.

Figure 6.1.2b shows a surface ξ that is independent of position (x or x') but has a displacement that varies with time. Then the second term in (b) is zero and the rate of change for an observer moving with velocity V is the same as for a stationary observer. This we would have known from Fig. 6.1.2b without recourse to a mathematical equation.

In Fig. 6.1.2c the surface elevation is independent of time, since $\xi = \xi(x)$ and the rate of change of ξ with respect to time for the fixed observer is zero. By contrast the time rate of change for an observer moving with the velocity V is

$$\frac{DA'}{Dt} = V \frac{\partial \xi}{\partial x} i_y. \tag{c}$$

This result is not surprising either, because an observer in the moving frame travels to the right with a velocity V and sees a deflection ξ that increases in proportion to the slope of the surface $\partial \xi / \partial x$ and in proportion to the velocity V. In particular, if

$$\xi = Sx, \tag{d}$$

then from (c)

$$\frac{DA'}{Dt} = VSi_y. \tag{e}$$

This result could be obtained by inspection of Fig. 6.1.2c.

We shall find it useful later to write (6.1.18) in a different form. Because $\mathbf{v}^r$ is constant, a vector identity* makes it possible to write (6.1.18) in the form

$$\frac{\partial A'}{\partial t'} = \frac{\partial A'}{\partial t} + \mathbf{v}^r(\nabla \cdot A') - \nabla \times (\mathbf{v}^r \times A'). \tag{6.1.20}$$

We are now in a position to obtain transformations for electromagnetic quantities from the field equations for magnetic and electric field systems.

6.1.1 Transformations for Magnetic Field Systems

The differential equations that define the relations of the field quantities to sources in quasi-static magnetic field systems were given in Section 6.0 (6.0.1) to (6.0.5) and are repeated here for convenience:

$$\nabla \times \mathbf{H} = \mathbf{J}_f, \tag{6.1.21}$$

$$\nabla \cdot \mathbf{B} = 0, \tag{6.1.22}$$

$$\nabla \cdot \mathbf{J}_f = 0, \tag{6.1.23}$$

$$\nabla \times \mathbf{E} = - \frac{\partial \mathbf{B}}{\partial t}, \tag{6.1.24}$$

$$\mathbf{B} = \mu_0(\mathbf{H} + \mathbf{M}). \tag{6.1.25}$$

* $\nabla \times (\mathbf{a} \times \mathbf{b}) = (\mathbf{b} \cdot \nabla)\mathbf{a} - (\mathbf{a} \cdot \nabla)\mathbf{b} + \mathbf{a}(\nabla \cdot \mathbf{b}) - \mathbf{b}(\nabla \cdot \mathbf{a}).$

These equations describe the field quantities measured by an observer who is fixed in the unprimed inertial coordinate system of Fig. 6.1.1.

It is a postulate of special relativity that physical laws must be the same in any inertial coordinate system. Consequently, we write the equations to describe the field quantities measured by an observer who is fixed in the primed inertial coordinate system of Fig. 6.1.1 as

$$\nabla' \times \mathbf{H}' = \mathbf{J}_f', \tag{6.1.26}$$

$$\nabla' \cdot \mathbf{B}' = 0, \tag{6.1.27}$$

$$\nabla' \cdot \mathbf{J}_f' = 0, \tag{6.1.28}$$

$$\nabla' \times \mathbf{E}' = -\frac{\partial \mathbf{B}'}{\partial t'}, \tag{6.1.29}$$

$$\mathbf{B}' = \mu_0(\mathbf{H}' + \mathbf{M}'). \tag{6.1.30}$$

Use is now made of (6.1.11), (6.1.12), and (6.1.20) to express (6.1.26) to (6.1.29) in the equivalent forms

$$\nabla \times \mathbf{H}' = \mathbf{J}_f', \tag{6.1.31}$$

$$\nabla \cdot \mathbf{B}' = 0, \tag{6.1.32}$$

$$\nabla \cdot \mathbf{J}_f' = 0, \tag{6.1.33}$$

$$\nabla \times (\mathbf{E}' - \mathbf{v}^r \times \mathbf{B}') = -\frac{\partial \mathbf{B}'}{\partial t}. \tag{6.1.34}$$

We have made use of (6.1.32) to simplify the form of (6.1.34).

It has been postulated that (6.1.31) to (6.1.34) describe the same physical laws as (6.1.21) to (6.1.24). A comparison of the two sets of equations shows that a consistent set of transformations which satisfies this requirement is

$$\mathbf{H}' = \mathbf{H}, \tag{6.1.35}$$

$$\mathbf{J}_f' = \mathbf{J}_f, \tag{6.1.36}$$

$$\mathbf{B}' = \mathbf{B}, \tag{6.1.37}$$

$$\mathbf{E}' = \mathbf{E} + \mathbf{v}^r \times \mathbf{B}. \tag{6.1.38}$$

We also use (6.1.35) and (6.1.37) with (6.1.25) and (6.1.30) to obtain the transformation for magnetization density

$$\mathbf{M}' = \mathbf{M}. \tag{6.1.39}$$

The transformations of (6.1.35) to (6.1.39) relate the values of electromagnetic quantities in a quasi-static, magnetic field system that would be measured by two observers in relative motion with constant relative velocity $\mathbf{v}^r$ at a particular point in space at a given instant of time. Note that there is no contradiction or inconsistency among these transformations as there would have been had we kept terms such as the displacement current in Ampère's law. Note also that the transformation for free current density (6.1.36) indicates that current flow by the convection of net free charge is consistently neglected in a magnetic field system. We can now return to the integral form of the magnetic system equations (Table 1.2) to see that the definition of $\mathbf{E}'$ postulated there is consistent with what we have found here. Still another derivation of the integral form of Ampère's law for deforming contours of integration is given in Section B.4.1.

It is interesting to interpret (6.1.38) in terms of the Lorentz force (6.1.1). Consider a charge q at rest in the primed coordinate system. The force measured by an observer in that system is simply

$$\mathbf{f}' = q\mathbf{E}'.$$

An observer in the unprimed system who measures fields $\mathbf{E}$ and $\mathbf{B}$ will see the charge moving with a velocity $\mathbf{v}^r$ and will therefore describe the force as

$$\mathbf{f} = q\mathbf{E} + q\mathbf{v}^r \times \mathbf{B}.$$

The transformation of (6.1.38) is just the relation between $\mathbf{E}$ and $\mathbf{E}'$ that must exist if the force on the charge is to be independent of the coordinate system in which it is expressed. Some writers actually use the Lorentz force to obtain the transformation for the electric field rather than the differential equations as we have.* Although this can be done, it is important to see that there is a close connection between the field transformations and the field equations. The field equations for the magnetic field systems do not include the displacement current, and it would be *inconsistent* to use field transformations based on equations that did not include this same approximation. For this reason it is not surprising that in the next section a *different* set of field transformations is found for the electric field systems.

Example 6.1.2. The most interesting of the field transformations introduced in this section is given by (6.1.38) and it is important to understand the close connection between this expression for $\mathbf{E}'$ in terms of the fields in the fixed frame and the lumped parameter models of preceding chapters. For this purpose consider the idealized problem shown in Fig. 6.1.3, in which a pair of perfectly conducting plates are shorted by a conducting bar. The bar moves to the right with the velocity V and there is a uniform magnetic flux density $\mathbf{B}$ imposed in the z-direction by an external source. We assume that the plates are terminated at the left in an essentially open circuit so that no currents flow to make additions to the field $\mathbf{B}$.

* R. M. Fano, L. J. Chu, and R. B. Adler, *Electromagnetic Fields, Energy, and Forces,* Wiley, New York, 1960, p. 390.

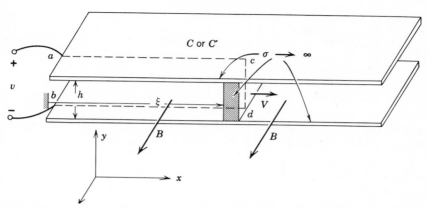

Fig. 6.1.3 A pair of parallel perfectly conducting plates are short-circuited by a moving perfectly conducting bar. Because of the magnetic field $\mathbf{B}$, a voltage v is induced which can be computed either by integrating the induction equation around the fixed loop C' that passes through the bar or by integrating the induction equation around a loop C that expands in area as the bar moves to the right. The field transformation of (6.1.38) guarantees that both integrations will give the same result.

First recall how the voltage v is computed in Chapter 2. A contour C, as shown in Fig. 6.1.3, passes through the perfectly conducting bar. Then the induction equation is written in the form (2.1.6) and (2.1.7)

$$\oint_C \mathbf{E}' \cdot d\mathbf{l} = -\frac{d}{dt} \int_S \mathbf{B} \cdot \mathbf{n}\, da, \tag{a}$$

where $\mathbf{E}'$ is the electric field in the frame of the conductor. Hence the integral of $\mathbf{E}'$ along the contour a-c-d-b makes no contribution and (a) reduces to the familiar form

$$v = \frac{d\lambda}{dt}, \tag{b}$$

where

$$\lambda = \int_S \mathbf{B} \cdot \mathbf{n}\, da = -\xi h B. \tag{c}$$

In the viewpoint represented by this derivation the voltage v arises because the contour C is expanding, thus enclosing more magnetic flux. In particular (b) and (c) give

$$v = -hBV. \tag{d}$$

The field transformations make it possible to take an alternative approach to this problem. The integral form of the induction equation can also be written for a contour that is fixed in space

$$\oint_{C'} \mathbf{E} \cdot d\mathbf{l} = -\frac{d}{dt} \int_{S'} \mathbf{B} \cdot \mathbf{n}\, da \tag{e}$$

This expression has the same form as (a), but now C' and S' are fixed and $\mathbf{E}$ is the electric field intensity evaluated in the fixed frame. In the present example we can consider the contour C' shown in Fig. 6.1.3, but even though this contour has the same instantaneous position as before it is now fixed in space rather than moving. As a direct consequence the right-hand side of (e) vanishes (remember, we assume that B is constant). If we further recognize that the integral of E through the perfectly conducting plates from a-c and d-b makes no contribution, (e) reduces to

$$\int_b^a \mathbf{E} \cdot d\mathbf{l} + \int_c^d \mathbf{E} \cdot d\mathbf{l} = 0. \tag{f}$$

In the region in which the terminals are located we assume (as in the preceding approach) that there is no time-varying magnetic field so that $\mathbf{E} = -\nabla\phi$ and

$$\int_b^a \mathbf{E} \cdot d\mathbf{l} = -(\phi_a - \phi_b) = -v. \tag{g}$$

Hence (f) reduces to

$$v = \int_c^d \mathbf{E} \cdot d\mathbf{l}. \tag{h}$$

The remaining integration from c-d must provide the voltage v. Note that this "speed voltage" is given by the term on the right in (a), but is now accounted for by the term on the left in (e). This term can be evaluated by recognizing that because $\mathbf{E}' = 0$ in the bar (6.1.38)

$$\mathbf{E} = -\mathbf{v} \times \mathbf{B} = VBi_y. \tag{i}$$

This result can be incorporated into (h) to give

$$v = -hBV, \tag{j}$$

which will be recognized as the same result obtained with the deforming contour of integration (d).

6.1.2 Transformations for Electric Field Systems

The differential equations that define the fields and their relations to sources in quasi-static, electric field systems were given in Table 1.2.

$$\nabla \times \mathbf{E} = 0, \tag{6.1.40}$$

$$\nabla \cdot \mathbf{D} = \rho_f, \tag{6.1.41}$$

$$\nabla \cdot \mathbf{J}_f = -\frac{\partial \rho_f}{\partial t}, \tag{6.1.42}$$

$$\nabla \times \mathbf{H} = \mathbf{J}_f + \frac{\partial \mathbf{D}}{\partial t}, \tag{6.1.43}$$

$$\mathbf{D} = \epsilon_0 \mathbf{E} + \mathbf{P}. \tag{6.1.44}$$

These equations describe the field quantities measured by an observer who is fixed in the unprimed inertial coordinate system of Fig. 6.1.1.

Our procedure here is analogous to that of the preceding section. We recognize, by postulate, that these physical laws must be the same in any other inertial coordinate system. We write them for the primed inertial coordinate system of Fig. 6.1.1 as

$$\nabla' \times \mathbf{E}' = 0, \tag{6.1.45}$$

$$\nabla' \cdot \mathbf{D}' = \rho'_f, \tag{6.1.46}$$

$$\nabla' \cdot \mathbf{J}'_f = -\frac{\partial \rho'_f}{\partial t'}, \tag{6.1.47}$$

$$\nabla' \times \mathbf{H}' = \mathbf{J}'_f + \frac{\partial \mathbf{D}'}{\partial t'}, \tag{6.1.48}$$

$$\mathbf{D}' = \epsilon_0 \mathbf{E}' + \mathbf{P}'. \tag{6.1.49}$$

We now use (6.1.11), (6.1.12), (6.1.17)*, and (6.1.20) to express (6.1.45) to (6.1.48) in the forms

$$\nabla \times \mathbf{E}' = 0, \tag{6.1.50}$$

$$\nabla \cdot \mathbf{D}' = \rho'_f, \tag{6.1.51}$$

$$\nabla \cdot (\mathbf{J}'_f + \rho'_f \mathbf{v}^r) = -\frac{\partial \rho'_f}{\partial t}, \tag{6.1.52}$$

$$\nabla \times (\mathbf{H}' + \mathbf{v}^r \times \mathbf{D}') = \mathbf{J}'_f + \rho'_f \mathbf{v}^r + \frac{\partial \mathbf{D}'}{\partial t}. \tag{6.1.53}$$

We have used (6.1.51) to obtain (6.1.53).

Using the postulate that (6.1.40) to (6.1.43) express the same physical laws as (6.1.50) to (6.1.53) we obtain the following consistent set of transformations:

$$\mathbf{E}' = \mathbf{E}, \tag{6.1.54}$$

$$\mathbf{D}' = \mathbf{D}, \tag{6.1.55}$$

$$\rho'_f = \rho_f, \tag{6.1.56}$$

$$\mathbf{H}' = \mathbf{H} - \mathbf{v}^r \times \mathbf{D}, \tag{6.1.57}$$

$$\mathbf{J}'_f = \mathbf{J}_f - \rho_f \mathbf{v}^r. \tag{6.1.58}$$

We use (6.1.54) and (6.1.55) with (6.1.44) and (6.1.49) to obtain the transformation for polarization density

$$\mathbf{P}' = \mathbf{P}. \tag{6.1.59}$$

Note that these transformations are consistent with those postulated in

* Remember $\mathbf{v}^r$ is constant, so $(\mathbf{v}^r \cdot \nabla)f' = \nabla \cdot (\mathbf{v}^r f)$.

Section 1.1.2b to express the integral form of the equations for an electric field system. Yet another derivation of these integral laws is given in Section B.4.2.

Example 6.1.3. The simple significance of the field transformations for the electric field systems can be illustrated by means of the parallel-plate capacitor shown in Fig. 6.1.4. Here a battery is used to induce surface charges on the plates, as shown. Hence in the laboratory (unprimed) frame there is an electric field intensity between the plates related to the surface charge density by

$$\mathbf{E} = \frac{\sigma_f}{\epsilon_0}\mathbf{i}_y, \tag{a}$$

whereas there is no magnetic field $\mathbf{H}$. (We assume here that there are no external currents that would induce a magnetic field in the laboratory frame.) For the purpose of the example consider that the plates have infinite extent in the x-direction. Then, according to the electric field transformations, an observer in the moving frame of Fig. 6.1.4a would measure the magnetic field intensity (6.1.57)

$$\mathbf{H}' = -V\epsilon_0 E_y \mathbf{i}_z = -V\sigma_f \mathbf{i}_z. \tag{b}$$

This magnetic field is present in the moving frame because in that frame of reference the surface charges give rise to surface currents. These currents induce the field $\mathbf{H}'$. To see this,

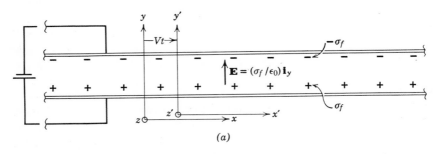

(a)

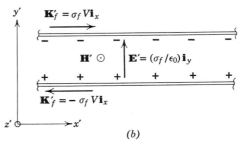

(b)

Fig. 6.1.4 (a) A parallel-plate capacitor is biased by a voltage source so that surface charges of opposite polarity are induced; (b) the fields in the moving frame can be found by computing the magnetic field induced by the convection of the surface charges or by using the field transformation of (6.1.57).

consider that the plates are being viewed from the moving frame of reference, as shown in Fig. 6.1.4b. In this frame surface currents flow in the x-direction, thus giving rise to the magnetic field of (b). Note that implicit to this reasoning is the transformation for the free current density (6.1.58).

In this and the preceding section we have obtained transformations that describe the relations between the field quantities measured by two observers in relative motion with a constant relative velocity. These transformations have been obtained for quasi-static systems and are valid only for such systems. We have stated that these transformations are consistent. By this we mean that we can use our transformation relations to transform field quantities repeatedly back and forth between two inertial reference frames without generating inconsistencies. A summary of transformations is given in Table 6.1.

6.2 BOUNDARY CONDITIONS

It is often found that electrical properties change significantly over distances that are infinitesimal with respect to significant dimensions of an electromechanical system. Such changes occur at the surface of a medium or at an interface between two media. In such cases we can represent the abrupt changes mathematically as spatial discontinuities in the electromagnetic variables. It is these discontinuities that provide boundary conditions on the electromagnetic variables.

The conventional treatment in electromagnetic theory considers conditions at stationary boundaries.* Because we are interested here in electromechanics we require boundary conditions at moving boundaries. The conditions derived are correct only for quasi-static systems.

First, we define the surface Σ, illustrated in Fig. 6.2.1, which separates medium a from medium b. Media a and b move with velocities $\mathbf{v}^a$ and $\mathbf{v}^b$ with respect to the inertial coordinate system $\mathbf{r}$ in which all field and source quantities $(\mathbf{E}, \mathbf{B}, \mathbf{P}, \mathbf{M}, \mathbf{J}_f, \rho_f)$ are defined. Superscripts a and b indicate the medium in which a quantity exists. The normal vector $\mathbf{n}$ is defined as normal to the surface Σ and has a positive direction from medium b to medium a, as shown.

In order that the surface Σ may be a well-defined boundary between the two media, the normal components of the two velocities $\mathbf{v}^a$ and $\mathbf{v}^b$ must be the same at the surface; thus

$$\mathbf{n} \cdot (\mathbf{v}^a - \mathbf{v}^b) = 0. \tag{6.2.1}$$

If this condition is not satisfied, the two materials are diffusing through each other or moving apart, leaving a vacuum between them. In either case a

* Fano et al., *op. cit.*, pp. 86–89.

Table 6.1 Differential Equations, Transformations, and Boundary Conditions for Quasi-static Electromagnetic Systems with Moving Media

	Differential Equations		Transformations		Boundary Conditions	
Magnetic field systems	$\nabla \times \mathbf{H} = \mathbf{J}_f$	(1.1.1)	$\mathbf{H}' = \mathbf{H}$	(6.1.35)	$\mathbf{n} \times (\mathbf{H}^a - \mathbf{H}^b) = \mathbf{K}_f$	(6.2.14)
	$\nabla \cdot \mathbf{B} = 0$	(1.1.2)	$\mathbf{B}' = \mathbf{B}$	(6.1.37)	$\mathbf{n} \cdot (\mathbf{B}^a - \mathbf{B}^b) = 0$	(6.2.7)
	$\nabla \cdot \mathbf{J}_f = 0$	(1.1.3)	$\mathbf{J}_f' = \mathbf{J}_f$	(6.1.36)	$\mathbf{n} \cdot (\mathbf{J}_f^a - \mathbf{J}_f^b) + \nabla_\Sigma \cdot \mathbf{K}_f = 0$	(6.2.9)
	$\nabla \times \mathbf{E} = -\dfrac{\partial \mathbf{B}}{\partial t}$	(1.1.5)	$\mathbf{E}' = \mathbf{E} + \mathbf{v}^r \times \mathbf{B}$	(6.1.38)	$\mathbf{n} \times (\mathbf{E}^a - \mathbf{E}^b) = v_n(\mathbf{B}^a - \mathbf{B}^b)$	(6.2.22)
	$\mathbf{B} = \mu_0(\mathbf{H} + \mathbf{M})$	(1.1.4)	$\mathbf{M}' = \mathbf{M}$	(6.1.39)		
Electric field systems	$\nabla \times \mathbf{E} = 0$	(1.1.11)	$\mathbf{E}' = \mathbf{E}$	(6.1.54)	$\mathbf{n} \times (\mathbf{E}^a - \mathbf{E}^b) = 0$	(6.2.31)
	$\nabla \cdot \mathbf{D} = \rho_f$	(1.1.12)	$\mathbf{D}' = \mathbf{D}$	(6.1.55)	$\mathbf{n} \cdot (\mathbf{D}^a - \mathbf{D}^b) = \sigma_f$	(6.2.33)
			$\rho_f' = \rho_f$	(6.1.56)		
	$\nabla \cdot \mathbf{J}_f = -\dfrac{\partial \rho_f}{\partial t}$	(1.1.14)	$\mathbf{J}_f' = \mathbf{J}_f - \rho_f \mathbf{v}^r$	(6.1.58)	$\mathbf{n} \cdot (\mathbf{J}_f^a - \mathbf{J}_f^b) + \nabla_\Sigma \cdot \mathbf{K}_f = v_n(\rho_f^a - \rho_f^b) - \dfrac{\partial \sigma_f}{\partial t}$	(6.2.36)
	$\nabla \times \mathbf{H} = \mathbf{J}_f + \dfrac{\partial \mathbf{D}}{\partial t}$	(1.1.15)	$\mathbf{H}' = \mathbf{H} - \mathbf{v}^r \times \mathbf{D}$	(6.1.57)	$\mathbf{n} \times (\mathbf{H}^a - \mathbf{H}^b) = \mathbf{K}_f + v_n \mathbf{n} \times [\mathbf{n} \times (\mathbf{D}^a - \mathbf{D}^b)]$	(6.2.38)
	$\mathbf{D} = \epsilon_0 \mathbf{E} + \mathbf{P}$	(1.1.13)	$\mathbf{P}' = \mathbf{P}$	(6.1.59)		

268

well-defined boundary of the type postulated does not exist. From the electromagnetic theory viewpoint no requirement is
necessary on the tangential velocities of
the media at the boundary. Consequently,
the media can slide past each other at the
boundary with no restrictions on the tangential components of the velocities. We
shall find that the boundary conditions
depend on the normal component of the
velocity of the boundary. One or both
media may be vacuum.

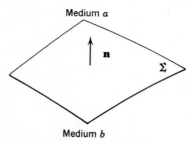

Fig. 6.2.1 Surface separating two media.

In general, the surface Σ is not plane and it is moving and deforming.
When a mathematical description of the surface is given, we must be able to
evaluate the normal vector $\mathbf{n}$. In the coordinate system $\mathbf{r}$ a surface can be
described by the general functional form

$$f(\mathbf{r}, t) = 0. \tag{6.2.2}$$

The normal vector $\mathbf{n}$ can then be evaluated as

$$\mathbf{n} = \frac{\nabla f}{|\nabla f|}. \tag{6.2.3}$$

This statement is familiar from electromagnetic field theory; that is, if we
assume that (6.2.2) defines one equipotential surface of the set

$$f(\mathbf{r}, t) = \phi,$$

where ϕ is the potential, the electric field is the negative gradient of the
potential and is normal to an equipotential surface. Hence we can think of
the normal vector $\mathbf{n}$, defined by (6.2.3) as the negative of the normalized
electric field, evaluated at the zero-potential surface.

Example 6.2.1. To illustrate the manner in which a surface is represented by an expression
like that in (6.2.2), consider the surface defined in Fig. 6.2.2 in which the height of the
surface above the x-z plane is given by

$$y = A \sin \omega t \cos \frac{2\pi x}{l} + B. \tag{a}$$

where A, B, ω, and l are positive constants. This represents a surface whose position is
independent of z and whose height varies as the cosine function with x. The amplitude of
the variation in height at a fixed position x is a sinusoidal function of time.

To obtain the equation for the surface in the form of (6.2.2) we write

$$f(x, y, t) = y - A \sin \omega t \cos \frac{2\pi x}{l} - B = 0. \tag{b}$$

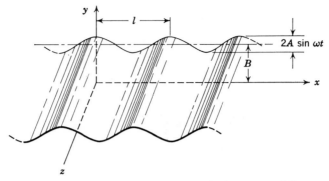

Fig. 6.2.2 Example of surface that varies in space and time.

Taking the gradient of this expression yields

$$\nabla f = \mathbf{i}_x \frac{2\pi A}{l} \sin \omega t \sin \frac{2\pi x}{l} + \mathbf{i}_y.$$

The magnitude of this gradient is

$$|\nabla f| = \left(1 + \frac{4\pi^2 A^2}{l^2} \sin^2 \omega t \sin^2 \frac{2\pi x}{l}\right)^{1/2}$$

and the normal vector is

$$\mathbf{n} = \frac{\mathbf{i}_x (2\pi A/l) \sin \omega t \sin (2\pi x/l) + \mathbf{i}_y}{\sqrt{1 + (4\pi^2 A^2/l^2) \sin^2 \omega t \sin^2 (2\pi x/l)}} \tag{c}$$

This normal vector becomes $\mathbf{i}_y$ at

$$\frac{2\pi x}{l} = \pm n\pi; \quad n = 0, 1, 2, \ldots;$$

that is, on the crests and in the troughs of the corrugations the normal vector is vertical. At other values of x the normal vector is not vertical and its direction can be determined from (c). The direction of the normal can be reversed by defining f as the negative of (b). Consequently, we can label media a and b and make sure that the definition of f yields a normal vector as described in Fig. 6.2.1 or we can define f and label the materials after the direction of the normal has been determined.

6.2.1 Boundary Conditions for Magnetic Field Systems

For studying boundary conditions in a quasi-static, magnetic field system we assume that the surface Σ carries a free surface current density $\mathbf{K}_f$ (amperes per meter) and a free surface charge density σ_f (coulombs per square meter). The free surface current density $\mathbf{K}_f$ is part of the primary excitation, whereas the surface charge density is a quantity that can be determined from auxiliary relations after the fields have been determined.

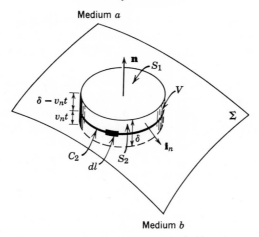

Fig. 6.2.3 Geometry for calculating discontinuities in normal components of field vectors.

Consider first the equations in integral form that determine how the sources excite the fields. They were given in (1.1.20) and (1.1.21) and are

$$\oint_C \mathbf{H} \cdot d\mathbf{l} = \int_S \mathbf{J}_f \cdot \mathbf{i}_n \, da, \tag{6.2.4}$$

$$\oint_S \mathbf{B} \cdot \mathbf{i}_n da = 0. \tag{6.2.5}$$

Here we have introduced $\mathbf{i}_n$ as the unit vector perpendicular to the area of integration so that it can be distinguished from the vector $\mathbf{n}$ normal to the surface Σ. To find the boundary condition imposed by (6.2.5) we define a small, right-circular cylindrical volume V, enclosed by a surface S consisting of the top and bottom surfaces of areas S_1 and a lateral surface of height δ and area S_2, as shown in Fig. 6.2.3. The volume V is fixed in the inertial coordinate system $\mathbf{r}$ and is so oriented that it intersects the boundary Σ as shown in Fig. 6.2.3. The surface S_1 is small enough that the boundary Σ can be assumed plane in its vicinity and the top and bottom surfaces S_1 are parallel to the boundary Σ. Hence the vector $\mathbf{n}$ is normal to both Σ and S_1. We assume that the height δ of the pillbox is so small that the lateral area S_2 is much smaller than the area of surface S_1. When we integrate (6.2.5) over the surface S and assume that S_1 is so small that $\mathbf{B}$ does not change appreciably over S_1, we obtain

$$(\mathbf{B}^a \cdot \mathbf{n})S_1 - (\mathbf{B}^b \cdot \mathbf{n})S_1 = 0. \tag{6.2.6}$$

We cancel S_1 from this expression to obtain

$$\mathbf{n} \cdot (\mathbf{B}^a - \mathbf{B}^b) = 0. \tag{6.2.7}$$

Equation 6.2.7 states that the normal component of $\mathbf{B}$ must be continuous at the boundary. This is the same result obtained in the electromagnetic theory of stationary systems; thus the motion has not affected this boundary condition.

Like the flux density the free-current density $\mathbf{J}_f$ in a quasi-static magnetic field system has no divergence [see (1.1.3) of Table 1.2]. However, when deriving the boundary condition on $\mathbf{J}_f$, the integral expression of (1.1.22) of Table 1.2 must be used with due regard for surface currents at the discontinuity. The current density $\mathbf{J}_f$, unlike $\mathbf{B}$, can be singular. If we use (1.1.22) ($\oint \mathbf{J}_f \cdot \mathbf{i}_n \, da = 0$) with the pillbox in Fig. 6.2.3 and neglect the contribution of volume current density $\mathbf{J}_f$ over the lateral surface S_2, we obtain

$$(\mathbf{J}_f^a \cdot \mathbf{n})S_1 - (\mathbf{J}_f^b \cdot \mathbf{n})S_1 + \oint_{C_2} \mathbf{K}_f \cdot \mathbf{i}_n \, dl = 0. \tag{6.2.8}$$

This is simply an expression of the fact that current into the pillbox from the two media must equal surface current across the contour C_2 because no appreciable free charge density (volume or surface) can exist in a magnetic field system. Dividing (6.2.8) by S_1 and taking the limit as $S_1 \rightarrow 0$ yields the desired boundary condition

$$\mathbf{n} \cdot (\mathbf{J}_f^a - \mathbf{J}_f^b) + \nabla_\Sigma \cdot \mathbf{K}_f = 0, \tag{6.2.9}$$

where

$$\nabla_\Sigma \cdot \mathbf{K}_f = \lim_{S_1 \rightarrow 0} \frac{\oint_{C_2} \mathbf{K}_f \cdot \mathbf{i}_n \, dl}{S_1} \tag{6.2.10}$$

is the surface (two-dimensional) divergence of $\mathbf{K}_f$ applied in the plane of the surface Σ at the point in question.*

We consider next the boundary condition imposed by (6.2.4). For this purpose we use the contour C which encloses the open surface S and is fixed in the coordinate system $\mathbf{r}$. The contour instantaneously intersects the boundary, as illustrated in Fig. 6.2.4. The surface S is a plane rectangle and is small enough for the boundary Σ to be assumed plane in its vicinity. The surface S is perpendicular to Σ and the height δ of the contour is much smaller than the length L.

$$\delta \ll L$$

---

* The two-dimensional divergence is simply the sum of the derivatives of the two orthogonal components of a vector in the surface with respect to the distance in the component directions; for example, assume a surface Σ with normal vector $\mathbf{n} = \mathbf{i}_z$. A vector $\mathbf{A}$ lying in the surface Σ will have only x- and y-components $\mathbf{A} = A_x \mathbf{i}_x + A_y \mathbf{i}_y$ and the surface divergence of this vector is $\nabla_\Sigma \cdot \mathbf{A} = [\mathbf{i}_x(\partial/\partial x) + \mathbf{i}_y(\partial/\partial y)] \cdot \mathbf{A} = \partial A_x/\partial x + \partial A_y/\partial y$. Note that the surface divergence in this case is just two terms of the volume divergence.

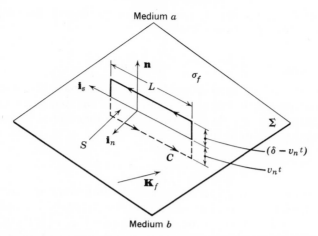

Medium a

Medium b

Fig. 6.2.4 Contour and surface for determining discontinuities in tangential components of field vectors.

The three unit vectors $\mathbf{n}$, $\mathbf{i}_n$, and $\mathbf{i}_s$, shown in Fig. 6.2.4, are mutually orthogonal. We assume that the contour C is small enough that fields do not vary appreciably over its length L. With these assumptions, and ignoring contributions from the ends (δ), we integrate (6.2.4) to obtain (after canceling out the length L)

$$(\mathbf{H}^a - \mathbf{H}^b) \cdot \mathbf{i}_s = \mathbf{K}_f \cdot \mathbf{i}_n. \tag{6.2.11}$$

This expression states that the discontinuity in the tangential component of $\mathbf{H}$ in the direction of $\mathbf{i}_s$ is equal to the component of $\mathbf{K}_f$ perpendicular to $\mathbf{i}_s$.

Equation 6.2.11 can be put into a more useful form in the following way. We substitute

$$\mathbf{i}_s = \mathbf{i}_n \times \mathbf{n} \tag{6.2.12}$$

into (6.2.11) and use a vector identity* to obtain

$$[\mathbf{n} \times (\mathbf{H}^a - \mathbf{H}^b)] \cdot \mathbf{i}_n = \mathbf{K}_f \cdot \mathbf{i}_n. \tag{6.2.13}$$

By definition, the vector $\mathbf{K}_f$ lies in the boundary Σ. The vector $[\mathbf{n} \times (\mathbf{H}^a - \mathbf{H}^b)]$ also lies in the boundary Σ. The vector $\mathbf{i}_n$ has an arbitrary direction except that it also lies in the boundary Σ. Therefore from (6.2.13) we obtain the result

$$\mathbf{n} \times (\mathbf{H}^a - \mathbf{H}^b) = \mathbf{K}_f. \tag{6.2.14}$$

Note once again that this is the same boundary condition obtained for stationary systems (it is independent of the boundary velocity).

*$\mathbf{a} \cdot \mathbf{b} \times \mathbf{c} = \mathbf{a} \times \mathbf{b} \cdot \mathbf{c}.$

We now derive the boundary condition for the electric field by starting with (1.1.23) written for a fixed contour C:

$$\oint_C \mathbf{E} \cdot dl = -\frac{d}{dt} \int_S \mathbf{B} \cdot \mathbf{i}_n \, da. \tag{6.2.15}$$

We integrate (6.2.15) by using the contour C and surface S defined in Fig. 6.2.4. The restrictions on orientation and size in the derivation of (6.2.14) also apply here. By using the unit vectors and dimensions defined in Fig. 6.2.4 we obtain the contour integral

$$\oint_C \mathbf{E} \cdot dl = (\mathbf{E}^a - \mathbf{E}^b) \cdot \mathbf{i}_s L. \tag{6.2.16}$$

In this expression we have neglected the contribution to this integral from the sides perpendicular to Σ because we require that $\delta \ll L$.* The time origin is defined as the instant in which the surface Σ coincides with the lower edge of the contour. Thus, defining the normal component of velocity of the boundary as

$$v_n = \mathbf{n} \cdot \mathbf{v}^a = \mathbf{n} \cdot \mathbf{v}^b, \tag{6.2.17}$$

we write the surface integral in (6.2.15) as

$$\int_S \mathbf{B} \cdot \mathbf{i}_n \, da = [\mathbf{B}^a(\delta - v_n t) + \mathbf{B}^b(v_n t)] \cdot \mathbf{i}_n L. \tag{6.2.18}$$

In this expression we have assumed that δ is small enough that v_n does not change appreciably as the boundary Σ passes the contour C. Note that this does not require that v_n be a constant, for we shall shortly take the limit in which $\delta \to 0$.

We take the time derivative of (6.2.18)

$$\frac{d}{dt} \int_S \mathbf{B} \cdot \mathbf{i}_n \, da = -v_n(\mathbf{B}^a - \mathbf{B}^b) \cdot \mathbf{i}_n L$$
$$+ \left[\frac{\partial v_n}{\partial t} t(\mathbf{B}^b - \mathbf{B}^a) + \frac{\partial \mathbf{B}^a}{\partial t}(\delta - v_n t) + \frac{\partial \mathbf{B}^b}{\partial t}(v_n t) \right] \cdot \mathbf{i}_n L. \tag{6.2.19}$$

The time derivatives of the fields are finite in the two media: consequently, in the limit as $\delta \to 0$ the term in brackets on the right of (6.2.19) vanishes. (Note that by definition $\delta \geq v_n t$ so that the interval of time during which the surface is within the volume V is the largest time t with which we are concerned. Hence, as $\delta \to 0$, so also does the largest value of t.) We equate the negative of (6.2.19) to (6.2.16) and cancel the length L to obtain

$$(\mathbf{E}^a - \mathbf{E}^b) \cdot \mathbf{i}_s = v_n(\mathbf{B}^a - \mathbf{B}^b) \cdot \mathbf{i}_n. \tag{6.2.20}$$

* There is the implicit assumption here that although $\mathbf{E}$ can be discontinuous at the boundary it must be finite. Otherwise we could not ignore the contribution to the integral along the sides of length δ.

By using the relation

$$\mathbf{i}_s = \mathbf{i}_n \times \mathbf{n}$$

and a vector identity,* we put (6.2.20) in the form

$$[\mathbf{n} \times (\mathbf{E}^a - \mathbf{E}^b)] \cdot \mathbf{i}_n = v_n(\mathbf{B}^a - \mathbf{B}^b) \cdot \mathbf{i}_n. \tag{6.2.21}$$

The vector $\mathbf{i}_n$ lies in the boundary Σ but otherwise it has an arbitrary direction. The vector $\mathbf{n} \times (\mathbf{E}^a - \mathbf{E}^b)$ also lies in the boundary Σ. The normal component of $\mathbf{B}$ is continuous [see (6.2.7)]; consequently, the vector $(\mathbf{B}^a - \mathbf{B}^b)$ lies in the boundary Σ. Therefore we conclude from (6.2.21) that

$$\mathbf{n} \times (\mathbf{E}^a - \mathbf{E}^b) = v_n(\mathbf{B}^a - \mathbf{B}^b). \tag{6.2.22}$$

This is the desired boundary condition on the electric field.

We indicate an alternative method of deriving (6.2.22) by putting it in a different form. We define the velocity $\mathbf{v}$ as

$$\mathbf{v} = \mathbf{n}v_n, \tag{6.2.23}$$

which is simply the normal velocity of the boundary Σ. We now write (6.2.22) in the form

$$\mathbf{n} \times (\mathbf{E}^a - \mathbf{E}^b) = (\mathbf{n} \cdot \mathbf{v})(\mathbf{B}^a - \mathbf{B}^b) \tag{6.2.24}$$

and use a vector identity† with the boundary condition on the normal component of $\mathbf{B}$ (6.2.7) to write (6.2.24) as

$$\mathbf{n} \times (\mathbf{E}^a - \mathbf{E}^b) = -\mathbf{n} \times [\mathbf{v} \times (\mathbf{B}^a - \mathbf{B}^b)]. \tag{6.2.25}$$

When we define $\mathbf{E}^{a'}$ and $\mathbf{E}^{b'}$ as

$$\mathbf{E}^{a'} = \mathbf{E}^a + \mathbf{v} \times \mathbf{B}^a, \tag{6.2.26}$$

$$\mathbf{E}^{b'} = \mathbf{E}^b + \mathbf{v} \times \mathbf{B}^b, \tag{6.2.27}$$

we can rewrite (6.2.25) as

$$\mathbf{n} \times (\mathbf{E}^{a'} - \mathbf{E}^{b'}) = 0. \tag{6.2.28}$$

From the transformation of (6.1.38) we recognize that $\mathbf{E}^{a'}$ and $\mathbf{E}^{b'}$ are the electric fields that an observer will measure when he is in a coordinate system moving with the normal velocity of the boundary. In this coordinate system the boundary is at rest; consequently, as (6.2.24) indicates, the tangential component of electric field must be continuous, as it must be in any stationary system.‡ This idea can be used as the basis for an alternative derivation of the boundary condition on the tangential component of electric field, once the condition on a fixed boundary has been obtained. Note, however, that our

---

* $\mathbf{a} \cdot \mathbf{b} \times \mathbf{c} = \mathbf{a} \times \mathbf{b} \cdot \mathbf{c}$.
† $(\mathbf{a} \cdot \mathbf{b})\mathbf{c} = -\mathbf{a} \times (\mathbf{b} \times \mathbf{c}) + \mathbf{b}(\mathbf{a} \cdot \mathbf{c})$.
‡ At least any stationary system in which $\mathbf{E}$ is finite everywhere.

transformations were derived for an inertial coordinate system. The boundary condition just derived is not restricted to boundaries that move with a constant velocity.

Example 6.2.2. Consider the system illustrated in Fig. 6.2.5 in which a surface Σ that is perpendicular to the y-axis moves with a speed v in the y-direction

$$\mathbf{v} = \mathbf{i}_y v.$$

We assume that the surface Σ has an infinite extent in the x- and z-directions so we can write its instantaneous position y_s as

$$y_s = vt.$$

We have chosen $t = 0$ as the instant when the surface contains the origin.

The surface Σ is immersed in vacuum and carries a uniform surface current density

$$\mathbf{K}_f = \mathbf{i}_z K_f.$$

The system is constrained so that to the right of the surface $(y > y_s)$ the fields are zero. A simple experiment in which this physical situation arises is shown in Fig. 6.2.5b, in which a moving conductor shorts parallel electrodes driven by a current source. Here the moving short is modeled as being very thin and carrying a surface current K_f. In practice, the moving short could be a sheet of highly ionized gas moving down a shock tube.

The electric and magnetic fields in the region $(y < y_s)$ to the left of the surface Σ are to be found.

We select as the normal vector $\mathbf{n}$ the vector $\mathbf{i}_y$,

$$\mathbf{n} = \mathbf{i}_y,$$

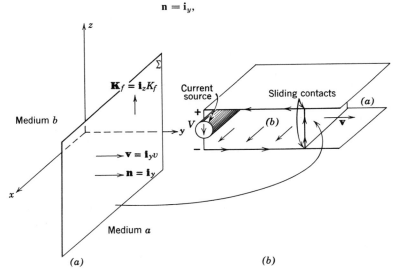

Fig. 6.2.5 (a) Plane surface in motion and carrying a surface current density; (b) the moving surface could constitute the moving conductor that short-circuits parallel plates excited by a current source distributed along the x-axis.

and thus medium b is $y < y_s$ and medium a is $y > y_s$. Our problem is specified such that

$$E^a = 0 \quad \text{and} \quad H^a = 0.$$

We first use (6.2.14) to find the magnetic field intensity H^b:

$$i_y \times (-H^b) = i_z K_f.$$

If we write H^b in component form,

$$H^b = i_x H_x^{\ b} + i_y H_y^{\ b} + i_z H_z^{\ b},$$

we can write the boundary condition as

$$i_z H_x^{\ b} - i_x H_z^{\ b} = i_z K_f.$$

Equating components in this expression yields

$$H_x^{\ b} = K_f,$$

$$H_z^{\ b} = 0.$$

Thus in vacuum $B = \mu_0 H$ and we can use the boundary condition on the normal component of B (6.2.7) with the given information that $H^a = 0$ to arrive at the result

$$H_y^{\ b} = 0.$$

Thus the magnetic field intensity adjacent to the surface in region b is completely determined.

To find the electric field intensity to the left of the moving current sheet we use (6.2.22) to obtain

$$i_y \times [-E^b] = -vB^b,$$

from which

$$E^b = i_z v \mu_0 K_f.$$

This is the electric field intensity to the left of the current sheet generated by the moving discontinuity in magnetic field intensity.

The discontinuity in electric field at the moving interface is necessary if concepts introduced earlier in this and preceding chapters are to remain consistent. We have already pointed out that the same boundary condition follows from the field transformation. If the moving surface is placed in the context of the problem shown in Fig. 6.2.5b, it is also possible to find the electric field behind the surface by using lumped parameter ideas to compute the voltage V, hence the electric field E between the plates.

6.2.2 Boundary Conditions for Electric Field Systems

For studying the boundary conditions in a quasi-static electric field system we assume a boundary surface Σ that carries a surface charge density σ_f and a surface current density K_f (see Figs. 6.2.3 and 6.2.4). The surface charge density σ_f is part of the primary excitation, whereas the surface current density K_f simply accounts for the conduction or convection of charge. The magnetic field generated by K_f can be computed once all of the other fields are known.

Two of the integral equations that determine the fields in a quasi-static electric field system are (see Table 1.2)

$$\oint_C \mathbf{E} \cdot d\mathbf{l} = 0, \tag{6.2.29}$$

$$\oint_S \mathbf{D} \cdot \mathbf{i}_n \, da = \int_V \rho_f \, dV. \tag{6.2.30}$$

The results derived in the preceding section can be used to obtain the boundary conditions implied by these equations.

In the preceding section the boundary condition on the tangential component of $\mathbf{E}$ was derived from (6.2.15) by using the contour defined in Fig. 6.2.4 to obtain the result of (6.2.22). We note that (6.2.29) is simply (6.2.15) with the right side set equal to zero; consequently, by setting the right side of (6.2.22) equal to zero, we obtain

$$\mathbf{n} \times (\mathbf{E}^a - \mathbf{E}^b) = 0. \tag{6.2.31}$$

To derive the boundary condition on the normal component of $\mathbf{D}$ we use the pillbox-shaped surface of Fig. 6.2.3 with the same restrictions on relative geometry that were used in deriving (6.2.7) in the preceding section. By performing the integration (6.2.30) and taking the limit as $\delta \to 0$, we obtain the result

$$(\mathbf{D}^a \cdot \mathbf{n})S_1 - (\mathbf{D}^b \cdot \mathbf{n})S_1 = \sigma_f S_1, \tag{6.2.32}$$

where S_1 is the area of the top and bottom of the closed surface S. Division of both sides by S_1 yields the desired boundary condition

$$\mathbf{n} \cdot (\mathbf{D}^a - \mathbf{D}^b) = \sigma_f, \tag{6.2.33}$$

which is the same as the corresponding boundary condition for stationary systems.

When the conductivity of a material is uniform, the free charges have only a transient existence in the bulk of the material. Surface charges play an important role in such cases. As we shall see in Chapter 7, the conduction process in the region of an interface is an important factor in many electric field systems. For this reason the boundary condition associated with the conservation of charge equation (Table 1.2)

$$\oint_S \mathbf{J}_f \cdot \mathbf{i}_n \, da = -\frac{d}{dt} \int_V \rho_f \, dV \tag{6.2.34}$$

assumes primary significance.

The evaluation of this boundary condition is much like the evaluation of the boundary condition on current density derived for magnetic field systems in (6.2.8) to (6.2.10), except that now we must include the effects of volume and surface charge densities. Using the pillbox-shaped volume of Fig. 6.2.3 and neglecting the contribution of volume current density $\mathbf{J}_f$ across the lateral surface S_2, we find that (6.2.34) becomes

$$S_1 \mathbf{n} \cdot (\mathbf{J}_f{}^a - \mathbf{J}_f{}^b) + \oint_{C_2} \mathbf{K}_f \cdot \mathbf{i}_n \, dl = -\frac{d}{dt} [\rho_f{}^a S_1(\delta - v_n t) + \rho_f{}^b S_1 v_n t + S_1 \sigma_f].$$

(6.2.35)

In the limit, as $\delta \to 0$, then $S_1 \to 0$, this expression becomes

$$\mathbf{n} \cdot (\mathbf{J}_f{}^a - \mathbf{J}_f{}^b) + \nabla_\Sigma \cdot \mathbf{K}_f = v_n(\rho_f{}^a - \rho_f{}^b) - \frac{\partial \sigma_f}{\partial t},$$

(6.2.36)

where we have used the definition of the surface divergence of surface current density $(\nabla_\Sigma \cdot \mathbf{K}_f)$ given in (6.2.10). It should be pointed out here that surface current density occurs in electric field systems most often as the convection of free surface charge density, as indicated by the application of the transformation in (6.1.58) to surface current density and surface charge density.

Equation 6.2.36 is the boundary condition implied by the conservation of charge equation. An example will help to clarify the significance of the terms.

Example 6.2.3. An application of the conservation of charge boundary condition that is considered in Section 7.2 is shown in Fig. 6.2.6. Here two slightly conducting materials form a common boundary that moves to the right with the velocity $U\mathbf{i}_x$. There are no free charges in the bulk of the materials in which $\mathbf{J}_f = \sigma \mathbf{E}$ (see Section 7.2.2). Hence in this particular case the boundary condition (6.2.36) becomes

$$\sigma_a E_y{}^a - \sigma_b E_y{}^b + \frac{\partial}{\partial x} K_{fx} + \frac{\partial}{\partial z} K_{fz} = -\frac{\partial \sigma_f}{\partial t}.$$

(a)

On the interface the only surface current is due to the convection of free charge σ_f; that is,

$$K_{fz} = 0; \qquad K_{fx} = U\sigma_f.$$

(b)

Moreover, σ_f is related to the electric field through the boundary condition (6.2.33) (we assume that $\mathbf{D} = \epsilon \mathbf{E}$ in both materials):

$$\sigma_f = \epsilon_a E_y{}^a - \epsilon_b E_y{}^b.$$

(c)

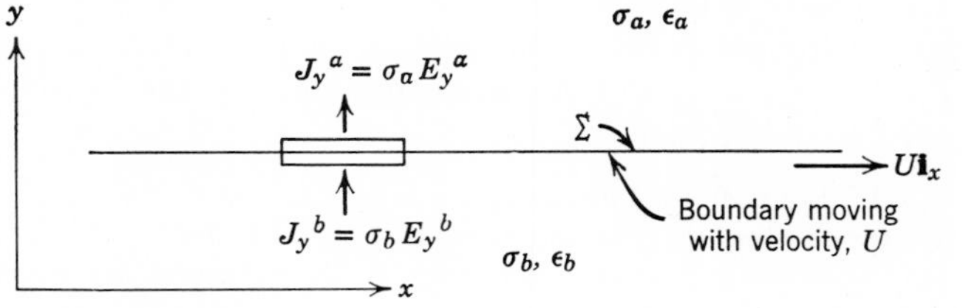

Fig. 6.2.6 A boundary between materials with conductivities σ_a and σ_b and permittivities ϵ_a and ϵ_b moves to the right with velocity U. Boundary condition (6.2.36) accounts for conservation of charge in a small section of the boundary.

It follows that (a) can be written as

$$\sigma_a E_y{}^a - \sigma_b E_y{}^b + \left(\frac{\partial \sigma_f}{\partial t} + U \frac{\partial \sigma_f}{\partial x} \right) = 0. \tag{d}$$

Note that (c) and (d) together constitute a single boundary condition on the electric field intensity at the moving surface. Remember that $\partial \sigma_f / \partial t + U \partial \sigma_f / \partial x$ is the rate of change with respect to time for an observer traveling with the velocity U [from (6.1.56) $\sigma_f = \sigma_f'$]. Hence (d) simply states that for such an observer the net current into a small section of the interface goes into an increase in the surface charge σ_f.

Equations 6.2.31, 6.2.33, and 6.2.36 are the only boundary conditions needed to solve problems for the electric fields in most quasi-static electric field systems. In these systems magnetic fields are generated by time-changing electric fields. Boundary conditions for these magnetic fields can be obtained from the integral form of Ampère's law (see Table 1.2)

$$\oint_C \mathbf{H} \cdot d\mathbf{l} = \int_S \mathbf{J}_f \cdot \mathbf{i}_n \, da + \frac{d}{dt} \int_S \mathbf{D} \cdot \mathbf{i}_n \, da, \tag{6.2.37}$$

where C and S are fixed as shown in Fig. 6.2.4. The process is analogous to that used in deriving (6.2.22) in the preceding section and leads to the boundary condition*

$$\mathbf{n} \times (\mathbf{H}^a - \mathbf{H}^b) = \mathbf{K}_f + v_n \mathbf{n} \times [\mathbf{n} \times (\mathbf{D}^a - \mathbf{D}^b)]. \tag{6.2.38}$$

Note that this boundary condition is essentially that of (6.2.14) for the magnetic field system, with an added term to account for displacement current.

A summary of field transformations and boundary conditions is given in Table 6.1, which is arranged so that the correspondence of transformations and boundary conditions with differential equations is emphasized. One of the most important concepts related in this chapter is the consistency that must exist among differential equations, transformations, and boundary conditions.

The most obvious effects on boundary conditions from material motion are brought in through the normal velocity v_n. It must be remembered, however, that the boundary is itself part of a mechanical system that can often deform in the presence of magnetic or electric forces. This geometric effect of the boundary conditions is represented by the normal vector $\mathbf{n}$ and illustrated by Example 6.2.4.

Example 6.2.4. Boundary conditions provide a mechanism by which mechanical motions can alter electrostatic field solutions. In Fig. 6.2.7 one of a pair of perfectly conducting electrodes is plane, whereas the other has the sinusoidal dependence on (x, t)

$$y = A \sin \omega t \cos kx + B, \tag{a}$$

---

* To show this note that $-\mathbf{n} \times (\mathbf{n} \times \mathbf{A})$ is the component of $\mathbf{A}$ in the surface to which $\mathbf{n}$ is normal.

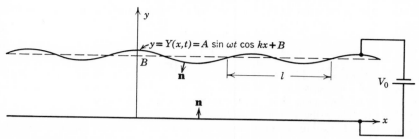

Fig. 6.2.7 Perfectly conducting electrodes at $y = 0$ and $y = A \sin \omega t \cos kx + B$ (where $k = 2\pi/l$) constrained to a constant potential difference.

where the dimension $A \ll B$, ω is the angular frequency, and $k = 2\pi/l$ (see Example 6.2.1). We wish to compute the electric field in the region between the electrodes when they are at the potential difference V_0 and to find the surface charge density on the lower electrode. It is assumed that the plates have infinite extent in the x- and z-directions.

The important boundary condition is (6.2.31). Because the electrodes are perfectly conducting, they can support no internal electric field. Hence at the surface of the electrodes

$$\mathbf{n} \times \mathbf{E} = 0, \tag{b}$$

where we have set $\mathbf{E}^a = \mathbf{E}$ in (6.2.31). On the lower electrode $\mathbf{n} = \mathbf{i}_y$ and (b) reduces to

$$E_x(x, 0, t) = 0. \tag{c}$$

Here we have used the fact that the upper surface position does not vary with z to set

$$E_z(x, y, t) = 0.$$

The normal vector $\mathbf{n}$ on the upper electrode is given by the negative of (c) of Example 6.2.1. We assume that the amplitude A is small enough $(4\pi^2 A^2/l^2 \ll 1)$ to justify setting the denominator of this expression equal to 1. Then

$$\mathbf{n} = -\mathbf{i}_x kA \sin \omega t \sin kx - \mathbf{i}_y. \tag{d}$$

The boundary condition (b), applied to the upper electrode, reduces to

$$n_y E_x(x, Y, t) = n_x E_y(x, Y, t), \tag{e}$$

where $Y = A \sin \omega t \cos kx + B$ is the position of the upper electrode. If A were zero (two parallel flat plates) the electric field would be $\mathbf{E} = (V_0/B)\mathbf{i}_y$. Hence we define a perturbation electric field $\mathbf{e}(x, y, t)$ and let

$$\mathbf{E} = e_x \mathbf{i}_x + \left(\frac{V_0}{B} + e_y\right)\mathbf{i}_y. \tag{f}$$

The perturbations e_x and e_y are proportional to the amplitude A. Introducing (f) into (e) [with n_x and n_y defined by (d)], we have

$$e_x(x, Y, t) = kA \sin \omega t \sin kx \left[\frac{V_0}{B} + e_y(x, Y, t)\right] \tag{g}$$

and now, if we ignore terms that are proportional to A^2 (compared with terms proportional to A),

$$e_x(x, B, t) = \frac{kAV_0}{B} \sin \omega t \sin kx. \tag{h}$$

Here e_x has been evaluated at $y = B$ rather than $y = Y$ because the difference in e_x evaluated at these points is proportional to A^2. The approximate effect of the corrugated surface on the electric field is found by using (h) and (c) as boundary conditions.

Between the plates the divergence and curl of the electric field are zero [(1.1.11) and (1.1.12) with no free charge)]. For the two-dimensional case under consideration this gives two expressions for the perturbation components.

$$\frac{\partial e_x}{\partial x} + \frac{\partial e_y}{\partial y} = 0, \tag{i}$$

$$\frac{\partial e_x}{\partial y} - \frac{\partial e_y}{\partial x} = 0. \tag{j}$$

If boundary condition (h) is to be satisfied, e_x must have the (x, t) dependence $\sin \omega t \sin kx$. Hence we assume (and later justify) that

$$e_x(x, y, t) = f(y) \sin \omega t \sin kx. \tag{k}$$

Then (i) and (j) will be satisfied for all values of t and x only if e_y has the (x, t) dependence $\sin \omega t \cos kx$:

$$e_y(x, y, t) = g(y) \sin \omega t \cos kx. \tag{l}$$

The dependence on (x, t) assumed for e_x and e_y is justified when we substitute (k) and (l) into (i) and (j) and find that the functions of x and t cancel out. After carrying out this process there remain the equations

$$fk + \frac{dg}{dy} = 0, \tag{m}$$

$$\frac{df}{dy} + kg = 0. \tag{n}$$

This pair of ordinary differential equations has the solution

$$f = C \sinh ky + D \cosh ky. \tag{o}$$

where C and D are arbitrary constants. Remember that e_x is proportional to f [see (k)]. Hence, if (c) is to hold for *all* values of y, $D = 0$. From (k) and (o)

$$e_x(x, y, t) = C \sinh ky \sin \omega t \sin kx, \tag{p}$$

where the constant C follows from boundary condition (h) as

$$C = \frac{kAV_0}{B \sinh kB}. \tag{q}$$

Note that it was our foresight in guessing the (x, t) dependence of (k) that allowed us to satisfy condition (h) for all values of x and t. We now know f and therefore can find g from (n). Hence (l) becomes

$$e_y = -C \cosh ky \sin \omega t \cos kx. \tag{r}$$

In the limiting case in which $B \ll l$ we can calculate these fields much more easily. This limiting case occurs when the wavelength l of the corrugation on the upper plate is long compared with the average spacing B between the plates. We expect a small section to have the same field as a parallel plate capacitor; that is,

$$E_y = \frac{V_0}{B + A \sin \omega t \cos kx} \cong \frac{V_0}{B} - \frac{V_0 A}{B^2} \sin \omega t \cos kx \tag{s}$$

and

$$E_x = 0. \tag{t}$$

If $B \ll l$, then $kB \ll 1$; and in this limit our solution [(f), (p), and (r)] reduces to the "long-wave" approximation of (s) and (t). In this limit all of the perturbation charges (those additional charges due to the corrugation) on one plate have image charges on the opposite plate. In the opposite extreme in which $kB \gg 1$ ($l \ll B$) there are few perturbation charges on the flat plate. To see this we can compute the surface charge density on the lower plate as

$$\sigma_f = \epsilon_0 \left[\frac{V_0}{B} + e_y(x, 0, t) \right], \tag{u}$$

which [from (q) and (r)] is

$$\sigma_f = \epsilon_0 \left[\frac{V_0}{B} - \frac{kA V_0 \sin \omega t \cos kx}{B \sinh kB} \right]. \tag{v}$$

As kB becomes large, the perturbation part of σ_f becomes small (as $kB \to \infty$, $\sinh kB \to \infty$).

A scheme for finding the deflection of a conducting surface would measure the charge on an electrode imbedded in the flat plate. Equation v shows that the perturbation surface charge density provides the (x, t) dependence of the deflection. The amplitude of σ_f however, would be inversely proportional to the wavelengths l to be detected.

6.3 CONSTITUENT RELATIONS FOR MATERIALS IN MOTION

Constituent relations, which are mathematical models of the electromagnetic properties of matter, were discussed briefly for stationary media in Section 1.1. At that point specific models that describe materials in a way that is useful in this study of electromechanical interactions were presented. As indicated in Section 6.0, however, the constituent relations expressed for stationary material may not be correct when the material is moving. In the next two sections we recast the constituent relations in forms that are correct when describing material that is in motion with respect to the reference frame in which electromagnetic quantities are measured. In general, a medium may be in motion relative to a particular inertial coordinate system in which we wish to define field and source quantities. We postulate that constituent relations, as conventionally defined for stationary media, still hold for moving media, provided they use source and field quantities defined in an inertial coordinate system with the same velocity as the material at the instant of time in question. It is therefore assumed that acceleration and rate of deformation do not affect local material properties. Constituent relations obtained with this postulate yield predictions that agree to a high degree of accuracy with experimental results.* To apply this postulate we shall use the transformations of Sections 6.1.1 and 6.1.2 with the constituent relations for stationary media given in Section 1.1. Because the transformations are different for quasi-static electric and magnetic field systems we consider constituent relations for the two systems separately.

6.3.1 Constituent Relations for Magnetic Field Systems

Reference to the differential equations of Section 1.1 (see Table 1.2) and the boundary conditions of Section 6.2.1 shows that the fields in a quasi-static magnetic field system are excited by free current density $\mathbf{J}_f$, free surface current density $\mathbf{K}_f$, and magnetization density $\mathbf{M}$. Thus we need consider here only how $\mathbf{J}_f$, $\mathbf{K}_f$, and $\mathbf{M}$ are affected by field quantities in the presence of material motion.

Consider first a linear isotropic conducting medium, which, when stationary, has the constituent relation introduced as (1.1.9),

$$\mathbf{J}_f = \sigma\mathbf{E}, \tag{6.3.1}$$

where σ is the electrical conductivity.

We now define an inertial coordinate system $\mathbf{r}$ in which we measure the quantities $\mathbf{E}$, $\mathbf{B}$, and $\mathbf{J}_f$ as functions of space ($\mathbf{r}$) and time (t). The material medium moves with respect to this coordinate system with a velocity $\mathbf{v}(\mathbf{r}, t)$. In general, the velocity $\mathbf{v}$ is different for each point within the material because it can be translating, rotating, and deforming. We wish to express the constituent relation describing electrical conduction in terms of quantities measured in the coordinate system $\mathbf{r}$. To do this we use the postulate given in the preceding section which states that the constituent relation for the material at rest is applicable in an inertial coordinate system with respect to which the material is instantaneously at rest. Thus to express the constituent relation for the material occupying position $\mathbf{r}$ at time t we define an inertial coordinate system having the velocity

$$\mathbf{v}^r = \mathbf{v}(\mathbf{r}, t), \tag{6.3.2}$$

that is, $\mathbf{v}^r$ is a constant with a value equal to the material velocity at position $\mathbf{r}$ at time t. We denote electromagnetic quantities as measured in this moving coordinate system with primes and apply our postulate along with (6.3.1) to write

$$\mathbf{J}'_f(\mathbf{r}, t) = \sigma(\mathbf{r}, t)\mathbf{E}'(\mathbf{r}, t). \tag{6.3.3}$$

---

* A case in which acceleration effects on conduction are computed is discussed in L. D. Landau and E. M. Lifshitz, *Electrodynamics of Continuous Media*, Addison-Wesley, Reading, Mass., 1960, pp. 210–212. These effects are usually ignorable.

We now use the transformations of (6.1.36) and (6.1.38) to rewrite (6.3.3) as

$$\mathbf{J}_f(\mathbf{r}, t) = \sigma(\mathbf{r}, t)[\mathbf{E}(\mathbf{r}, t) + \mathbf{v}(\mathbf{r}, t) \times \mathbf{B}(\mathbf{r}, t)]. \tag{6.3.4}$$

This equation is the desired result in that it is the relation imposed among electromagnetic variables expressed in the fixed frame by linear isotropic electrical conduction in a moving medium.

The functional notation $(\mathbf{r}, t)$ has been included in the preceding equations to make the meanings of the terms more explicit. Equation 6.3.4 is more compactly expressed without the functional notation as

$$\mathbf{J}_f = \sigma(\mathbf{E} + \mathbf{v} \times \mathbf{B}). \tag{6.3.5}$$

Next consider surface conduction on a material with surface conductivity σ_s as described for stationary materials by (1.1.10).

$$\mathbf{K}_f = \sigma_s[-\mathbf{n} \times (\mathbf{n} \times \mathbf{E})], \tag{6.3.6}$$

where $\mathbf{n}$ is the normal to the surface and $[-\mathbf{n} \times (\mathbf{n} \times \mathbf{E})]$ is the component of $\mathbf{E}$ tangent to the surface. When the surface is moving, we use a process analogous to that used for volume conduction to obtain the result

$$\mathbf{K}_f = \sigma_s\{-\mathbf{n} \times [\mathbf{n} \times (\mathbf{E} + \mathbf{v} \times \mathbf{B})]\}. \tag{6.3.7}$$

The velocity $\mathbf{v}$ is the velocity of the surface with respect to the coordinate system in which the electromagnetic quantities are measured.

The final constituent relation that must be defined for magnetic field systems is the relation between magnetization density $\mathbf{M}$ and magnetic field intensity $\mathbf{H}$.

The constituent relation for an isotropic, linear, magnetic material was written as (1.1.6)

$$\mathbf{M} = \chi_m\mathbf{H}, \tag{6.3.8}$$

where χ_m is the magnetic susceptibility. Using (1.1.4) we wrote

$$\mathbf{B} = \mu\mathbf{H}, \tag{6.3.9}$$

where the permeability μ is defined as

$$\mu = \mu_0(1 + \chi_m). \tag{6.3.10}$$

Although the constituent relation as expressed by (6.3.8) or (6.3.9) was written for stationary material, the transformations of (6.1.35), (6.1.37), and (6.1.39) show that in a quasi-static magnetic field system $\mathbf{B}$, $\mathbf{H}$, and $\mathbf{M}$ are unaffected by relative motion. Consequently, (6.3.8) and (6.3.9) hold also when the material is moving with respect to the coordinate system in which the electromagnetic quantities are to be measured.

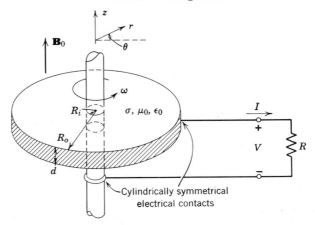

Fig. 6.3.1   A homopolar generator.

Example 6.3.1.   As an example of transformations and constituent relations for moving materials, consider the device illustrated schematically in Fig. 6.3.1. This is a Faraday disk (also called a homopolar machine or an acyclic machine). Machines with the basic configuration of Fig. 6.3.1 or alternative configurations that operate physically in the same way are manufactured for supplying dc power at low voltage and high current.* A cutaway view of one such configuration is shown in Fig. 6.3.2.

With reference to Fig. 6.3.1, the device consists essentially of a right circular cylinder of conducting material that is rotated about its axis. Electrical contacts, usually made of liquid metal (see Fig. 6.3.2), are made symmetrically at inner and outer radii. Not shown in the figure is the electromagnet which produces a uniform axial flux density $\mathbf{B}_0$.

We specify that the applied flux density $\mathbf{B}_0$ is constant and that the shaft is driven by a constant angular velocity source ω. The electrical terminals are loaded by a resistance R. The material of the rotating disk is homogeneous, isotropic, and electrically linear with the material constants σ, μ_0, ϵ_0. The dimensions are defined in the figure.

We wish to find the terminal voltage and current for all values of load resistance R and steady-state operation.

It should be clear from an inspection of Fig. 6.3.1 that the current in the disk is radial and the current density is uniform around the periphery at any radius. Thus the magnetic field generated by this current density is tangential and has no effect on the terminal voltage. Hence we neglect the field due to current in the disk. The validity of this assumption becomes clearer in the analysis to follow.

We select the cylindrical coordinate system r, θ, z shown in Fig. 6.3.1. The cylindrical symmetry and the uniformity of variables in the z-direction indicate that we can assume

$$\frac{\partial}{\partial \theta} = \frac{\partial}{\partial z} = 0,$$

---

* D. A. Watt, "Development and Operation of a 10KW Homopolar Generator with Mercury Brushes," *Proc. I.E.E. (London)*, **105A**, 33–40, (June 1958). A. K. Das Gupta, "Design of Self-Compensated High-Current Comparatively Higher Voltage Homopolar Generators," *Trans. AIEE*, **80**, Part III, 567–573, 1961–1962.

STATIONARY
COLLECTOR UNIT

ROTATING
COLLECTOR RING

OIL SEAL

MAIN BEARING

GUIDE BEARINGS

FLEXIBLE COUPLING

Fig. 6.3.2 Cutaway view of an acyclic generator. The solid rotor is made of magnetically soft steel, the flux density is radial, and current is axial between two liquid metal collector rings, one of which is shown. (Courtesy of General Electric Company.)

so that electromagnetic quantities of interest will vary with radius only. The electromagnetic equations for this quasi-static magnetic field system are those of Section 1.1.1a (see Table 1.2).

We first use the conservation of charge in integral form (1.1.22)

$$\oint \mathbf{J}_f \cdot \mathbf{n} \, da = 0, \tag{a}$$

to establish that the radial component of current density is related to the terminal current by

$$J_r = \frac{I}{2\pi r d}. \tag{b}$$

We next write Ohm's law for a grain of matter at the radius r by writing the r component of (6.3.5).

$$J_r = \sigma(E_r + \omega r B_0), \tag{c}$$

where B_0 is the magnitude (z-component) of $\mathbf{B}_0$ and E_r is the radial component of electric field intensity. A tangential (θ) component of flux density is parallel to the material velocity and does not contribute a $\mathbf{v} \times \mathbf{B}$ term. Thus the neglect of the field generated by current in the disk is justified.

We now use (b) in (c) to find E_r:

$$E_r = \frac{I}{2\pi\sigma dr} - \omega B_0 r. \tag{d}$$

Recognizing that there is no time rate of change of magnetic field in the fixed reference frame, we can write the terminal voltage as

$$V = -\int_{R_i}^{R_o} E_r\, dr = -\frac{I}{2\pi\sigma d} \ln\frac{R_o}{R_i} + \frac{\omega B_0}{2}(R_o^2 - R_i^2). \tag{e}$$

Use of the terminal relation required by the resistance R yields

$$I = \frac{V_{oc}}{R + R_{int}} \tag{f}$$

where $V_{oc} = (\omega B_0/2)(R_o^2 - R_i^2)$ is the open circuit $(R \to \infty)$ voltage of the generator, and $R_{int} = [\ln(R_o/R_i)]/2\pi\sigma d$ is the internal resistance of the generator.

To obtain some idea of the kinds of numbers obtainable with real materials consider a copper disk with the following parameters and dimensions:

$$\sigma = 5.9 \times 10^7 \text{ mhos/m} \qquad \omega = 400 \text{ rad/sec}$$
$$d = 0.005 \text{ m} \qquad\qquad B_0 = 1 \text{ Wb/m}^2$$
$$R_i = 0.01 \text{ m} \qquad\qquad R_o = 0.1 \text{ m}$$

The open-circuit voltage is then

$$V_{oc} = 2 \text{ V}$$

and the internal resistance is

$$R_{int} = 1.25 \times 10^{-6}\ \Omega.$$

The short-circuit current is

$$I_{sc} = \frac{V_{oc}}{R_{int}} = 1.6 \times 10^6 \text{ A}.$$

The maximum power that can theoretically be delivered by this generator is

$$P_{max} = \frac{V_{oc}I_{sc}}{4} = 8 \times 10^5 \text{ W}.$$

For steady-state operation, however, the output power would be limited to a much lower value by allowable $I^2 R_{int}$ heating of the rotating disk. These figures indicate, though, that this device is suitable for supplying large pulses of power.*

We now use (d) and (f) to write the radial component of electric field intensity as

$$E_r = \left[\frac{R_{int}V_{oc}}{(R + R_{int})\ln(R_o/R_i)}\right]\frac{1}{r} - \omega B_0 r. \tag{g}$$

In the spirit of the discussion of quasi-static systems in Section B.2.2 we can calculate the volume charge density necessary to satisfy Gauss's law:

$$\rho_f = \nabla \cdot \epsilon_0 E. \tag{h}$$

---

* T. J. Crawford, "Kinetic Energy Storage for Resistance Welding," *Welding Engineer*, **33**, 36 (1948).

Using the equation for the divergence in cylindrical coordinates,* we have

$$\rho_f = -2\epsilon_0 \omega B_0. \tag{i}$$

This charge density arises from the second term in (g); the first term is divergenceless. The finite volume charge density results because the electric field is generated by nonuniform motion in a uniform magnetic field. There is, however, no net charge on the disk because an equal amount of charge of opposite sign occurs as a surface charge density at $r = R_o$ and $r = R_i$.

As discussed in Section B.2.2 this charge density was derived *after* the field problem was solved and its presence has negligible effect on the field solutions. To illustrate, consider the current density that results from the convection of this charge density by the rotating disk. The result is a θ-component of current density that has the value

$$J_\theta = -2\epsilon_0 \omega^2 B_0 r.$$

We use the θ-component of Ampere's law in cylindrical coordinates to find the change in B_z caused by this current:

$$\frac{\partial B_z}{\partial r} = -\mu_0 J_\theta = 2\mu_0 \epsilon_0 \omega^2 B_0 r.$$

Integrating this expression, we find the maximum possible fractional change in B_z as

$$\frac{\Delta B_z}{B_0} = \omega^2 R_o^2 \mu_0 \epsilon_0 = \frac{\omega^2 R_o^2}{c^2},$$

where c is the speed of light (Section B.2.1). For any disk made of real material the peripheral speed (ωR_0) must be much smaller than the speed of light; thus the change in B_z due to convection current is negligible.

We reconsider the homopolar machine and complete its terminal description as an electromechanical coupling device in Section 6.4.

6.3.2 Constituent Relations for Electric Field Systems

The differential equations in Section 1.1.1*b* (see Table 1.2) and the boundary conditions of Section 6.2.2 indicate that fields in quasi-static, electric field systems are excited by free charge density ρ_f, free surface charge density σ_f, and polarization density **P**. The constituent relations for these source quantities are given for stationary media in Section 1.1.1*b*. We generalize those constituent relations appropriate for electric field systems to include the effects of material motion.

In Section 1.1.1*b* the conduction process in a stationary medium was modeled by (1.1.16):

$$\mathbf{J}_f = (\rho_{f+}\mu_+ + \rho_{f-}\mu_-)\mathbf{E}, \tag{6.3.11}$$

where ρ_{f+} and ρ_{f-} are the densities of free charge and μ_+ and μ_- are the mobilities of the free charges defined in Section B.3.3. When the material is moving, (6.3.11) must be modified according to the transformations of

* $[d(\epsilon_0 r E_r)/dr]/r$

(6.1.56) and (6.1.58). Thus, if the material is moving with velocity $\mathbf{v}$, we must write (6.3.11) in the form

$$\mathbf{J}_f = (\rho_{f+}\mu_+ + \rho_{f-}\mu_-)\mathbf{E} + \rho_f\mathbf{v}, \tag{6.3.12}$$

where the net charge density ρ_f is given by

$$\rho_f = \rho_{f+} + \rho_{f-}. \tag{6.3.13}$$

The first term $[(\rho_{f+}\mu_+ + \rho_{f-}\mu_-)\mathbf{E}]$ of (6.3.12) describes the motion of charge carriers with respect to the material and the second term $(\rho_f\mathbf{v})$ describes the convection of net charge by the motion of the material.

The transformations of (6.1.54), (6.1.55), and (6.1.59) show that in a quasi-static electric field system $\mathbf{D}$, $\mathbf{E}$, and $\mathbf{P}$ are unaffected by relative motion. Consequently, (1.1.17) and (1.1.19), which were written for stationary material, are still valid when the material is moving with respect to the coordinate system in which electromagnetic quantities are measured. For convenience we repeat these two equations here:

$$\mathbf{P} = \epsilon_0 \chi_e \mathbf{E}, \tag{6.3.14}$$

$$\mathbf{D} = \epsilon \mathbf{E}, \tag{6.3.15}$$

where the dielectric susceptibility χ_e and permittivity ϵ are related by

$$\epsilon = \epsilon_0(1 + \chi_e). \tag{6.3.16}$$

We conclude this section with an example that involves a particularly simple form of (6.3.12). Other examples of the use of these constituent relations are given in Chapter 7.

Example 6.3.2. A simple example in which the constituent relation (6.3.12) is used, is shown in Fig. 6.3.3. Here a cylindrical beam of charge carriers moves with the velocity V in the z-direction. We assume that the charge density is uniform throughout the beam and that the carriers (for example electrons) have zero mobility.

In a primed frame moving to the right at the velocity V the current is zero (6.3.12) and we have the simple fields associated with a uniform cylinder of charge density ρ_0. Note that we have assumed $\rho_f = \rho_f'$, as given by (6.1.56). In this moving frame there is no magnetic field because there is no current $\mathbf{J}_f'$. Because the beam is uniform in the z-direction,

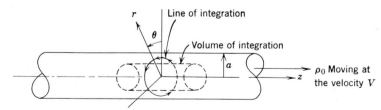

Fig. 6.3.3 Charged beam moving at velocity V to the right.

the electric field follows from Gauss's law (1.1.25) integrated over a cylinder of radius r and unit length in the z-direction:

$$\epsilon_0 E_r'(2\pi r) = \int_0^r \rho_f 2\pi r \, dr. \tag{a}$$

Hence inside the beam

$$E_r' = \frac{\rho_0 r}{2\epsilon_0}, \qquad r < a, \tag{b}$$

and outside the beam

$$E_r' = \frac{\rho_0 a^2}{2\epsilon_0 r}, \qquad r > a. \tag{c}$$

To find the fields in the fixed frame is a simple matter, for (6.1.54) requires that $\mathbf{E} = \mathbf{E}'$ and (6.1.58) gives the current as

$$\mathbf{J}_f = \rho_0 V \mathbf{i}_z, \qquad r < a. \tag{d}$$

The magnetic field follows from (6.1.57) and (6.1.54) as $\mathbf{H} = V \mathbf{i}_z \times \epsilon_0 \mathbf{E}$ or, by use of (b) and (c),

$$\mathbf{H} = \mathbf{i}_\theta \frac{V \rho_0 r}{2}, \qquad r < a,$$

$$\mathbf{H} = \mathbf{i}_\theta \frac{V \rho_0 a^2}{2r}, \qquad r > a. \tag{e}$$

The last result could be found alternatively by using the current density $\mathbf{J}_f$ from (d) in the integral form of Ampère's law (1.1.20). A line integral of $\mathbf{H}$ around the beam at a radius r gives

$$2\pi r H_\theta = \int_0^r J_z 2\pi r \, dr \tag{f}$$

or

$$H_\theta = \frac{V \rho_0 r}{2}, \qquad r < a,$$

$$H_\theta = \frac{V \rho_0 a^2}{2r}, \qquad r > a. \tag{g}$$

in agreement with (e).

6.4 DC ROTATING MACHINES

As stated in Section 4.1.6c, the dc machine is the most widely used rotating machine for control applications, especially when precise and versatile control of mechanical power or torque is required. Control can be achieved with high efficiency so that dc motors are used widely in high-power systems such as traction applications for driving locomotives and subway trains, rolling mills in steel plants, and ship propulsion. In electrically propelled ships and in diesel-electric locomotives the prime mover produces mechanical power and an electrical system is used for control rather than a mechanical system of gears. The primary reason for this substitution is the versatility of the electrical power transmission system from the viewpoint of control.

The use of dc motors for controllable drives requires dc generators to supply the necessary power. Moreover, there are many applications of electric power in which direct current is necessary; for example, the production of aluminum is accomplished by the use of large quantities of direct current. Direct-current generators driven by alternating-current motors are used to supply power in many of these cases.

Because of the wide and extensive use of dc machines, we consider some of the important features of the more common types in use. Our treatment is introductory and intended to provide an understanding of the essential physics of dc machine operation and to indicate how the terminal behavior can be analyzed. In spite of our special attention to the topic at this point the reader should remember that although the dc machines we treat illustrate the basic material introduced in this chapter they are also specific examples of lumped-parameter, magnetic field-type, electromechanical devices introduced in Chapters 2 and 3. As we complete the analyses, we shall indicate the relation to the earlier chapters.

In the next two sections we treat two configurations of dc machines: commutator machines discussed briefly in Section 4.1.6c and homopolar machines, an example of which was introduced in Example 6.3.1.

6.4.1 Commutator Machines

6.4.1a Physical Characteristics

As discussed in Section 4.1.6c, a commutator can be viewed as a mechanically controlled frequency changer that causes rotor-current frequencies to satisfy automatically the condition for average power conversion (4.1.18) when rotor and stator electrical sources are at the same frequency (usually zero). To analyze the terminal behavior of a commutator machine, other viewpoints are used. (In some cases the techniques of Chapter 3 are employed, but this kind of treatment makes physical insight difficult.) We use a field approach to obtain equations of motion and indicate how the connection is made to the techniques of Chapter 3.*

To develop the equations of motion for a commutator machine from a field viewpoint we need to specify the geometry of the windings, the commutator, the brushes, and the magnetic material. To do this we use simplified schematic drawings. To put these representations in perspective a cutaway view

---

* For some alternative viewpoints on analytical techniques to be used with commutators see, for example, D. C. White and H. H. Woodson, *Electromechanical Energy Conversion*, Wiley, New York, 1959, Chapter 4; A. J. Thaler and M. I. Wilcox, *Electric Machines*, Wiley, New York, 1966, Chapters 3 and 4; A. E. Fitzgerald and C. Kingsley, Jr., *Electric Machinery*, 2nd ed., McGraw-Hill, New York, 1961, Chapter 3.

MAIN FIELD COIL AND POLE · ARMATURE COIL · COMMUTATING COIL AND POLE · POLE-FACE BAR CONNECTION · BRUSH HOLDER · COMMUTATOR

Fig. 6.4.1 Cutaway view of a 2250-hp, 300/600-rpm, 600-V, dc motor. (Courtesy of General Electric Company.)

of a commutator machine is shown in Fig. 6.4.1 with the principal parts labeled. When using the simplified schematic drawings, frequent reference should be made to this practical configuration.

First, consider the schematic end view of a two-pole commutator machine shown in Fig. 6.4.2. This is a salient-pole structure, as defined and discussed in Section 4.2, with the salient poles on the stator. A commutator machine can have any even number of poles (see Sections 4.1.8 and 4.2.4), but we treat a two-pole machine in the interest of simplicity. The rotor is essentially cylindrical with conductors placed in axial slots as indicated. The stator winding is excited directly at its terminals and the rotor conductors are excited through brushes (usually carbon) that make sliding contact with the commutator.

To follow the usual convention, we call the stator winding the *field* winding and denote quantities associated with it by the subscript f; we call the rotor winding the *armature* winding and denote quantities associated with it by the subscript a.

Currents in the field windings, with directions indicated by dots and crosses in Fig. 6.4.2, produce a flux density distribution that is symmetrical about the field magnetic axis, as indicated in the developed view of the machine in Fig. 6.4.3. Currents in the armature conductors, maintained by the commutator

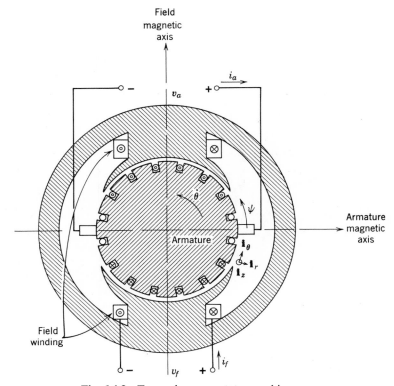

Fig. 6.4.2 Two-pole, commutator machine.

and brushes, have the directions indicated by the dots and crosses in Fig. 6.4.2, independent of armature (rotor) position or speed. Thus armature current produces a flux density distribution that is symmetrical about the armature magnetic axis, as indicated in Fig. 6.4.3.

To indicate qualitatively the shapes of the flux density distributions and to illustrate how armature conductors are connected to the commutator bars, a developed view of the machine is shown in Fig. 6.4.3. The shape of the field flux density distribution is understandable in terms of Ampère's law (1.1.20). For analytical purposes it is often assumed that fringing at the pole edges can be neglected because the air gap is small, that slot and teeth effects are negligible, and that there is no magnetic saturation. Then the flux density distribution has the square shape shown by dashed lines. As developed subsequently, the important quantity is the total magnetic flux per pole; consequently, the idealized curve is a good representation of the actual curve with respect to total flux (area under the curve).

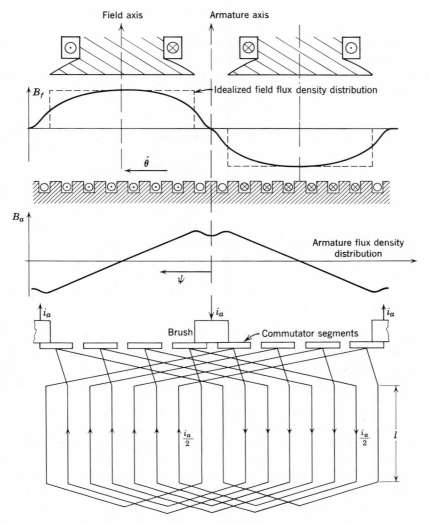

Fig. 6.4.3 Developed views of two-pole commutator machine showing flux distributions and armature connections.

The armature flux density distribution in Fig. 6.4.3 is idealized in two ways: the effects of slots and teeth are neglected and the armature current is assumed to be uniformly distributed along the armature surface. This approximation may seem rather gross with respect to the number and size of slots in Fig. 6.4.3; in practical machines, however, the number of slots is much greater and the slots are smaller; thus the approximate flux density distribution in Fig. 6.4.3 is quite accurate.

The developed view at the bottom of Fig. 6.4.3 shows how armature conductors are connected to commutator bars. A tracing of conducting paths will show that any one-turn coil has its ends connected to adjacent commutator bars and that there are two parallel conducting paths between brushes, each containing three coils in series. Two coils are short-circuited by the brushes. In practical machines with lap windings,* the coils may have one or more turns, with the coil terminals connected as shown in Fig. 6.4.3. Also, in practical machines each slot normally contains two coil sides, one each from two different coils, rather than the one we show for simplicity.

By visualizing what happens to the conductor currents in Fig. 6.4.3 as the armature conductors and commutator bars slide past the brushes, it will become clear that the armature current pattern will shift back and forth by about the distance between two slots. In a practical machine with a large number of armature conductors and commutator bars, this variation will be much less, and it is quite reasonable to assume that the current pattern is fixed at its average position. This switching of current pattern by the commutator can be interpreted as the electrical equivalent of a mechanical ratchet.

As indicated in Fig. 6.4.3 and noted earlier, two coils have no current because the brushes short-circuit them. As the armature turns, armature coils are successively shorted by the brushes. Before a coil is shorted it carries current in one direction, and after the short is removed the current direction is reversed. The process of current reversal is called commutation, and it is complicated by speed voltage and inductive voltages in the shorted coil and by arcing of the contact between brush and commutator. The process of commutation is complex and its practical realization imposes a limitation on the characteristics that can be achieved with commutator machines.† For the purpose of analyzing the terminal behavior of commutator machines we need to know only the geometry of the windings and the fact

---

* An alternative scheme is called a wave winding. Both schemes, lap and wave windings, essentially yield a continuous armature winding. For a discussion of the two schemes see, for example, A. E. Knowlton, ed., *Standard Handbook for Electrical Engineers*, 9th ed., McGraw-Hill, New York, 1957, Section 8.25.

† For a discussion of commutation and a list of good references see Knowlton, *op. cit.*, Sections 8.33 to 8.55.

that the commutator keeps the armature current pattern fixed in space with respect to the brushes, as illustrated in Figs. 6.4.2 and 6.4.3.

6.4.1b Equations of Motion

To develop the equations of motion for commutator machines we use the field transformations of Section 6.1.1 and the constituent relations of Section 6.3.1. We consider the effects of field flux density and armature flux density separately and superimpose the results. Such a process provides adequate accuracy; when the two flux density distributions in Fig. 6.4.3 are superimposed, however, they add in some regions and subtract in others. In the region in which they add, there may be saturation and resulting distortion of the flux patterns. When this occurs, the armature flux density distribution is skewed and there is a net linkage of armature flux with the field winding. This phenomenon is called armature reaction.* We neglect saturation, and thus the effects of armature reaction, in our analysis.

Consider first the field winding in Fig. 6.4.2. With reference to the flux density distributions of Fig. 6.4.3, it is clear that the armature produces no net flux linkage with the field winding because the axes of symmetry of the flux density distributions are orthogonal. Thus the field winding links only its own flux and we can write the equation (see Section 2.1.1)

$$v_f = R_f i_f + L_f \frac{di_f}{dt}, \qquad (6.4.1)$$

where R_f = the field winding resistance,

L_f = the field winding self-inductance.

Effects of armature slots and teeth are neglected in defining the constant field inductance L_f.

Because the armature conductors are in motion with respect to the reference frame in which we are defining fields, we must be careful when writing the voltage equation for the armature circuit. We use Faraday's law in integral form with a *fixed* contour (see Table 1.2):

$$-\oint_C \mathbf{E} \cdot d\mathbf{l} = \frac{d}{dt} \int_S \mathbf{B} \cdot \mathbf{n} \, da. \qquad (6.4.2)$$

The contour C is fixed so the $\mathbf{E}$ is measured in the fixed reference frame. The contour to be used (shown schematically in Fig. 6.4.4) follows one of the conducting paths through the armature conductors between the brushes (see Fig. 6.4.3). The contour is fixed and the conductors are moving; thus they coincide only instantaneously.

* See, for example, Knowlton, *op. cit.*, Sections 8.27 to 8.32.

To evaluate (6.4.2) we break the contour integration into two parts:

$$-\int_a^b \mathbf{E} \cdot d\mathbf{l} - \int_b^a \mathbf{E} \cdot d\mathbf{l} = \frac{d}{dt} \int_S \mathbf{B} \cdot \mathbf{n} \, da. \tag{6.4.3}$$

The first term on the left is the integral between the terminals external to the machine and is

$$-\int_a^b \mathbf{E} \cdot d\mathbf{l} = v_a. \tag{6.4.4}$$

The second integral on the left is taken through the armature circuit of the machine. If the armature conductor material has a conductivity σ, then (6.3.5) indicates that we must write

$$\mathbf{J} = \sigma(\mathbf{E} + \mathbf{v} \times \mathbf{B}) \tag{6.4.5}$$

for the armature conductors in which $\mathbf{J}$ is the armature conductor current density and $\mathbf{v}$ is the armature conductor velocity. This expression can be used for all armature circuit conductors, including those from the terminals to the brushes, because $\mathbf{v} = 0$ and $\mathbf{J} = \sigma\mathbf{E}$, as it should be for a conductor at rest.

Solution of (6.4.5) for $\mathbf{E}$ and the use of that result in the second term of (6.4.3) yields

$$-\int_b^a \mathbf{E} \cdot d\mathbf{l} = -\int_b^a \frac{\mathbf{J}}{\sigma} \cdot d\mathbf{l} + \int_b^a (\mathbf{v} \times \mathbf{B}) \cdot d\mathbf{l}. \tag{6.4.6}$$

The first term on the right is just the drop in voltage across the armature resistance and can be written as

$$-\int_b^a \frac{\mathbf{J}}{\sigma} \cdot d\mathbf{l} = -i_a R_a, \tag{6.4.7}$$

where R_a is the armature circuit resistance. To show this for the armature conductors between brushes, assume that the current $(i_a/2)$ (see Fig. 6.4.3) is distributed uniformly over the cross section A_w of the wire. Then the magnitude of $\mathbf{J}$ is

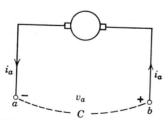

$$J = \frac{i_a}{2A_w}. \tag{6.4.8}$$

Fig. 6.4.4 Illustration of the contour for finding an armature voltage equation. The contour is completed on the armature, where it follows one of the two conducting paths joining the brushes in Fig. 6.4.3.

Specify the total length of wire between brushes as l_w and

$$-\int_b^a \frac{\mathbf{J}}{\sigma} \cdot d\mathbf{l} = -\int_0^{l_w} \frac{i_a}{2A_w\sigma} \, dl = \frac{-i_a l_w}{2A_w\sigma}. \tag{6.4.9}$$

The quantity $(l_w/2A_w\sigma)$ is just the resistance

of two wires in parallel, each having length l_w, and A_w, and conductivity σ.

The second term on the right of (6.4.6) is a *speed voltage*, which is evaluated as follows. The velocity of a conductor is

$$\mathbf{v} = \mathbf{i}_\theta \dot{\theta} R, \tag{6.4.10}$$

where R = the radius measured from the axis of rotation to the conductor location,

$\dot{\theta}$ = the angular speed of the armature,

$\mathbf{i}_\theta$ = the unit vector in the tangential direction taken as positive in the counterclockwise direction in Fig. 6.4.2.

If we assume that appreciable flux density occurs only over the axial length l shown in Fig. 6.4.3 and that this flux density is radial and independent of axial position,* then

$$\mathbf{B} = \mathbf{i}_r\, B_r(\psi), \tag{6.4.11}$$

where $\mathbf{i}_r$ = the unit vector in the radial direction,

ψ = an angle measured with respect to the fixed reference frame, as indicated in Fig. 6.4.2.

Equations 6.4.10 and 6.4.11 are used to write

$$\mathbf{v} \times \mathbf{B} = -\mathbf{i}_z \dot{\theta} R B_r(\psi), \tag{6.4.12}$$

where $\mathbf{i}_z$ is the unit vector in the axial direction and is positive out of the paper in Fig. 6.4.2. Use of this term in the integral

$$\int_b^a (\mathbf{v} \times \mathbf{B}) \cdot d\mathbf{l},$$

with the flux density distributions of Fig. 6.4.3 and the contour defined in Fig. 6.4.4, shows that there is no net contribution from armature flux density but there is from field flux density. To evaluate this contribution we can evaluate B_r at the value of ψ for each conductor, multiply by the length, and add up the contributions of each conductor to get the total. In real machines there are many armature conductors such that it is a good approximation to use the average flux density due to the field winding

$$(B_{rf})_{\mathrm{av}} = \frac{\displaystyle\int_0^\pi B_{rf}(\psi)\, d\psi}{\pi} \tag{6.4.13}$$

and write

$$\mathbf{v} \times \mathbf{B} = -\mathbf{i}_z\, \dot{\theta} R (B_{rf})_{\mathrm{av}}. \tag{6.4.14}$$

* This restriction is necessary only for simplicity. The method is general and can include axial variation of radial flux density and effects of the axial component of $\mathbf{B}$ on the radially directed end turns.

We then take twice the axial length ($2l$) for the voltage generated in one turn and the total number of turns N in one path between brushes to write

$$\int_b^a (\mathbf{v} \times \mathbf{B}) \cdot d\mathbf{l} = -2lN \dot{\theta} R (B_{rf})_{\text{av}}. \tag{6.4.15}$$

Because $(B_{rf})_{\text{av}}$ is proportional to field current i_f, it is conventional to write this term as

$$\int_b^a (\mathbf{v} \times \mathbf{B}) \cdot d\mathbf{l} = -G\dot{\theta} i_f, \tag{6.4.16}$$

where G is the *speed coefficient* that depends only on geometry and magnetic material properties.

To evaluate the final term, the right side of (6.4.3), we recognize that

$$\int_S \mathbf{B} \cdot \mathbf{n} \, da = \lambda_a \tag{6.4.17}$$

is the flux linking the armature circuit. As indicated earlier, all of this flux linkage is due to armature current, the system is assumed to be electrically linear, and the effects of slots and teeth are neglected; thus

$$\lambda_a = L_a i_a, \tag{6.4.18}$$

where L_a is the constant armature self-inductance and

$$\frac{d}{dt} \int_S \mathbf{B} \cdot \mathbf{n} \, da = \frac{d\lambda_a}{dt} = L_a \frac{di_a}{dt}. \tag{6.4.19}$$

The armature voltage equation is now written by combining (6.4.4), (6.4.6), (6.4.7), (6.4.16), and (6.4.19) in (6.4.3); thus

$$v_a = i_a R_a + L_a \frac{di_a}{dt} + G\dot{\theta} i_f. \tag{6.4.20}$$

This is the desired armature circuit equation.

It is clear from this result that the electrical consequence of mechanical motion is represented by the last term on the right of (6.4.20). This term was derived in (6.4.10) to (6.4.20) with a fixed contour and Ohm's law for a moving conductor. It could have been derived with a contour that moves with the armature conductor. In this case we assume a contour from b to a in Fig. 6.4.4 that is moving with the armature conductors and write (6.4.3) in the alternate form

$$-\int_a^b \mathbf{E} \cdot d\mathbf{l} - \int_b^a \mathbf{E}' \cdot d\mathbf{l} = \frac{d}{dt} \int_S \mathbf{B} \cdot \mathbf{n} \, da. \tag{6.4.21}$$

We must remember that the contour C is now moving and thus the surface S varies with time. In the frame moving with the conductor

$$\mathbf{J'} = \sigma \mathbf{E'}$$

and the transformation of (6.1.36) gives

$$\mathbf{J'} = \mathbf{J}.$$

Thus the second term on the left of (6.4.21) produces only the resistive voltage drop (6.4.7). The speed voltage (6.4.16) is now generated by the time-varying surface in the term on the right of (6.4.21). This can be verified in a straightforward manner and is not done here. The method corresponds to that of Chapter 3 in which speed voltages were obtained from time rates of change of fluxes. These alternate ways of computing the terminal voltage were also illustrated in Example 6.1.2.

To complete the terminal description of the commutator machine we must evaluate the torque of electric origin. There are several equally valid ways of doing this. The torque is evaluated here by using the Lorentz force density for magnetic field systems.

We shall use the force density (1.1.30)

$$\mathbf{F} = \mathbf{J} \times \mathbf{B}, \qquad (6.4.22)$$

with current density in the armature conductors and the radial component of flux density sketched in Fig. 6.4.3. It should be recognized that the teeth shield the conductors in the slots so that the conductors experience only a small fraction of the flux, most of which passes through the teeth. The result is that most of the torque is produced by magnetic forces on the magnetic material of the teeth. Nonetheless, we still get the correct answer by assuming that all the magnetic forces act on the conductors. That it is immaterial whether the force acts on the conductors or teeth but depends only on the magnetic fields in the air gap adjacent to the armature can be verified by using the Maxwell stress tensor to be introduced in Section 8.2.1.*

Making assumptions consistent with those in the derivation of the armature voltage equation, we assume (for mathematical convenience, not necessity) that appreciable flux density exists only along the length l of axial conductors (see Fig. 6.4.3 for definition of l) and that the flux density is radial and does not vary with axial position

$$\mathbf{B} = \mathbf{i}_r B_r(\psi). \qquad (6.4.23)$$

---

* The fact that the force acts on the armature teeth and not on the conductors has the practical advantage that the mechanical forces applied to the conductor insulation are small and the insulation problem is more easily solved.

The current density in the region of interest is uniform across the conductor and axial

$$\mathbf{J} = \mathbf{i}_z J_z. \tag{6.4.24}$$

We use (6.4.23) and (6.4.24) in (6.4.22) to get the force density

$$\mathbf{F} = \mathbf{i}_\theta J_z \, B_r(\psi). \tag{6.4.25}$$

For uniform current density the magnitude of the current density in one armature conductor (see Fig. 6.4.3) is

$$|J_z| = \frac{i_a}{2A_w}, \tag{6.4.26}$$

where A_w is the cross-sectional area of the conductor. By integrating throughout the volume of one conductor over the active length l, the total force on one conductor is

$$\bar{\mathbf{F}}_1 = \pm \mathbf{i}_\theta \frac{i_a l \, B_r(\psi)}{2}. \tag{6.4.27}$$

The $\pm$ is determined by the relative directions of current and flux density.

For the system of Fig. 6.4.2 we could simply superimpose the field and armature flux density distributions in Fig. 6.4.3, find the force on each conductor, add the forces, and multiply by the lever arm to get the torque. It is more instructive, however, to consider the two flux densities separately. First, it should be evident from the relative shapes of the armature current distribution and the armature flux density distribution (see Fig. 6.4.3) that no net torque results from their interaction. Furthermore, the relative directions of field flux density and armature current are such that each conductor produces a torque in the $+\theta$-direction. Thus, with a lever arm (conductor radial position) of R, the torque from one conductor in the $+\theta$-direction is

$$T_1 = \frac{i_a l R \, B_{rf}(\psi)}{2}. \tag{6.4.28}$$

We could add the contributions from the 12 active conductors (six coils) in Fig. 6.4.2; there are, however, many conductors, and the practice is to use the average field flux density defined in (6.4.13) and multiply by the number of active conductors, which is four times the number N of coils introduced in (6.4.15) (remember that there are two parallel paths between the brushes); thus the total torque is

$$T^e = 2Nl \, R(B_{rf})_{av} i_a. \tag{6.4.29}$$

Note that the coefficient of i_a in this expression is the same as the coefficient of $\dot\theta$ in (6.4.15), and we use the speed coefficient G defined by (6.4.15) and (6.4.16) to write

$$T^e = Gi_f i_a. \tag{6.4.30}$$

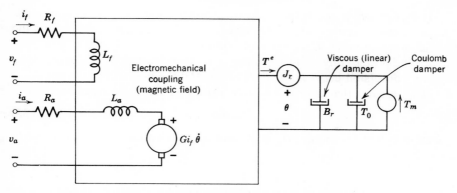

Fig. 6.4.5 Equivalent circuit of the commutator machine in Fig. 6.4.2.

In addition to the Maxwell stress tensor method mentioned earlier, this same torque can be derived by the energy method of Chapter 3, although with the commutator, care must be taken when applying this technique.

We have now completed the description of the electromechanical coupling properties of the commutator machine of Fig. 6.4.2. We complete the terminal description in the nomenclature introduced in Chapters 2 and 3 by drawing the equivalent circuit in Fig. 6.4.5. All losses are taken outside the coupling network which contains only magnetic field energy storage. On the mechanical side the rotor (armature) moment of inertia is J_r and both viscous (B_r) and coulomb (T_0) damping are included. A commutator machine normally has significant coulomb damping from the brushes sliding on the commutator. The sources T_m, v_a, and v_f are general and can be independent or dependent on some variable.

6.4.1c   Machine Properties

We shall now study some properties of the commutator machine by using the equivalent circuit of Fig. 6.4.5. The instantaneous power converted to mechanical form by the coupling network is

$$p_m = T^e \dot{\theta} = G i_f i_a \dot{\theta}, \tag{6.4.31}$$

where (6.4.30) has been used for torque T^e. The instantaneous power absorbed from the armature circuit by the speed voltage $G\dot{\theta}i_f$ is

$$p_e = G\dot{\theta}i_f i_a, \tag{6.4.32}$$

which is equal to the mechanical power output. This leads to the following immediate conclusions:

1. Power conversion between electrical and mechanical form in a commutator machine occurs instantaneously between the mechanical system and the speed voltage source in the armature circuit.

2. The power conversion is proportional to field current, but there is no power conversion between the field circuit and the mechanical system.

Next, assume that the rotor is to be driven by a constant-speed source

$$\dot{\theta} = \omega_m, \tag{6.4.33}$$

open circuit the armature $(i_a = 0)$, and apply a battery to the field circuit terminals

$$v_f = V_f. \tag{6.4.34}$$

The open-circuit armature voltage varies with field voltage, as can be seen by considering steady-state conditions and (6.4.1) to find

$$i_f = \frac{V_f}{R_f}. \tag{6.4.35}$$

From (6.4.20) with $i_a = 0$ we find

$$v_a = \frac{G\omega_m}{R_f} V_f. \tag{6.4.36}$$

The armature voltage is proportional to the field voltage. This has the makings of a linear amplifier.

Now with the constraints of (6.4.33) and (6.4.34) applied, put a load resistance R_L across the armature terminals; the armature terminal voltage in the steady-state is

$$v_a = \left(\frac{R_L}{R_L + R_a}\right) \frac{G\omega_m}{R_f} V_f. \tag{6.4.37}$$

The load voltage is linear with field voltage and all the load power comes from the mechanical source. This illustrates the basic mode of operation of a dc generator, but it also indicates that the machine can be operated as an electromechanical amplifier. Direct-current machines are used as power amplifiers in many control applications. The power gain in a single machine is usually in the range of 20 to 30 and the bandwidth over which the amplification factor is constant is limited by field inductance to a few Hertz. Nonetheless, for control applications in which devices and power requirements are large, the required bandwidth is often small. It is difficult to think of a more economical way to make a 100,000-W, linear dc amplifier.

Commutator machines are used widely as electromechanical amplifiers, especially when considerable power is to be handled in control applications. Some amplifiers involve special constraints on a machine like that in Fig. 6.4.2 (Rototrol and Regulex); others have special configurations that involve

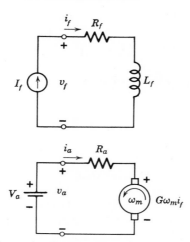

Fig. 6.4.6   Constraints for study of energy conversion properties in a dc machine.

a second set of brushes placed 90° from the original set to form a second armature circuit and a second field circuit placed 90° from the original field circuit (metadyne and amplidyne). All of these amplifiers are analyzed with the same basic techniques we used earlier.*

To learn some of the characteristics of the commutator machine as a dc energy converter we consider a steady-state problem with the constraints indicated in Fig. 6.4.6. The rotor position is constrained by a constant speed source

$$\dot{\theta} = \omega_m;$$

the field is constrained by a direct-current source

$$i_f = I_f;$$

and the armature terminals are constrained by a constant-voltage source

$$v_a = V_a.$$

We have left out armature inductance because we are treating the steady state.

The use of these constraints with the armature circuit equation (6.4.20) yields for the armature current

$$i_a = \frac{V_a - G\omega_m I_f}{R_a}. \tag{6.4.38}$$

---

* For a good discussion of rotating amplifiers in general and analyses of the specific configurations named see G. J. Thaler and M. L. Wilcox, *Electric Machines*, Wiley, New York, 1966, pp. 135–149.

The electric power fed into the armature terminals is

$$p_a = v_a i_a = V_a \left(\frac{V_a - G\omega_m I_f}{R_a} \right).$$
(6.4.39)

The torque of electric origin (6.4.30) is

$$T^e = GI_f \left(\frac{V_a - G\omega_m I_f}{R_a} \right)$$
(6.4.40)

and the mechanical power out of the coupling network (6.4.31) is

$$p_m = T^e \omega_m = GI_f \omega_m \left(\frac{V_a - G\omega_m I_f}{R_a} \right).$$
(6.4.41)

The quantities given by (6.4.38) to (6.4.41) are sketched as functions of ω_m for constant V_a and I_f in Fig. 6.4.7. As indicated in this figure, there are three regions of operation as defined by energy flow. Generator operation has mechanical power input ($p_m < 0$) and armature power output ($p_a < 0$) and occurs at values of speed at which the speed voltage ($G\omega_m I_f$) is greater than the armature voltage (V_a). The speed voltage then makes current flow to charge the battery on the armature terminals. Motor operation has armature power input ($p_a > 0$) and mechanical power output ($p_m > 0$) and occurs in a range of speed in which the armature terminal voltage V_a is greater than the speed voltage $G\omega_m I_f$ and can feed power into the speed voltage. Brake operation occurs when power is put into the machine both from the armature terminals ($p_a > 0$) and from the mechanical terminals ($p_m < 0$) and all of this power is dissipated in the armature resistance R_a. To see this refer to Fig. 6.4.6 and recognize that with $\omega_m < 0$ the speed voltage $G\omega_m I_f$ and armature battery V_a have aiding polarities and both feed power to R_a.

Figures 6.4.6 and 6.4.7 give the essential features of the operation of a dc machine with separate excitation; that is, the field winding is excited independently from a source separate from the armature excitation. The characteristics of a dc generator with separate excitation can be derived quite easily by using an equivalent circuit like that of Fig. 6.4.6. The transient performance of a separately excited dc generator is limited by field inductance, armature inductance, load inductance, or capacitance, and prime mover characteristics. The study of the characteristics is straightforward and is left to the problems at the end of the chapter.

The principal characteristics of a separately excited dc motor are shown in Fig. 6.4.8 in the sketch of torque-speed curves with armature voltage as parameter and field current constant. For practical machines the relatively small armature resistance leads to the steep slope of the curves. Thus at constant armature voltage there is little variation of speed with torque and the speed can be controlled quite closely by controlling the armature voltage.

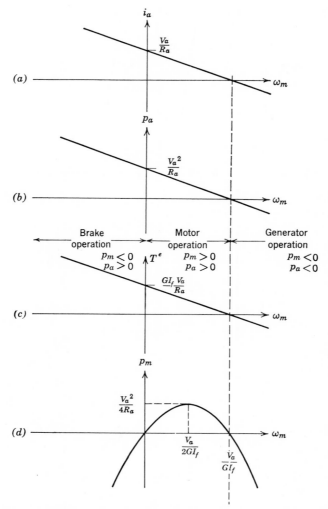

Fig. 6.4.7 Terminal characteristics of commutator machine with constant armature voltage and constant field current: (a) armature current; (b) armature power input; (c) torque of electric origin; (d) mechanical power out of coupling network.

This is the most common mode of operation of a dc motor when speed control is required. More precise speed regulation is obtained by using a feedback control system to sense the speed error and correct the armature voltage accordingly. When a dc generator is used to supply motor armature power in such a system it is called a Ward-Leonard system.*

* See, for example, Thaler and Wilcox, *op. cit.*, p. 291.

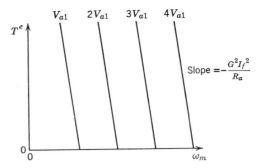

Fig. 6.4.8 Torque speed curves of separately excited dc motor.

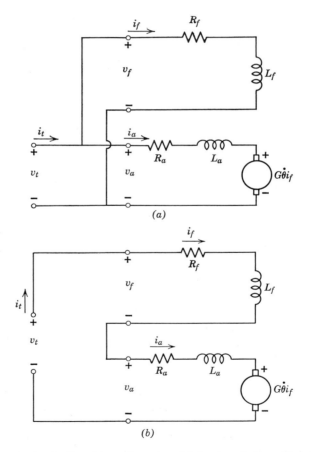

Fig. 6.4.9 Methods of self-exciting a dc motor: (a) shunt excitation; (b) series excitation.

There are two other fundamental ways of providing field excitation in dc motors; shunt excitation, illustrated schematically in Fig. 6.4.9a, and series excitation, illustrated in Fig. 6.4.9b. Considering shunt excitation with a steady state dc problem, we neglect the inductance and write

$$v_f = i_f R_f, \tag{6.4.42}$$

$$v_a = i_a R_a + G\dot{\theta} i_f. \tag{6.4.43}$$

The shunt terminal constraints of Fig. 6.4.9a are

$$v_t = v_a = v_f,$$

$$i_t = i_a + i_f.$$

Using these constraints with (6.4.42) and (6.4.43) yields for the armature current and terminal current

$$i_a = \left(1 - \frac{G\dot{\theta}}{R_f}\right) \frac{v_t}{R_a}, \tag{6.4.44}$$

$$i_t = \left(\frac{1}{R_f} + \frac{1}{R_a} - \frac{G\dot{\theta}}{R_f R_a}\right) v_t. \tag{6.4.45}$$

The torque of electric origin is (6.4.30)

$$T^e = G\left(1 - \frac{G\dot{\theta}}{R_f}\right) \frac{v_t^2}{R_f R_a}. \tag{6.4.46}$$

The torque-speed and terminal-current-speed curves for shunt excitation are sketched in Fig. 6.4.10. Because of the steep slope of the torque-speed curve, speed control is most effectively and efficiently achieved by the control of field resistance R_f because it determines the intercept with the speed axis.

Now consider a steady-state dc problem with series excitation as in Fig. 6.4.9b; (6.4.42) and (6.4.43) still hold but now the series connection imposes the constraints

$$v_t = v_a + v_f,$$

$$i_t = i_a = i_f.$$

Using these constraints with (6.4.42) and (6.4.43), we get for the terminal current

$$i_t = \frac{v_t}{R_f + R_a + G\dot{\theta}}, \tag{6.4.47}$$

and the torque of electric origin is (6.4.30)

$$T^e = G i_t^2 = \frac{G v_t^2}{(R_f + R_a + G\dot{\theta})^2}. \tag{6.4.48}$$

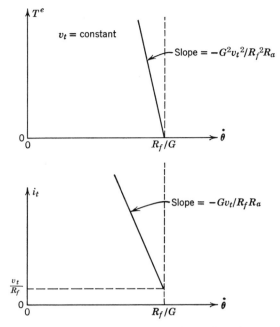

Fig. 6.4.10 Torque and terminal current as functions of speed in a shunt-excited dc motor with constant terminal voltage.

The torque and terminal current are sketched as functions of speed for constant terminal voltage in Fig. 6.4.11. Series-excited motors are used for traction drives and other applications in which high starting torque is required. The starting current is usually limited by variable series resistance, as is the running current.

A commutator machine like that of Fig. 6.4.2 may have more than one field winding on the same field structure. Oftentimes two field windings are used, one for shunt excitation and one for series excitation, in which case the machine is called a *compound* motor. It should be clear that combinations of the characteristics of Fig. 6.4.10 and 6.4.11 in varying amounts can lead to a wide variety of motor characteristics.*

We consider one final example of the possible steady-state characteristics of the commutator machine in Fig. 6.4.2, and that is as a shunt, self-excited, dc generator. By self-excited, we mean that only mechanical input is required to produce an electrical output. The field current is generated by the armature. The successful operation of this machine depends on saturation in the magnetic material, which shows up in the speed coefficient G, thus reducing

* See, for example, Fitzgerald and Kingsley, *op. cit.*, pp. 141–142.

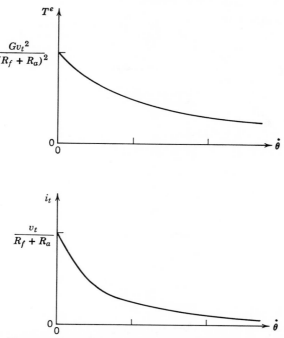

Fig. 6.4.11 Torque and terminal current as functions of speed for series-excited dc motor with constant terminal voltage.

the value of G as the excitation current i_f, hence the speed voltage increase. This saturation is usually represented by a plot of armature open-circuit voltage v_{oc} in Fig. 6.4.12 (the speed voltage $G\omega_m i_f$) as a function of field current with speed held fixed. Such a curve is sketched in Fig. 6.4.12a. Now connect the field winding in parallel with the armature terminals with no load connected, as shown in Fig. 6.4.12b; the field current is determined in the steady state by the field resistance line in Fig. 6.4.12a. The steady-state operating point at which the circuit equations are satisfied in the steady state is shown in Fig. 6.4.12a. If the field current is below the steady-state value, the excess of generated voltage over the iR drop goes into increasing the current as illustrated. Thus, if a small amount of voltage is produced (usually by residual field flux), the terminal voltage will build up automatically to the operating point, the rate of buildup being determined by the relative shapes of the two curves in Fig. 6.4.12a and by the machine inductances. The addition of a load causes a little additional voltage drop in R_a but does not change the essential features of the argument. A moderate range of voltage control is achieved by varying the field resistance R_f, the slope of the field resistance line, hence the intersection of the two curves in Fig. 6.4.12a.

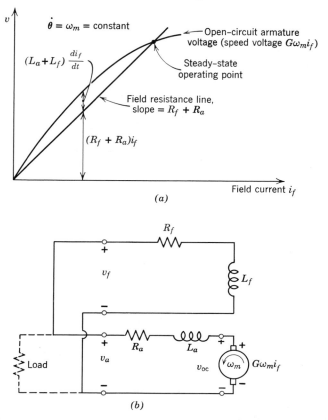

(a)

(b)

Fig. 6.4.12 Illustrating shunt self-excitation in a dc generator: (a) voltage versus field current curves; (b) shunt-connected generator with no load.

Generators can be series-excited and can use both series and shunt excitation. The techniques of analysis are similar to those used for shunt excitation and a great variety of terminal characteristics can be obtained.*

All of our examples have been based on dc excitation. Commutator machines are also used with alternating current. The techniques of analysis are essentially the same, but the inductances play a vital role in determining steady-state characteristics. Some examples of ac commutator machines are studied in the problems at the end of this chapter.

6.4.2　Homopolar Machines

A physically different type of dc rotating device is the homopolar machine, but, as we shall see, it has terminal behavior much like that of a commutator

* Fitzgerald and Kingsley, *op. cit.*, pp. 139–141.

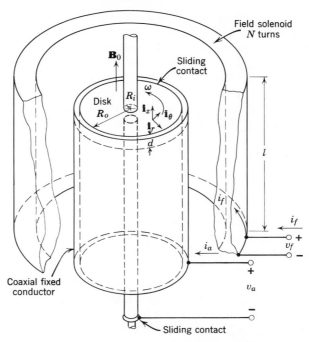

Fig. 6.4.13 Configuration for analysis of homopolar machine.

machine. One version of a homopolar machine is introduced in Example 6.3.1 to illustrate the application of Ohm's law for a moving conductor. A cutaway view of a practical homopolar generator appears in Fig. 6.3.2.

In Example 6.3.1 a limited analysis is made of the armature characteristics under steady-state conditions. In this section that analysis is generalized to include transients in the armature circuit and extended to find the terminal equations for the field circuit and the mechanical system.

For the analysis we use the configuration of Fig. 6.4.13 which is representative of a homopolar machine that would use a superconducting field coil. The system consists of a disk of the dimensions shown and connected to a shaft that is rotating with angular speed ω. A coaxial fixed conductor makes sliding electrical contact (conventionally through a liquid metal) with the outside surface of the disk. Another sliding contact is made with the shaft as shown and these two connections to the disk form the armature terminals. The whole assembly is surrounded by a coaxial solenoid that produces an axial flux density at the disk. The terminals of the solenoid are the field circuit terminals. The reason for the carefully specified cylindrical symmetry is mathematical simplicity and is not necessary for the analytical techniques to be correct. In many practical cases, however, symmetry is desirable to cut down on harmful electrical and electromechanical effects like circulating currents, thrust on bearings, and forces on the solenoid.

Current to and from the disk in the shaft and in the coaxial conductor is axial and has cylindrical symmetry. (We assume that the armature terminals are far enough removed from the disk and solenoid that the end effects can be ignored.) Current in the disk is radial and distributed uniformly at any radius. Consequently, the flux density produced by armature current is tangential and none of it will link the field solenoid. Therefore, we can write the field circuit equation immediately as

$$v_f = R_f i_f + L_f \frac{di_f}{dt}, \qquad (6.4.49)$$

where R_f = field circuit resistance,
  L_f = field circuit inductance.
This is exactly the same form as (6.4.1) for the commutator machine.

The electromagnetic behavior of the disk was analyzed for steady-state conditions in Example 6.3.1. When we assume that any transients occur slowly enough not to disturb appreciably the uniformity of current density in the disk, (we pursue this point in Chapter 7), the results of Example 6.3.1 are still valid, provided we add a self-inductance term. (There is no net field-produced flux linkage with the armature.) Thus the armature voltage equation is

$$v_a = R_a i_a + L_a \frac{di_a}{dt} + G\omega i_f, \qquad (6.4.50)$$

where R_a is the armature resistance found in Example 6.3.1 (where it is called R_{int})

$$R_a = \frac{\ln (R_o/R_i)}{2\pi\sigma d}; \qquad (6.4.51)$$

L_a is the armature self-inductance that can be calculated from the geometry and G is a speed coefficient found from equating the open-circuit voltage in Example 6.3.1 to the speed voltage.

$$G\omega i_f = \frac{\omega B_0}{2} (R_o^2 - R_i^2). \qquad (6.4.52)$$

As for the commutator machine, this speed coefficient G depends only on geometry and material properties.

We obtain an approximate value for G by assuming that the solenoid has N total turns and is axially long with small radial buildup. With an axial length l, the value of flux density near the center is (from Ampère's law)

$$\mathbf{B}_0 = \mathbf{i}_z B_0 = \mathbf{i}_z \frac{\mu_0 N i_f}{l}. \tag{6.4.53}$$

The use of this result in (6.4.52) and the solution for G yields

$$G = \frac{\mu_0 N}{2l}(R_o{}^2 - R_i{}^2). \tag{6.4.54}$$

Equation 6.4.50, which is the armature voltage equation for the homopolar machine, is the same form as the armature equation for the commutator machine (6.4.20). We could have derived this equation in a manner analogous to that used for the commutator machine; for example, if we had chosen a contour C, illustrated schematically in Fig. 6.4.14, then, with the contour fixed in the laboratory frame, we could write Faraday's law as

$$-\int_a^b \mathbf{E} \cdot d\mathbf{l} - \int_b^a \mathbf{E} \cdot d\mathbf{l} = \frac{d}{dt}\int_S \mathbf{B} \cdot \mathbf{n}\, da. \tag{6.4.55}$$

The first term on the left is the terminal voltage, the second term on the left contains the resistive voltage drop and the speed voltage, and that on the right is the self-inductance term. To complete such an analysis we must simply follow the steps used in going from (6.4.3) to (6.4.20) for the commutator machine.

Alternatively, the contour C can be fixed to the disk in Fig. 6.4.14, and Faraday's law is written as

$$-\int_a^b \mathbf{E} \cdot d\mathbf{l} - \int_b^a \mathbf{E}' \cdot d\mathbf{l} = \frac{d}{dt}\int_S \mathbf{B} \cdot \mathbf{n}\, da. \tag{6.4.56}$$

In this case the first term is still the terminal voltage, but now the second term on the left contains only the resistance voltage drop, and because of the time-varying surface S the term on the right includes both the speed voltage and voltage of self-inductance.

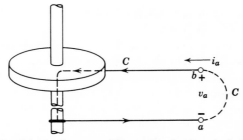

Fig. 6.4.14 Contour of integration for Faraday's law.

To complete the description of the homopolar machine, the torque of electric origin must be obtained. For this we use the force density of electric origin for magnetic field systems (1.1.30).

$$\mathbf{F} = \mathbf{J} \times \mathbf{B}. \tag{6.4.57}$$

Using the unit vectors for a cylindrical coordinate system shown in Fig. 6.4.13, the current density in the disk at a radius r is

$$\mathbf{J} = \mathbf{i}_r J_r = -\mathbf{i}_r \frac{i_a}{2\pi rd}. \tag{6.4.58}$$

[See (b) of Example 6.3.1 and note that the assumed positive direction of armature current has been reversed.] The only flux density that interacts with this current density to produce a torque about the axis of rotation is the field flux density given by (6.4.53). The use of these two quantities in (6.4.57) yields

$$\mathbf{F} = \mathbf{i}_\theta \frac{\mu_0 N i_f i_a}{2\pi ldr}. \tag{6.4.59}$$

The force is tangential; thus we multiply by the lever arm r and integrate throughout the volume of the disk to find the torque T^e in the direction of positive rotation ω

$$T^e = \int_{R_i}^{R_o} \int_0^{2\pi} \left(\frac{\mu_0 N i_f i_a}{2\pi l} \right) r \, dr \, d\theta. \tag{6.4.60}$$

Evaluation of the integral yields

$$T^e = \frac{\mu_0 N}{2l} (R_o^{\,2} - R_i^{\,2}) i_a i_f = G i_a i_f, \tag{6.4.61}$$

where the speed coefficient was defined in (6.4.54).

The results of (6.4.61) can be derived also by the energy methods of Chapter 3, provided great care is exercised in defining the moving circuit. It is much more reasonable and straightforward to evaluate the torque in the manner we did.

We now use the results of (6.4.49), (6.4.50), and (6.4.61) to redraw the equivalent circuit of Fig. 6.4.5. We have included the usual mechanical elements, and it would be well to remark that with liquid-metal brushes there is little coulomb friction (T_0) in a homopolar machine.

The equivalent circuit of Fig. 6.4.5 was originally drawn for the commutator machine discussed in Section 6.4.1. This emphasizes the similarity of commutator and homopolar machines. All of the discussion of the properties of commutator machines holds equally well for homopolar machines, with the qualification that relative parameter values in the two types of machine are different; for example, the homopolar machine has essentially a one-turn armature and is always a low-voltage, high-current device. Thus matching a wire-wound coil to this low impedance is difficult and few homopolar machines can be self-excited, either with series field windings or with shunt field windings. Consequently, most homopolar machines have separately excited field windings.

Because of the similarity between homopolar and commutator machine characteristics we terminate the discussion here and treat homopolar machines further in the problems at the end of this chapter.

6.5 DISCUSSION

In this chapter we have made the necessary generalizations of electromagnetic theory that are needed for analyzing quasistatic systems with materials in relative motion. This has involved transformations for source and field quantities between inertial reference frames, boundary conditions for moving boundaries, and constituent relations for moving materials. In addition to some simple examples, we have made an extensive analysis of dc rotating machines because they are devices that are particularly amenable to analysis by the generalized field theory.

Having completed the generalization of field theory with illustrative examples of lumped-parameter systems, we are now prepared to proceed to continuum electromechanical problems. In Chapter 7 we consider systems with specified mechanical motion and in which electromagnetic phenomena must be described with a continuum viewpoint.

PROBLEMS

6.1. Two frames of reference have a relative angular velocity Ω, as shown in Fig. 6P.1. In the fixed frame a point in space is designated by the cylindrical coordinates (r, θ, z). In the rotating frame the same point is designated by (r', θ', z'). Assume that $t = t'$.

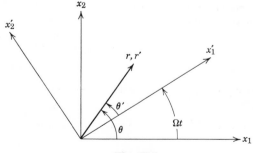

Fig. 6P.1

(a) Write the transformation laws [like (6.1.6)] that relate primed coordinates to the unprimed coordinates.

(b) Given that ψ is a function of (r, θ, z, t), find $\partial\psi/\partial t'$ (the rate of change with respect to time of ψ for an observer in the rotating frame) in terms of derivatives with respect to (r, θ, z, t).

6.2. A magnetic field distribution $\mathbf{B} = B_0 \sin kx_1 \mathbf{i}_2$ exists in the laboratory frame. What is the time rate of change for the magnetic field as viewed from the following:

(a) An inertial frame traveling parallel to the x_1-axis with speed V?

(b) An inertial frame traveling parallel to the x_2-axis with speed V?

6.3. A magnetic field traveling wave of the form $\mathbf{B} = \mathbf{i}_y B_0 \cos(\omega t - kx)$ is produced in the laboratory by two windings distributed in space such that the number of turns per unit length varies sinusoidally in space. The windings are identical except for a 90° separation. They are excited by currents of equal amplitude but 90° out of time phase. This is a linear version of Problem 4.10, which was cylindrical.

ω = radial frequency = $2\pi f$,

k = wavenumber = $\dfrac{2\pi}{\lambda}$,

λ = wavelength,

$v_p = \dfrac{\omega}{k} = f\lambda$ = phase velocity of wave.

(a) If an observer is in an inertial frame traveling with speed V in the x-direction, what is the apparent frequency of the magnetic wave?

(b) For what velocity will the wave appear stationary?

6.4. The following equations describe the motions of an inviscid fluid in the absence of external forces:

$$\rho \frac{\partial \mathbf{v}}{\partial t} + \rho(\mathbf{v} \cdot \nabla)\mathbf{v} + \nabla p = 0, \tag{1}$$

$$\frac{\partial \rho}{\partial t} + \nabla \cdot \rho \mathbf{v} = 0, \tag{2}$$

$$p = p(\rho), \tag{3}$$

where p is the pressure, ρ, the mass density, and $\mathbf{v}$ the velocity of the fluid. Equation 1 is Newton's law for a fluid, (2) is the law of conservation of mass, and (3) is a constitutive relation relating the pressure and density. Are these equations invariant to a Galilean transformation to a coordinate system given by $\mathbf{r}' = \mathbf{r} - \mathbf{v}_r t$? If so, find $\mathbf{v}'$, ρ', p' as a function of the unprimed quantities $\mathbf{v}$, ρ, p.

6.5. A cylindrical beam of electrons has radius a, a charge density $\rho_0(1 - r/a)$ ($\rho_0 < 0$) in the stationary frame, and velocity $\mathbf{v} = v_0 \mathbf{i}_z$. (See Fig. 6P.5.)

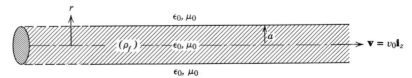

Fig. 6P.5

(a) Using only the transformation law for charge density, find the electric and magnetic fields in a reference frame that is at rest with the electrons.

(b) Without using any transformation laws, find the electric and magnetic fields in the stationary frame.

(c) Show that (a) and (b) are consistent with the electric field system transformation laws for **E**, **H**, and $\mathbf{J}_f$.

6.6. A pair of cylinders coaxial with the z-axis, as shown in Fig. 6P.6, forms a capacitor. The inner and outer surfaces have the potential difference V and radii a and b, respectively. The cylinders are only very slightly conducting, so that as they rotate with the

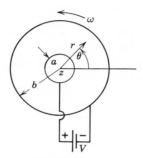

Fig. 6P.6

angular velocity ω they carry along the charges induced on their surfaces. As viewed from a frame rotating with the cylinders, the charges are stationary. We wish to compute the resulting fields.

(a) Compute the electric field between the cylinders and the surface charge densities σ_a and σ_b on the inner and outer cylinders, respectively.

(b) Use the transformation for the current density to compute the current density from the results of part (a).

(c) In turn, use the current density to compute the magnetic field intensity **H** between the cylinders.

(d) Now use the field transformation for the magnetic field intensity to check the result of part (c).

6.7. A pair of perfectly conducting electrodes traps a magnetic field, as shown in Fig. 6P.7. One electrode is planar and at $y = 0$, the other has a small sinusoidal variation given as a

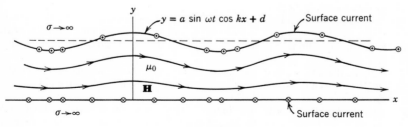

Fig. 6P.7

function of space and time. Both boundaries can be considered perfect conductors, so that $\mathbf{n} \cdot \mathbf{B} = 0$ on their surfaces. In what follows, assume that $a \ll d$ and that the magnetic field intensity between the plates takes the form

$$\mathbf{H} = \left[\frac{\Lambda}{\mu_0 d} + h_x(x, y, t) \right] \mathbf{i}_x + h_y(x, y, t) \mathbf{i}_y,$$

where Λ is the flux trapped between the plates (per unit length in the z-direction) and h_x and h_y are small compared with $\Lambda/\mu_0 d$.

(a) Find the perturbation components h_x and h_y.

(b) The solutions in part (a) must satisfy the boundary conditions: $\mathbf{n} \times \mathbf{E} = (\mathbf{n} \cdot \mathbf{v})\mathbf{B}$ [boundary condition (6.2.22) of Table 6.1]. Compute the electric field intensity by using the magnetic field found in part (a). Now check to see that this boundary condition is satisfied to linear terms.

6.8. The system shown in Fig. 6P.8 consists of a coaxial line of inner radius a and outer radius b, with an annular conductor that makes perfect electrical contact with the inner and outer conductors. The annular conductor is constrained to move to the right with constant velocity v. All conductors can be assumed to have infinite conductivity. A battery V_0 supplies a current I to the system through a resistance R. This excitation is physically arranged to

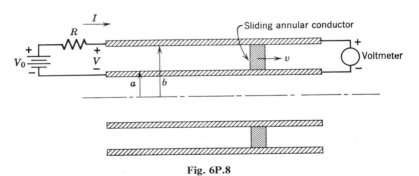

Fig. 6P.8

maintain cylindrical symmetry about the center line. Fringing fields at the left end can be neglected. A voltmeter is connected between the inner and outer conductors at the extreme right end as shown.

(a) In terms of the current I, find the fields $\mathbf{E}$ and $\mathbf{H}$ throughout the length of the line between the conductors.

(b) Using the constraints imposed by the battery and resistance, find $\mathbf{E}$, $\mathbf{H}$, and the terminal variables I and V in terms of V_0 and the other constants of the system.

(c) What does the voltmeter read? Why can this be different from the terminal voltage V?

(d) Compute the rate of change of stored magnetic energy and the power VI into the line. If there is a discrepancy between these values, explain where the power goes (or comes from).

(e) Treat the problem as a lumped inductor with a mechanical variable. Find $L(x)$ and the force f^e acting on the sliding short. Use this to explain your answer to part (d).

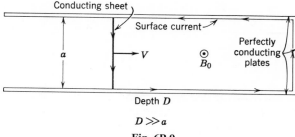

Depth D

$$D \gg a$$

Fig. 6P.9

6.9. A sheet of metal (with surface conductivity σ_s) slides between plane-parallel, perfectly conducting plates, as shown in Fig. 6P.9. The perfectly conducting plates are shorted at the right end. At time $t = 0$ a current flows on the inside surfaces of the plates and through the metal sheet to generate the magnetic field B_0. If the sheet were stationary, we would expect that the initial magnetic flux would decay with time. The sheet, however, moves to the right with a constant velocity V, hence tends to compress the magnetic field and prevent its decay. At what constant velocity V must the sheet move to keep B_0 constant?

6.10. A slab of conducting material with mass M and conductivity σ has the position $x(t)$, as shown in Fig. 6P.10. Fixed side and top plates form a closed circuit for currents

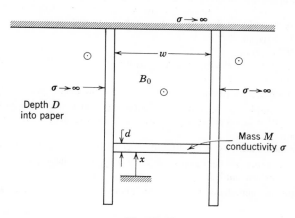

Fig. 6P.10

induced in the movable plate. A uniform magnetic field B_0 (directed out of the paper) extends throughout the system. The system is so constructed that $D \gg w$.

(a) Assume that contributions to the magnetic field induced by currents resulting from motions of the movable slab can be ignored. Find the magnetic force on the slab in the x-direction as a function of the velocity v.

(b) Given that the initial velocity of the slab is $(dx/dt)(t = 0) = v_0$, find $v(t)$ (ignore gravity).

(c) Under what conditions will the assumptions used in (a) be valid? (Remember, v_0 is given.)

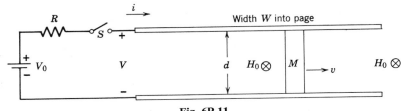

Fig. 6P.11

6.11. The system shown in Fig. 6P.11 is composed of a pair of parallel plates of width W and separation d, connected by a sliding conductor of mass M. The sliding conductor makes frictionless and perfect electrical contact with the plates. The entire system is immersed in a static magnetic field H_0 into the page and the plates are excited by the battery V_0 through the resistance R and the switch S. All conductors may be assumed to be perfect, fringing fields may be neglected, and you may assume that $i/W \ll H_0$.

(a) Find the force on the sliding conductor in terms of the current i.

(b) With the system at rest, the switch S is closed at $t = 0$. Find the velocity of the sliding conductor $v(t)$ for $t > 0$.

6.12. The system shown in Fig. 6P.12 consists of two parallel, perfectly conducting plates with depth D and separation W. Between these plates is placed a perfectly conducting short-circuit which has mass M and slides with viscous coefficient of friction B. You may assume that $W \ll D$ and that fringing fields may be neglected.

(a) Find $\lambda = \lambda(i, x)$.

(b) Find $W'_m(i, x)$ or $W_m(\lambda, x)$.

(c) Find the force of electric origin f^e (from $W'_m(i, x)$ or $W_m(\lambda, x)$) exerted by the fields on the sliding short.

Assume now that a battery is placed across the electric terminals so that $v = V_0 = $ constant.

(d) Write a complete set of differential equations that would allow you to find $x(t)$.

(e) If the system has reached a state in which the velocity of the plate (dx/dt) is a constant, find (dx/dt).

(f) Under the conditions of (e), find the current supplied by the battery $i(t)$.

You will now repeat this problem and solve it by using field theory. Do not assume that $v = V_0$ and $x = $ constant until part (l).

(g) Find the magnetic field $\mathbf{H}$ between the plates as a function of the current $i = i(t)$.

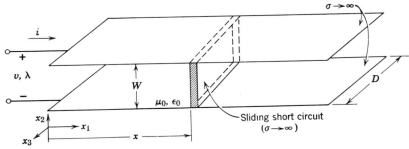

Fig. 6P.12

(h) Find the force exerted by this **H** field on the sliding short in terms of i and x by using the Lorentz force law to show that it agrees with (c).

(i) Compute the electric field everywhere between the plates. Evaluate the constant of integration by requiring that the voltage at the terminals be $v(t)$.

(j) Relate the terminal voltage $v(t)$ to the current $i(t)$ and plate position $x(t)$ by explicitly using Faraday's law in integral form.

(k) Show by using (i) and (j) that the boundary conditions on the electric field at the moving plate are satisfied.

(l) Convince yourself that the results of (g) through (k) are formally equivalent to the lumped-parameter approach of parts (a) through (f); that is, again find (dx/dt) and $i(t)$ by assuming that $v = V_0$ and $(dx/dt) = $ constant.

(m) Under the conditions of part (l) evaluate the electric field of part (i) explicitly.

6.13. The device shown in Fig. 6P.13 is a model of an MHD system that is studied in greater detail in Chapters 12 to 14. It consists of a *rigid* annular ring of high but finite conductivity σ, depth D, and inner and outer radii R_1 and R_2, respectively. The entire system is immersed in an externally applied, uniform, magnetic field $\mathbf{H} = H_0 \mathbf{i}_z$. A set of fixed, perfectly conducting electrodes, each subtending an angle 2α, closely fits the conducting shell. The conducting shell rotates without friction and has a moment of inertia K about the origin (z-axis). The position of the shell is described by the angle ψ. You may assume that the average radius R of the shell is large compared with its thickness $[R \gg (R_2 - R_1)]$.

1. *Ignore* the reaction **H** field produced by the flow of current in the shell between the electrodes.

2. Since $R \gg (R_2 - R_1)$, assume that both the current density *and* the electric field exist only between the electrodes (no fringing) and that they are uniform, radially directed, and independent of r and θ.

(a) Write the differential equation of motion for the shell in terms of T_1^e and T_2^e, the torques of electric origin produced by the two electrode regions.

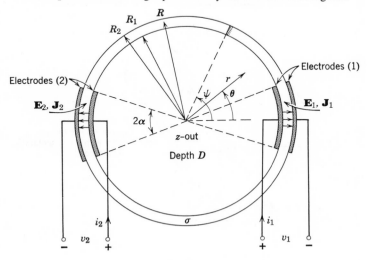

Fig. 6P.13

(b) Find the Lorentz force *density* in the region between each pair of electrodes in terms of the currents i_1 and i_2 and H_0.

(c) Find the torques T_1^e and T_2^e you used in part (a) in terms of the currents i_1, i_2, and H_0 by appropriately integrating the force density you found in part (b).

(d) Relate the electrode voltages v_1 and v_2 to the electric fields E_1 and E_2 as measured in a fixed frame.

(e) Use the magnetic field system transformation laws with your answer to part (d) to find the electrode voltages v_1 and v_2 in terms of the currents i_1 and i_2 and the velocity of the cylindrical shell $R(d\psi/dt)$.

Your answers to parts (a), (c), and (e) should give you a set of three differential equations in ψ, v_1, v_2, i_1, and i_2. (If the electrical terminal constraints, namely, relations between v_1 and i_1 and v_2 and i_2 were specified, you should have as many equations as unknowns.)

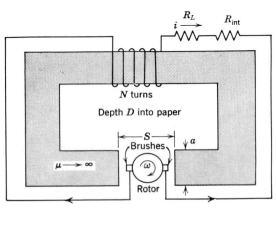

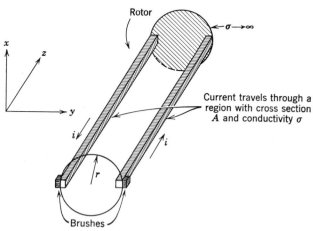

Fig. 6P.14

(f) Suppose $i_2 = 0$ and $i_1(t) = i_0 u_{-1}(t)$; find and sketch $\psi(t)$, $v_2(t)$, and $v_1(t)$ for $t \geq 0$, assuming that for $t < 0$ the system is at rest ($\psi = $ constant $= 0$).

(g) Suppose $i_2 = 0$ and $v_1(t) = (v_0 \sin \omega t)u_{-1}(t)$; find and sketch $\psi(t)$, $v_2(t)$, and $i_1(t)$ for $t \geq 0$, again assuming that the system is at rest for $t < 0$.

(h) A resistance R_0 is placed across terminal pair 2. Assuming that $i_1(t) = i_0 \cos \omega t$, find the steady-state current $i_2(t) = \text{Re}\ (\hat{i}_2 e^{j\omega t})$. Plot $|\hat{i}_2|$ versus ω to show that the device could be used as a transformer at *low* frequencies.

6.14. Figure 6P.14 shows a model for a self-excited dc machine. The rotor is laminated in such a way that i flows only in the z-direction. The brushes have an effective area A, hence the current density on either side of the rotor is i/A. The rotor has a conductivity σ over the area of the brushes. Neglect the thickness of the brushes compared with r. The far end of the rotor is assumed to be infinitely conducting, as shown. The rotor is driven at a constant angular velocity ω; R_{int} does not include the effect of the conductivity of the rotor.

(a) Find the differential equation for $i(t)$. Neglect the inductance of the rotor.

(b) If $i(t = 0) = I_0$, calculate the power dissipated in the load resistor R_L as a function of time. For what values of the parameters is this power unbounded as $t \to \infty$?

(c) In a real system what would prevent the current from becoming infinite?

6.15. A 150-kw, 240-V, separately-excited, dc generator has the following constants (see Fig. 6P.15):

$$R_f = 30 \text{ ohms} \qquad R_a = 0.02 \text{ ohm,}$$
$$L_f = 12 \text{ H} \qquad L_a = 0.001 \text{ H,}$$
$$G = 0.30 \text{ H.}$$

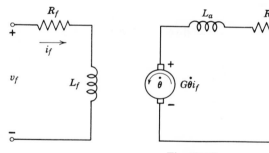

Fig. 6P.15

The generator is driven by a constant speed source at its rated speed of 900 rpm. The field current is constant at 9.0 A. The purely resistive load of $R_L = 0.385$ ohms is switched onto the armature at $t = 0$. Calculate and plot the ensuing transients in load current and shaft torque.

6.16. The generator of Problem 6.15 is connected as shown in Fig. 6P.16. The constants are the same as those given in Problem 6.15, plus $V_f = 270$ V. The machine is driven by a constant-speed source at 900 rpm.

(a) With switch S_2 open, S_1 is closed at $t = 0$, calculate and plot the transient in open-circuit armature voltage v_a.

(b) With switch S_2 closed, S_1 is closed at $t = 0$, calculate and plot the transient in armature voltage v_a.

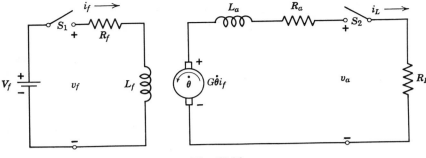

Fig. 6P.16

6.17. The generator of Problem 6.15 is connected in the circuit of Fig. 6P.17 and driven with a speed source having a torque-speed characteristic expressible as

$$T_m = T_0\left(1 - \frac{\omega}{\omega_0}\right),$$

where $\omega_0 = 1000$ rpm, $\omega = \dot{\theta} =$ shaft speed, $T_0 = 1.6 \times 10^4$ N-m, $T_m =$ torque applied to generator shaft. In addition the constant field voltage is $V_f = 270$ V and the rotor moment

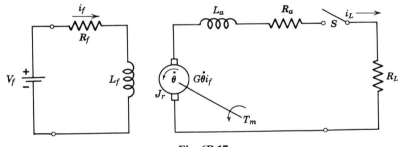

Fig. 6P.17

of inertia is $J_r = 12$ kg-m^2. Neglect mechanical damping. The switch in the armature circuit is closed at $t = 0$. Calculate and plot the ensuing transients in load current, shaft speed, and torque.

6.18. Consider a dc machine with moment of inertia J_0 and operating in the steady state at its rated speed ω_0. Consider the stopping transient with electrical excitation removed. This is a purely mechanical transient. Consider three cases and calculate and plot speed as a function of time for each case.

(a) There is only coulomb friction.
(b) There is only viscous friction.
(c) Both types of friction are present and produce equal torques at rated speed.

6.19. A dc motor has the following constants and ratings:

Field resistance,	$R_f = 230$ ohms	
Field inductance,	$L_f = 90$ H	
Armature resistance,	$R_a = 0.15$ ohm	
Armature inductance,	$L_a = 0.01$ H	
Speed coefficient,	$G = 1.5$ H	
Armature inertia,	$J_r = 0.5$ kg-m^2	
Rated line voltage	230 V	

The rated supply voltage of 230 V is applied to the field winding and the field current is 1 A. Assume that the motor shaft is unloaded and neglect mechanical losses.

(a) The 230-V supply is connected to the armature terminals at $t = 0$. Calculate and plot the ensuing transients in armature current and shaft speed.

(b) Repeat part (a), but with 1.35 ohms of resistance added in series with the armature.

6.20. A dc machine is often used as an energy storage element. With constant field current, negligible mechanical losses, and negligible armature inductance the machine, as viewed from the armature terminals, appears as the RC circuit of Fig. 6P.20.

(a) Find the equivalent capacitance C in terms of G, I_f, and J_r.

(b) Evaluate C for the machine in Problem 6.19 with $I_f = 1$ A.

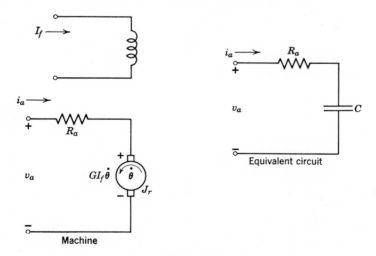

Machine

Equivalent circuit

Fig. 6P.20

6.21. Discuss the problem of operating a commutator machine on alternating voltage from the viewpoint of armature and field currents drawn and torque produced. More specifically, contrast series and parallel operation of field and armature and explain why the series arrangement is used almost exclusively.

6.22. A homopolar generator is constructed as shown in Fig. 6P.22. The disk rotates with the angular velocity ω and has a conductivity σ. It is connected by slip rings to an N-turn

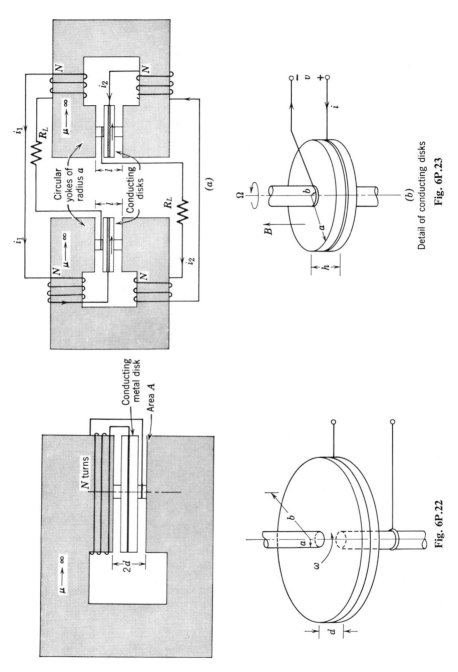

Circular yokes of radius a

Conducting disks

(a)

B

Detail of conducting disks

Fig. 6P.23 (b)

Conducting metal disk

Area A

N turns

Fig. 6P.22

coil. Under what condition can this system be self-excited (generate its own magnetic field)? The coil resistance can be taken as negligible.

6.23. Disks of conductivity σ rotate with the constant angular velocity Ω, as shown in Fig. 6P.23. Each disk is symmetrically connected to slip rings at the inner radii b and outer radii a. Magnetic yokes ($\mu \to \infty$) impose uniform magnetic fields over the volume of the disks. These fields are generated by the disks interconnected with the windings.

(a) Find an expression for the terminal voltage v for one of the disks as a function of Ω, i, and the magnetic flux density B.

(b) Determine the condition under which the interconnected disks will deliver steady-state ac current to the load resistances R_L. The disks are constrained to have a *constant* angular velocity.

(c) Determine the frequency of this current under the condition of part (b).

Appendix A

GLOSSARY OF COMMONLY USED SYMBOLS

Section references indicate where symbols of a given significance are introduced; grouped symbols are accompanied by their respective references. The absence of a section reference indicates that a symbol has been applied for a variety of purposes. Nomenclature used in examples is not included.

Symbol	Meaning	Section
A	cross-sectional area	
A_i	coefficient in differential equation	5.1.1
(A_n^+, A_n^-)	complex amplitudes of components of nth mode	9.2.1
A_w	cross-sectional area of armature conductor	6.4.1
a	spacing of pole faces in magnetic circuit	8.5.1
$a, (a_c, a_s)$	phase velocity of acoustic related waves	13.2.1, 11.4.1
a_b	Alfvén velocity	12.2.3
(a, b, c)	Lagrangian coordinates	11.1
a_i	constant coefficient in differential equation	5.1.1
$\mathbf{a}_p$	instantaneous acceleration of point p fixed in material	2.2.1c
B, B_r, B_s	damping constant for linear, angular and square law dampers	2.2.1b, 4.1.1, 5.2.2
$\mathbf{B}, \mathbf{B}_i, B_0$	magnetic flux density	1.1.1a, 8.1, 6.4.2
B_i	induced flux density	7.0
$(B_r, B_{ra}, B_{rb}, B_{rm})$	radial components of air-gap flux densities	4.1.4
$[B_{rf}, (B_{rf})_{\mathrm{av}}]$	radial flux density due to field current	6.4.1
b	width of pole faces in magnetic circuit	8.5
b	half thickness of thin beam	11.4.2b
C	contour of integration	1.1.2a
$C, (C_a, C_b), C_o$	capacitance	2.1.2, 7.2.1a, 5.2.1
C	coefficient in boundary condition	9.1.1
$\mathbf{C}$	the curl of the displacement	11.4
(C^+, C^-)	designation of characteristic lines	9.1.1

A1

Symbol	Meaning	Section
c_p	specific heat capacity at constant pressure	13.1.2
c_v	specific heat capacity at constant volume	13.1.2
$\mathbf{D}$	electric displacement	1.1.1a
d	length	
da	elemental area	1.1.2a
$d\mathbf{f}_n$	total elemental force on material in rigid body	2.2.1c
$d\mathbf{l}$	elemental line segment	1.1.2a
$d\mathbf{T}_n$	torque on elemental volume of material	2.2.1c
dV	elemental volume	1.1.2b
E	constant of motion	5.2.1
E	Young's modulus or the modulus of elasticity	9.1
$\mathbf{E}, E_o$	electric field intensity	1.1.1a, 5.1.2d
E_f	magnitude of armature voltage generated by field current in a synchronous machine	4.1.6a
E_i	induced electric field intensity	7.0
e_{11}, e_{ij}	strain tensor	9.1, 11.2
$\dot{e}_{ij}$	strain-rate tensor	14.1.1a
F	magnetomotive force (mmf)	13.2.2
$\mathbf{F}$	force density	1.1.1a
$\hat{F}$	complex amplitude of $f(t)$	5.1.1
F_0	amplitude of sinusoidal driving force	9.1.3
f	equilibrium tension of string	9.2
f	driving function	5.1.1
$f, \mathbf{f}, f^e, f^s, f_j, f_i, f_1$	force	2.2.1, 2.2.1c, 3.1, 5.1.2a, 3.1.2b, 8.1, 9.1
f	arbitrary scalar function	6.1
f'	scalar function in moving coordinate system	6.1
f	three-dimensional surface	6.2
f	integration constant	11.4.2a
G	a constant	5.1.2c
G	shear modulus of elasticity	11.2.2
G	speed coefficient	6.4.1
G	conductance	3.1
g	air-gap length	5.2.1
$g, \mathbf{g}$	acceleration of gravity	5.1.2c, 12.1.3
$(\mathbf{H}, H_x, H_y, H_z)$	magnetic field intensity	1.1.1a
h	specific enthalpy	13.1.2
$\mathbf{I}, I, (I_r, I_s), I_f$	electrical current	10.4.3, 12.2.1a, 4.1.2, 6.4.1
$(i, i_1, i_2, \ldots, i_k),$ $(i_{ar}, i_{as}, i_{br}, i_{bs}),$ $i_a, (i_a, i_b, i_c),$ $(i_f, i_t), (i_r, i_s)$	electrical current	2.1, 4.1.3, 6.4.1, 4.1.7, 6.4.1, 4.1

Symbol	Meaning	Section
$\mathbf{i}_n$	unit vector perpendicular to area of integration	6.2.1
$\mathbf{i}_s$	unit vector normal to surface of integration	6.2.1
$(\mathbf{i}_x, \mathbf{i}_y, \mathbf{i}_z), (\mathbf{i}_1, \mathbf{i}_2, \mathbf{i}_3)$	unit vectors in coordinate directions	2.2.1c
$J, \mathbf{J}_f$	current density	7.0, 1.1.1a
$J, J_r, (J_x, J_y, J_z)$	moment of inertia	5.1.2b, 4.1.1, 2.2.1c
J_{xz}, J_{yz}	products of inertia	2.2.1c
j	$\sqrt{-1}$	4.1.6a
K	loading factor	13.2.2
$K, \mathbf{K}_f$	surface current density	7.0, 1.1.1a
K	linear or torsional spring constant	2.2.1a
K_i	induced surface current density	7.0
$k, k_c, (k_r, k_i)$	wavenumber	7.1.3, 10.1.3, 10.0
k	summation index	2.1.1
k	maximum coefficient of coupling	4.1.6b
k_n	nth eigenvalue	9.2
$(L, L_1, L_2), (L_a, L_f), L_m, (L_0, L_2), (L_r, L_s, L_{sr}), L_{ss}$	inductance	2.1.1, 6.4.1, 2.1.1, 4.2.1, 4.1.1, 4.2.4
L	length of incremental line segment	6.2.1
l	value of relative displacement for which spring force is zero	2.2.1a
l, l_w, l_y	length	
M	Hartmann number	14.2.2
M	mass of one mole of gas in kilograms	13.1.2
M	Mach number	13.2.1
M	mass	2.2.1c
M	number of mechanical terminal pairs	2.1.1
M, M_s	mutual inductance	4.1.1, 4.2.4
$\mathbf{M}$	magnetization density	1.1.1a
m	mass/unit length of string	9.2
N	number of electrical terminal pairs	2.1.1
N	number of turns	5.2.2
n	number density of ions	12.3.1
n	integer	7.1.1
$\mathbf{n}$	unit normal vector	1.1.2
$\mathbf{P}$	polarization density	1.1.1a
P	power	12.2.1a
p	number of pole pairs in a machine	4.1.8
p	power per unit area	14.2.1
p	pressure	5.1.2d and 12.1.4
P_e, P_g, P_m, P_r	power	4.1.6a, 4.1.6b, 4.1.2, 4.1.6b
Q	electric charge	7.2.1a
q, q_i, q_k	electric charge	1.1.3 and 2.1.2, 8.1, 2.1.2
R, R_i, R_o	radius	

Symbol	Meaning	Section
$R, R_a, R_b, R_f, R_r, R_s$	resistance	
(R, R_g)	gas constant	13.1.2
R_e	electric Reynolds number	7.0
R_m	magnetic Reynolds number	7.0
r	radial coordinate	
$\mathbf{r}$	position vector of material	2.2.1c
$\mathbf{r}'$	position vector in moving reference frame	6.1
$\mathbf{r}_m$	center of mass of rigid body	2.2.1c
S	reciprocal modulus of elasticity	11.5.2c
S	surface of integration	1.1.2a
S	normalized frequency	7.2.4
S	membrane tension	9.2
S_z	transverse force/unit length acting on string	9.2
s	complex frequency	5.1.1
(s, s_{mT})	slip	4.1.6b
s_i	ith root of characteristic equation, a natural frequency	5.1.1
T	period of oscillation	5.2.1
T	temperature	13.1.2
$\mathbf{T}, T, T^e, T_{em}, T_m, T_0, T_1$	torque	2.2.1c, 5.1.2b, 3.1.1, 4.1.6b, 4.1.1, 6.4.1, 6.4.1
$\mathbf{T}$	surface force	8.4
$T_{ij}{}^m$	mechanical stress tensor	13.1.2
T_{mn}	the component of the stress-tensor in the mth-direction on a cartesian surface with a normal vector in the nth-direction	8.1
T_{or}	constant of coulomb damping	4.1.1
T_o	initial stress distribution on thin rod	9.1.1
T	longitudinal stress on a thin rod	9.1.1
T_z	transverse force per unit area on membrane	9.2
T_2	transverse force per unit area acting on thin beam	11.4.2b
t	time	1.1.1
t'	time measured in moving reference frame	6.1
U	gravitational potential	12.1.3
U	longitudinal steady velocity of string or membrane	10.2
u	internal energy per unit mass	13.1.1
u	surface coordinate	11.3
$u_0(x - x_0)$	unit impulse at $x = x_0$	9.2.1
u	transverse deflection of wire in x-direction	10.4.3
$u_{-1}(t)$	unit step occurring at $t = 0$	5.1.2b
V, V_m	velocity	7.0, 13.2.3
V	volume	1.1.2
V, V_a, V_f, V_o, V_s	voltage	
V	potential energy	5.2.1

Symbol	Meaning	Section
v, $\mathbf{v}$	velocity	
$(v, v_1, \ldots, v_k)$	voltage	2.1.1
v', (v_a, v_b, v_c), v_f, v_{oc}, v_t	voltage	
v_n	velocity of surface in normal direction	6.2.1
v_o	initial velocity distribution on thin rod	9.1.1
v_p	phase velocity	9.1.1 and 10.2
$\mathbf{v}^r$	relative velocity of inertial reference frames	6.1
v_s	$\sqrt{f/m}$ for a string under tension f and having mass/unit length m	10.1.1
v	longitudinal material velocity on thin rod	9.1.1
v	transverse deflection of wire in y-direction	10.4.3
(W_e, W_m)	energy stored in electromechanical coupling	3.1.1
(W_e', W_m', W')	coenergy stored in electromechanical coupling	3.1.2b
W''	hybrid energy function	5.2.1
w	width	5.2.2
w	energy density	11.5.2c
w'	coenergy density	8.5
X	equilibrium position	5.1.2a
$(x, x_1, x_2, \ldots, x_k)$	displacement of mechanical node	2.1.1
x	dependent variable	5.1.1
x_p	particular solution of differential equation	5.1.1
(x_1, x_2, x_3), (x, y, z)	cartesian coordinates	8.1, 6.1
(x', y', z')	cartesian coordinates of moving frame	6.1
(α, β)	constants along C^+ and C^- characteristics, respectively	9.1.1
(α, β)	see (10.2.20) or (10.2.27)	
α	transverse wavenumber	11.4.3
(α, β)	angles used to define shear strain	11.2
(α, β)	constant angles	4.1.6b
α	space decay parameter	7.1.4
α	damping constant	5.1.2b
α	equilibrium angle of torsional spring	2.2.1a
γ	ratio of specific heats	13.1.2
γ	piezoelectric constant	11.5.2c
$\gamma, \gamma_0, \gamma'$	angular position	
$\Delta_d(t)$	slope excitation of string	10.2.1b
Δ_0	amplitude of sinusoidal slope excitation	10.2.1b
$\Delta\mathbf{r}$	distance between unstressed material points	11.2.1a
$\Delta\mathbf{s}$	distance between stressed positions of material points	11.2.1a
$\delta(\ )$	incremental change in $(\ )$	8.5
$\boldsymbol{\delta}, \delta_1, \delta_0$	displacement of elastic material	11.1, 9.1, 11.4.2a
δ	thickness of incremental volume element	6.2.1
δ	torque angle	4.1.6a

Symbol	Meaning	Section
δ_{ij}	Kronecker delta	8.1
(δ_+, δ_-)	wave components traveling in the $\pm x$-directions	9.1.1
ϵ	linear permittivity	1.1.1b
ϵ_0	permittivity of free space	1.1.1a
η	efficiency of an induction motor	4.1.6b
η	second coefficient of viscosity	14.1.1c
$\theta, \theta_i, \theta_m$	angular displacement	2.1.1, 3.1.1, 5.2.1
θ	power factor angle; phase angle between current and voltage	4.1.6a
θ	equilibrium angle	5.2.1
$\dot{\theta}$	angular velocity of armature	6.4.1
θ_m	maximum angular deflection	5.2.1
$(\lambda, \lambda_1, \lambda_2, \ldots, \lambda_k)$ λ_a $(\lambda_a, \lambda_b, \lambda_c)$ $(\lambda_{ar}, \lambda_{as}, \lambda_{br}, \lambda_{bs})$ (λ_r, λ_s)	magnetic flux linkage	2.1.1, 6.4.1, 4.1.7, 4.1.3, 4.1
λ	Lamé constant for elastic material	11.2.3
λ	wavelength	7.1.4
μ	linear permeability	1.1.1a
$\mu, (\mu_+, \mu_-)$	mobility	12.3.1, 1.1.1b
μ	coefficient of viscosity	14.1.1
μ_d	coefficient of dynamic friction	2.2.1b
μ_0	permeability of free space	1.1.1a
μ_s	coefficient of static friction	2.2.1b
ν	Poisson's ratio for elastic material	11.2.2
ν	damping frequency	10.1.4
$(\boldsymbol{\xi}, \xi)$	continuum displacement	8.5
ξ_0	initial deflection of string	9.2
ξ_d	amplitude of sinusoidal driving deflection	9.2
$(\xi_n(x), \hat{\xi}_n(x))$	nth eigenfunctions	9.2.1b
(ξ_+, ξ_-)	amplitudes of forward and backward traveling waves	9.2
$\dot{\xi}_0(x)$	initial velocity of string	9.2
ρ	mass density	2.2.1c
ρ_f	free charge density	1.1.1a
ρ_s	surface mass density	11.3
Σ	surface of discontinuity	6.2
σ	conductivity	1.1.1a
σ_f	free surface charge density	1.1.1a
σ_m	surface mass density of membrane	9.2
σ_o	surface charge density	7.2.3
σ_s	surface conductivity	1.1.1a
σ_u	surface charge density	7.2.3
τ	surface traction	8.2.1
τ, τ_d	diffusion time constant	7.1.1, 7.1.2a
τ	relaxation time	7.2.1a

Symbol	Meaning	Section
τ_e	electrical time constant	5.2.2
τ_m	time for air gap to close	5.2.2
τ_o	time constant	5.1.3
τ_t	traversal time	7.1.2a
ϕ	electric potential	7.2
ϕ	magnetic flux	2.1.1
ϕ	cylindrical coordinate	2.1.1
ϕ	potential for $\mathbf{H}$ when $\mathbf{J}_f = 0$	8.5.2
ϕ	flow potential	12.2
χ_e	electric susceptibility	1.1.1b
χ_m	magnetic susceptibility	1.1.1a
ψ	the divergence of the material displacement	11.4
ψ	angle defined in Fig. 6.4.2	6.4.1
ψ	angular position in the air gap measured from stator winding (a) magnetic axis	4.1.4
ψ	electromagnetic force potential	12.2
ψ	angular deflection of wire	10.4.3
Ω	equilibrium rotational speed	5.1.2b
$\boldsymbol{\Omega}$	rotation vector in elastic material	11.2.1a
Ω_n	real part of eigenfrequency (10.1.47)	10.1.4
$\omega, (\omega_r, \omega_s)$	radian frequency of electrical excitation	4.1.6a, 4.1.2
ω	natural angular frequency (Im s)	5.1.2b
$\boldsymbol{\omega}, \omega_m$	angular velocity	2.2.1c, 4.1.2
ω_c	cutoff frequency for evanescent waves	10.1.2
ω_d	driving frequency	9.2
ω_n	nth eigenfrequency	9.2
ω_o	natural angular frequency	5.1.3
(ω_r, ω_i)	real and imaginary parts of ω	10.0
$\boldsymbol{\nabla}$	nabla	6.1
$\boldsymbol{\nabla}_\Sigma$	surface divergence	6.2.1

Appendix B

REVIEW OF ELECTROMAGNETIC THEORY

B.1 BASIC LAWS AND DEFINITIONS

The laws of electricity and magnetism are empirical. Fortunately they can be traced to a few fundamental experiments and definitions, which are reviewed in the following sections. The rationalized MKS system of units is used.

B.1.1 Coulomb's Law, Electric Fields and Forces

Coulomb found that when a charge q (coulombs) is brought into the vicinity of a distribution of *charge density* $\rho_e(\mathbf{r}')$ (coulombs per cubic meter), as shown in Fig. B.1.1, a force of repulsion $\mathbf{f}$ (newtons) is given by

$$\mathbf{f} = q\mathbf{E}, \tag{B.1.1}$$

where the *electric field intensity* $\mathbf{E}$ (volts per meter) is evaluated at the position

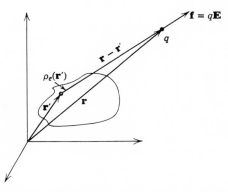

Fig. B.1.1 The force $\mathbf{f}$ on the point charge q in the vicinity of charges with density $\rho_e(\mathbf{r}')$ is represented by the electric field intensity $\mathbf{E}$ times q, where $\mathbf{E}$ is found from (B.1.2).

B1

$\mathbf{r}$ of the charge q and determined from the distribution of charge density by

$$E(\mathbf{r}) = \frac{1}{4\pi\epsilon_0} \int_{V'} \rho_e(\mathbf{r}') \frac{(\mathbf{r} - \mathbf{r}')}{|\mathbf{r} - \mathbf{r}'|^3} \, dV'. \tag{B.1.2}$$

In the rationalized MKS system of units the permittivity ϵ_0 of free space is

$$\epsilon_0 = 8.854 \times 10^{-12} \approx \frac{1}{36\pi} \times 10^{-9} \, F/m. \tag{B.1.3}$$

Note that the integration of (B.1.2) is carried out over all the charge distribution (excluding q), hence represents a superposition (at the location $\mathbf{r}$ of q) of the electric field intensities due to elements of charge density at the positions $\mathbf{r}'$.

As an example, suppose that the charge distribution $\rho_e(\mathbf{r}')$ is simply a point charge Q (coulombs) at the origin (Fig. B.1.2); that is,

$$\rho_e = Q \, \delta(\mathbf{r}'), \tag{B.1.4}$$

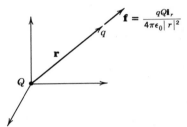

where $\delta(\mathbf{r}')$ is the *delta function* defined by

$$\delta(\mathbf{r}') = 0, \qquad \mathbf{r}' \neq 0,$$

$$\int_{V'} \delta(\mathbf{r}') \, dV' = 1. \tag{B.1.5}$$

Fig. B.1.2 Coulomb's law for point charges Q (at the origin) and q (at the position $\mathbf{r}$).

For the charge distribution of (B.1.4) integration of (B.1.2) gives

$$E(\mathbf{r}) = \frac{Q\mathbf{r}}{4\pi\epsilon_0 |r|^3}. \tag{B.1.6}$$

Hence the force on the point charge q, due to the point charge Q, is from (B.1.1)

$$\mathbf{f} = \frac{qQ\mathbf{r}}{4\pi\epsilon_0 |r|^3}. \tag{B.1.7}$$

This expression takes the familiar form of *Coulomb's law* for the force of repulsion between point charges of like sign.

We know that electric charge occurs in integral multiples of the electronic charge (1.60×10^{-19} C). The charge density ρ_e, introduced with (B.1.2), is defined as

$$\rho_e(\mathbf{r}) = \lim_{\delta V \to 0} \frac{1}{\delta V} \sum_i q_i, \tag{B.1.8}$$

where δV is a small volume enclosing the point $\mathbf{r}$ and $\sum_i q_i$ is the algebraic sum of charges within δV. The charge density is an example of a continuum model. To be valid the limit $\delta V \to 0$ must represent a volume large enough to contain a large number of charges q_i, yet small enough to appear infinitesimal when compared with the significant dimensions of the system being analyzed. This condition is met in most electromechanical systems.

For example, in copper at a temperature of 20°C the number density of free electrons available for carrying current is approximately 10^{23} electrons/cm^3. If we consider a typical device dimension to be on the order of 1 cm, a reasonable size for δV would be a cube with 1-mm sides. The number of electrons in δV would be 10^{20}, which certainly justifies the continuum model.

The force, as expressed by (B.1.1), gives the total force on a single test charge in vacuum and, as such, is not appropriate for use in a continuum model of electromechanical systems. It is necessary to use an *electric force density* $\mathbf{F}$ (newtons per cubic meter) that can be found by averaging (B.1.1) over a small volume.

$$ \mathbf{F} = \lim_{\delta V \to 0} \frac{\sum_i \mathbf{f}_i}{\delta V} = \lim_{\delta V \to 0} \frac{\sum q_i \mathbf{E}_i}{\delta V}. \tag{B.1.9} $$

Here q_i represents all of the charges in δV, $\mathbf{E}_i$ is the electric field intensity acting on the ith charge, and $\mathbf{f}_i$ is the force on the ith charge. As in the charge density defined by (B.1.8), the limit of (B.1.9) leads to a continuum model if the volume δV can be defined so that it is small compared with macroscopic dimensions of significance, yet large enough to contain many electronic charges. Further, there must be a sufficient amount of charge external to the volume δV that the electric field experienced by each of the test charges is essentially determined by the sources of field outside the volume. Fortunately these requirements are met in almost all physical situations that lead to useful electromechanical interactions. Because all charges in the volume δV experience essentially the same electric field $\mathbf{E}$, we use the definition of free charge density given by (B.1.8) to write (B.1.9) as

$$ \mathbf{F} = \rho_e \mathbf{E}. \tag{B.1.10} $$

Although the static electric field intensity $\mathbf{E}$ can be computed from (B.1.2), it is often more convenient to state the relation between charge density and field intensity in the form of *Gauss's law:*

$$ \oint_S \epsilon_0 \mathbf{E} \cdot \mathbf{n} \, da = \int_V \rho_e \, dV. \tag{B.1.11} $$

In this integral law $\mathbf{n}$ is the outward-directed unit vector normal to the surface S, which encloses the volume V. It is not our purpose in this brief review to show that (B.1.11) is implied by (B.1.2). It is helpful, however, to note that

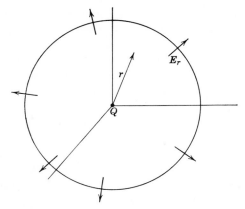

Fig. B.1.3 A hypothetical sphere of radius r encloses a charge Q at the origin. The integral of $\epsilon_0 E_r$ over the surface of the sphere is equal to the charge Q enclosed.

in the case of a point charge Q at the origin it predicts the same electric field intensity (B.1.6) as found by using (B.1.2). For this purpose the surface S is taken as the sphere of radius r centered at the origin, as shown in Fig. B.1.3. By symmetry the only component of $\mathbf{E}$ is radial (E_r), and this is constant at a given radius r. Hence (B.1.11) becomes

$$4\pi r^2 E_r \epsilon_0 = Q. \tag{B.1.12}$$

Here the integration of the charge density over the volume V enclosed by S is the total charge enclosed Q but can be formally taken by using (B.1.4) with the definition provided by (B.1.5). It follows from (B.1.12) that

$$E_r = \frac{Q}{4\pi\epsilon_0 r^2}, \tag{B.1.13}$$

a result that is in agreement with (B.1.6).

Because the volume and surface of integration in (B.1.11) are arbitrary, the integral equation implies a differential law. This is found by making use of the *divergence theorem**

$$\oint_S \mathbf{A} \cdot \mathbf{n} \, da = \int_V \mathbf{\nabla} \cdot \mathbf{A} \, dV \tag{B.1.14}$$

to write (B.1.11) as

$$\int_V (\mathbf{\nabla} \cdot \epsilon_0 \mathbf{E} - \rho_e) \, dV = 0. \tag{B.1.15}$$

---

* For a discussion of the divergence theorem see F. B. Hildebrand, *Advanced Calculus for Engineers*, Prentice-Hall, New York, 1949, p. 312.

Since the volume of integration is arbitrary, it follows that

$$\nabla \cdot \epsilon_0 \mathbf{E} = \rho_e. \tag{B.1.16}$$

From this discussion it should be apparent that this *differential* form of *Gauss's law* is implied by Coulomb's law, with the electric field intensity defined as a force per unit charge.

B.1.2 Conservation of Charge

Experimental evidence supports the postulate that electric charge is conserved. When a negative charge appears (e.g., when an electron is removed from a previously neutral atom), an equal positive charge also appears (e.g., the positive ion remaining when the electron is removed from the atom).

We can make a mathematical statement of this postulate in the following way. Consider a volume V enclosed by a surface S. If charge is conserved, the net rate of flow of electric charge out through the surface S must equal the rate at which the total charge in the volume V decreases. The current density $\mathbf{J}$ (coulombs per square meter-second) is defined as having the direction of flow of positive charge and a magnitude proportional to the net rate of flow of charge per unit area. Then the statement of conservation of charge is

$$\oint_S \mathbf{J} \cdot \mathbf{n}\, da = -\frac{d}{dt} \int_V \rho_e\, dV. \tag{B.1.17}$$

Once again it follows from the arbitrary nature of S (which is fixed in space) and the divergence theorem (B.1.14) that

$$\nabla \cdot \mathbf{J} + \frac{\partial \rho_e}{\partial t} = 0. \tag{B.1.18}$$

It is this equation that is used as a *differential* statement of *conservation of charge.*

To express conservation of charge it has been necessary to introduce a new continuum variable, the current density $\mathbf{J}$. Further insight into the relation between this quantity and the charge density ρ_e is obtained by considering a situation in which two types of charge contribute to the current, charges q_+ with velocity $\mathbf{v}_+$ and charges q_- with velocity $\mathbf{v}_-$. The current density $\mathbf{J}_+$ that results from the flow of positive charge is

$$\mathbf{J}_+ = \lim_{\delta V \to 0} \frac{1}{\delta V} \sum_i q_{+i} \mathbf{v}_{+i}. \tag{B.1.19}$$

If we define a *charge-average velocity* $\mathbf{v}_+$ for the positive charges as

$$\mathbf{v}_+ = \frac{\displaystyle\sum_i q_{+i} \mathbf{v}_{+i}}{\displaystyle\sum_i q_{+i}} \tag{B.1.20}$$

and the density ρ_+ of positive charges from (B.1.8) as

$$\rho_+ = \lim_{\delta V \to 0} \frac{1}{\delta V} \sum_i q_{+i}, \tag{B.1.21}$$

we can write the current density of (B.1.19) as

$$\mathbf{J}_+ = \rho_+ \mathbf{v}_+. \tag{B.1.22}$$

Similar definitions for the charge-average velocity $\mathbf{v}_-$ and charge density ρ_- of negative charges yields the component of current density

$$\mathbf{J}_- = \rho_- \mathbf{v}_-. \tag{B.1.23}$$

The total current density $\mathbf{J}$ is the vector sum of the two components

$$\mathbf{J} = \mathbf{J}_+ + \mathbf{J}_-. \tag{B.1.24}$$

Now consider the situation of a material that contains charge densities ρ_+ and ρ_- which have charge-average velocities $\mathbf{v}_+$ and $\mathbf{v}_-$ with respect to the material. Assume further that the material is moving with a velocity $\mathbf{v}$ with respect to an observer who is to measure the current. The net average velocities of positive and negative charges as seen by the observer are $\mathbf{v}_+ + \mathbf{v}$ and $\mathbf{v}_- + \mathbf{v}$, respectively. The current density measured by the observer is then from (B.1.24)

$$\mathbf{J} = (\rho_+ \mathbf{v}_+ + \rho_- \mathbf{v}_-) + \rho_e \mathbf{v}, \tag{B.1.25}$$

where the net charge density ρ_e is given by

$$\rho_e = \rho_+ + \rho_-. \tag{B.1.26}$$

The first term of (B.1.25) is a net flow of charge with respect to the material and is normally called a *conduction current*. (It is often described by Ohm's law.) The last term represents the transport of net charge and is conventionally called a *convection current*. It is crucial that *net flow of charge* be distinguished from *flow of net charge*. The net charge may be zero but a current can still be accounted for by the conduction term. This is the case in metallic conductors.

B.1.3   Ampère's Law, Magnetic Fields and Forces

The *magnetic flux density* $\mathbf{B}$ is defined to express the force on a current element $i\,d\mathbf{l}$ placed in the vicinity of other currents. This element is shown in Fig. B.1.4 at the position $\mathbf{r}$. Then, according to Ampère's experiments, the force is given by

$$\mathbf{f} = i\,d\mathbf{l} \times \mathbf{B}, \tag{B.1.27}$$

where

$$\mathbf{B} = \frac{\mu_0}{4\pi} \int_{V'} \frac{\mathbf{J} \times (\mathbf{r} - \mathbf{r}')}{|\mathbf{r} - \mathbf{r}'|^3}\, dV'. \tag{B.1.28}$$

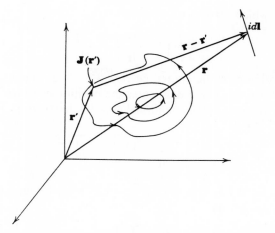

Fig. B.1.4 A distribution of current density $J(r')$ produces a force on the current element $id\mathbf{l}$ which is represented in terms of the magnetic flux density $\mathbf{B}$ by (B.1.27) and (B.1.28).

Hence the flux density at the position $\mathbf{r}$ of the current element $i\,d\mathbf{l}$ is the superposition of fields produced by currents at the positions $\mathbf{r}'$. In this expression the permeability of free space μ_0 is

$$\mu_0 = 4\pi \times 10^{-7} \text{ H/m.} \tag{B.1.29}$$

As an example, suppose that the distribution of current density J is composed of a current I (amperes) in the z direction and along the z-axis, as shown in Fig. B.1.5. The magnetic flux density at the position $\mathbf{r}$ can be computed

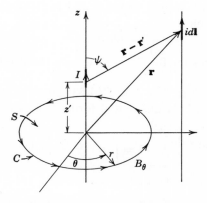

Fig. B.1.5 A current I (amperes) along the z-axis produces a magnetic field at the position $\mathbf{r}$ of the current element $id\mathbf{l}$.

from (B.1.28), which for this case reduces to*

$$\mathbf{B} = \frac{\mu_0 I}{4\pi} \int_{-\infty}^{+\infty} \frac{\mathbf{i}_z \times (\mathbf{r} - z'\mathbf{i}_z)}{|\mathbf{r} - z'\mathbf{i}_z|^3} \, dz'. \tag{B.1.30}$$

Here the coordinate of the source current I is z', as shown in Fig. B.1.5, whereas the coordinate $\mathbf{r}$ that designates the position at which $\mathbf{B}$ is evaluated can be written in terms of the cylindrical coordinates (r, θ, z). Hence (B.1.30) becomes

$$\mathbf{B} = \frac{\mu_0 I \mathbf{i}_\theta}{4\pi} \int_{-\infty}^{+\infty} \frac{\sin \psi \sqrt{(z - z')^2 + r^2}}{[(z - z')^2 + r^2]^{3/2}} \, dz', \tag{B.1.31}$$

where, from Fig. B.1.5, $\sin \psi = r/\sqrt{(z - z')^2 + r^2}$. Integration on z' gives the magnetic flux density

$$\mathbf{B} = \frac{\mu_0 I \mathbf{i}_\theta}{2\pi r}. \tag{B.1.32}$$

It is often more convenient to relate the magnetic flux density to the current density $\mathbf{J}$ by the integral of *Ampère's law* for static fields, which takes the form

$$\oint_C \mathbf{B} \cdot d\mathbf{l} = \mu_0 \int_S \mathbf{J} \cdot \mathbf{n} \, da. \tag{B.1.33}$$

Here C is a closed contour of line integration and S is a surface enclosed by C. We wish to present a review of electromagnetic theory and therefore we shall not embark on a proof that (B.1.33) is implied by (B.1.28). Our purpose is served by recognizing that (B.1.33) can also be used to predict the flux density in the situation in Fig. B.1.5. By symmetry we recognize that $\mathbf{B}$ is azimuthally directed and independent of θ and z. Then, if we select the contour C in a plane z equals constant and at a radius r, as shown in Fig. B.1.5, (B.1.33) becomes

$$2\pi r B_\theta = \mu_0 I. \tag{B.1.34}$$

Solution of this expression for B_θ gives the same result as predicted by (B.1.28). [See (B.1.32).]

The contour C and surface S in (B.1.33) are arbitrary and therefore the equation can be cast in a differential form. This is done by using Stokes' theorem†,

$$\oint_C \mathbf{A} \cdot d\mathbf{l} = \int_S \mathbf{n} \cdot (\nabla \times \mathbf{A}) \, da, \tag{B.1.35}$$

---

* Unit vectors in the coordinate directions are designated by i. Thus $\mathbf{i}_z$ is a unit vector in the z-direction.

† See F. B. Hildebrand, *Advanced Calculus for Engineers*, Prentice-Hall, New York, 1949, p. 318.

to write (B.1.33) as

$$\int_S (\nabla \times \mathbf{B} - \mu_0 \mathbf{J}) \cdot \mathbf{n}\, da = 0, \tag{B.1.36}$$

from which the differential form of Ampère's law follows as

$$\nabla \times \mathbf{B} = \mu_0 \mathbf{J}. \tag{B.1.37}$$

So far the assumption has been made that the current $\mathbf{J}$ is constant in time. Maxwell's contribution consisted in recognizing that if the sources ρ_e and $\mathbf{J}$ (hence the fields $\mathbf{E}$ and $\mathbf{B}$) are time varying the displacement current $\epsilon_0 \partial \mathbf{E}/\partial t$ must be included on the right-hand side of (B.1.37). Thus for dynamic fields Ampère's law takes the form

$$\nabla \times \mathbf{B} = \mu_0 \mathbf{J} + \mu_0 \frac{\partial \epsilon_0 \mathbf{E}}{\partial t}. \tag{B.1.38}$$

This alteration of (B.1.37) is necessary if conservation of charge expressed by (B.1.18) is to be satisfied. Because the divergence of any vector having the form $\nabla \times \mathbf{A}$ is zero, the divergence of (B.1.38) becomes

$$\nabla \cdot \mathbf{J} + \frac{\partial (\nabla \cdot \epsilon_0 \mathbf{E})}{\partial t} = 0. \tag{B.1.39}$$

Then, if we recall that ρ_e is related to $\mathbf{E}$ by Gauss's law (B.1.16), the conservation of charge equation (B.1.18) follows. The displacement current in (B.1.38) accounts for the rate of change of ρ_e in (B.1.18).

We shall make considerable use of Ampère's law, as expressed by (B.1.38), with Maxwell's displacement current included. From our discussion it is clear that the static form of this law results from the force law of interaction between currents. The magnetic flux density is defined in terms of the force produced on a current element. Here we are interested primarily in a continuum description of the force, hence require (B.1.27) expressed as a force density. With the same continuum restrictions implied in writing (B.1.10), we write the magnetic force density (newtons per cubic meter) as

$$\mathbf{F} = \mathbf{J} \times \mathbf{B}. \tag{B.1.40}$$

In view of our remarks it should be clear that this force density is not something that we have derived but rather arises from the definition of the flux density $\mathbf{B}$. Further remarks on this subject are found in Section 8.1.

B.1.4   Faraday's Law of Induction and the Potential Difference

Two extensions of static field theory are required to describe dynamic fields. One of these, the introduction of the displacement current in Ampère's law, was discussed in the preceding section. Much of the significance of this generalization stems from the apparent fact that an electric field can lead to the generation of a magnetic field. As a second extension of static field theory, Faraday discovered that, conversely, time-varying magnetic fields can lead to the generation of electric fields.

Faraday's law of induction can be written in the integral form

$$\oint_C \mathbf{E} \cdot d\mathbf{l} = -\frac{d}{dt} \int_S \mathbf{B} \cdot \mathbf{n} \, da, \qquad (B.1.41)$$

where again C is a contour that encloses the surface S. The contour and surface are arbitrary; hence it follows from Stokes' theorem (B.1.35) that Faraday's law has the differential form

$$\nabla \times \mathbf{E} = -\frac{\partial \mathbf{B}}{\partial t}. \qquad (B.1.42)$$

Note that in the static case this expression reduces to $\nabla \times \mathbf{E} = 0$, which is, in addition to Gauss's law, a condition on the static electric field. That this further equation is consistent with the electric field, as given by (B.1.2), is not shown in this review. Clearly the one differential equation represented by Gauss's law could not alone determine the three components of $\mathbf{E}$.

In regions in which the magnetic field is either static or negligible the electric field intensity can be derived as the gradient of a scalar potential ϕ:

$$\mathbf{E} = -\nabla\phi. \qquad (B.1.43)$$

This is true because the curl of the gradient is zero and (B.1.42) is satisfied. The difference in potential between two points, say a and b, is a measure of the line integral of $\mathbf{E}$, for

$$\int_a^b \mathbf{E} \cdot d\mathbf{l} = -\int_a^b \nabla\phi \cdot d\mathbf{l} = \phi_a - \phi_b. \qquad (B.1.44)$$

The potential difference $\phi_a - \phi_b$ is referred to as the voltage of point a with respect to b. If there is no magnetic field $\mathbf{B}$ in the region of interest, the integral of (B.1.44) is independent of path. In the presence of a time-varying magnetic field the integral of $\mathbf{E}$ around a closed path is not in general zero, and if a potential is defined in some region by (B.1.43) the path of integration will in part determine the measured potential difference.

The physical situation shown in Fig. B.1.6 serves as an illustration of the implications of Faraday's law. A magnetic circuit is excited by a current source $I(t)$ as shown. Because the magnetic material is highly permeable, the induced flux density $B(t)$ is confined to the cross section A which links a circuit formed by resistances R_a and R_b in series. A cross-sectional view of the

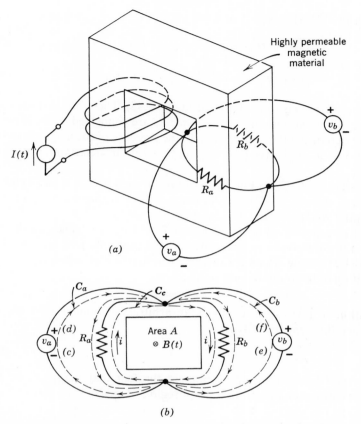

Fig. B.1.6 (a) A magnetic circuit excited by $I(t)$ so that flux $AB(t)$ links the resistive loop (b) a cross-sectional view of the loop showing connection of the voltmeters.

circuit is shown in Fig. B.1.6b, in which high impedance voltmeters v_a and v_b are shown connected to the same nodes. Under the assumption that no current is drawn by the voltmeters, and given the flux density $B(t)$, we wish to compute the voltages that would be indicated by v_a and v_b.

Three contours of integration C are defined in Fig. B.1.6b and are used with Faraday's integral law (B.1.41). The integral of $\mathbf{E}$ around the contour C_c is equal to the drop in potential across both of the resistances, which carry the same current i. Hence, since this path encloses a total flux $AB(t)$, we have

$$i(R_a + R_b) = -\frac{d}{dt}[AB(t)].$$ (B.1.45)

The paths of integration C_a and C_b do not enclose a magnetic flux; hence for these paths (B.1.41) gives

$$v_a = -iR_a = \frac{R_a}{R_a + R_b}\frac{d}{dt}[AB(t)] \quad \text{for} \quad C_a, \quad (B.1.46)$$

$$v_b = iR_b = \frac{-R_b}{R_a + R_b}\frac{d}{dt}[AB(t)] \quad \text{for} \quad C_b, \quad (B.1.47)$$

where the current i is evaluated by using (B.1.45). The most obvious attribute of this result is that although the voltmeters are connected to the same nodes they do not indicate the same values. In the presence of the magnetic induction the contour of the voltmeter leads plays a role in determining the voltage indicated.

The situation shown in Fig. B.1.6 can be thought of as a transformer with a single turn secondary. With this in mind, it is clear that Faraday's law plays an essential role in electrical technology.

The divergence of an arbitrary vector $\nabla \times \mathbf{A}$ is zero. Hence the divergence of (B.1.42) shows that the divergence of $\mathbf{B}$ is constant. This fact also follows from (B.1.28), from which it can be shown that this constant is zero. Hence an additional differential equation for $\mathbf{B}$ is

$$\nabla \cdot \mathbf{B} = 0. \quad (B.1.48)$$

Integration of this expression over an arbitrary volume V and use of the divergence theorem (B.1.14) gives

$$\oint_S \mathbf{B} \cdot \mathbf{n}\, da = 0. \quad (B.1.49)$$

This integral law makes more apparent the fact that there can be no net magnetic flux emanating from a given region of space.

B.2 MAXWELL'S EQUATIONS

The generality and far-reaching applications of the laws of electricity and magnetism are not immediately obvious; for example, the law of induction given by (B.1.42) was recognized by Faraday as true when applied to a conducting circuit. The fact that (B.1.42) has significance even in regions of space unoccupied by matter is a generalization that is crucial to the theory of electricity and magnetism. We can summarize the differential laws introduced in Section B.1 as

$$\nabla \cdot \epsilon_0 \mathbf{E} = \rho_e, \quad (B.2.1)$$

$$\nabla \cdot \mathbf{J} + \frac{\partial \rho_e}{\partial t} = 0, \quad (B.2.2)$$

$$\nabla \times \mathbf{B} = \mu_0 \mathbf{J} + \mu_0 \frac{\partial \epsilon_0 \mathbf{E}}{\partial t}, \quad (B.2.3)$$

$$\nabla \times \mathbf{E} = -\frac{\partial \mathbf{B}}{\partial t}, \quad (B.2.4)$$

$$\nabla \cdot \mathbf{B} = 0. \quad (B.2.5)$$

Taken together, these laws are called *Maxwell's equations* in honor of the man who was instrumental in recognizing that they have a more general significance than any one of the experiments from which they originate. For example, we can think of a time-varying magnetic flux that induces an electric field according to (B.2.4) even in the absence of a material circuit. Similarly, (B.2.3) is taken to mean that even in regions of space in which there is no circuit, hence $J = 0$, a time-varying electric field leads to an induced magnetic flux density $\mathbf{B}$.

The coupling between time-varying electric and magnetic fields, as predicted by (B.2.1 to B.2.5), accounts for the existence of electromagnetic waves, whether they be radio or light waves or even gamma rays. As we might guess from the electromechanical origins of electromagnetic theory, the propagation of electromagnetic waves is of secondary importance in the study of most electromechanical phenomena. This does not mean that electromechanical interactions are confined to frequencies that are low compared with radio frequencies. Indeed, electromechanical interactions of practical significance extend into the gigahertz range of frequencies.

To take a mature approach to the study of electromechanics it is necessary that we discriminate at the outset between essential and nonessential aspects of interactions between fields and media. This makes it possible to embark immediately on a study of nontrivial interactions. An essential purpose of this section is the motivation of approximations used in this book.

Although electromagnetic waves usually represent an unimportant consideration in electromechanics and are not discussed here in depth, they are important to an understanding of the quasi-static approximations that are introduced in Section B.2.2. Hence we begin with a brief simplified discussion of electromagnetic waves.

B.2.1   Electromagnetic Waves

Consider fields predicted by (B.2.3) and (B.2.4) in a region of free space in which $J = 0$. In particular, we confine our interest to situations in which the fields depend only on (x, t) (the fields are one-dimensional) and write the y-component of (B.2.3) and the z-component of (B.2.4)

$$-\frac{\partial B_z}{\partial x} = \mu_0 \epsilon_0 \frac{\partial E_y}{\partial t}, \tag{B.2.6}$$

$$\frac{\partial E_y}{\partial x} = -\frac{\partial B_z}{\partial t}. \tag{B.2.7}$$

This pair of equations, which make evident the coupling between the dynamic electric and magnetic fields, is sufficient to determine the field components B_z and E_y. In fact, if we take the time derivative of (B.2.6) and use the resulting expression to eliminate B_z from the derivative with respect to x of (B.2.7), we obtain

$$\frac{\partial^2 E_y}{\partial x^2} = \frac{1}{c^2}\frac{\partial^2 E_y}{\partial t^2}, \qquad (B.2.8)$$

where

$$c = \frac{1}{\sqrt{\mu_0\epsilon_0}} = 3 \times 10^8 \quad (\text{m/sec}).$$

This equation for E_y is called the *wave equation* because it has solutions in the form of

$$E_y(x, t) = E_+(x - ct) + E_-(x + ct). \qquad (B.2.9)$$

That this is true may be verified by substituting (B.2.9) into (B.2.8). Hence solutions for E_y can be analyzed into components E_+ and E_- that represent waves traveling, respectively, in the $+x$- and $-x$-directions with the *velocity of light c*, given by (B.2.8). The prediction of electromagnetic wave propagation is a salient feature of Maxwell's equations. It results, as is evident from the derivation, because time-varying magnetic fields can induce electric fields [Faraday's law, (B.2.7)] while at the same time dynamic electric fields induce magnetic fields [Ampère's law with the displacement current included (B.2.6)]. It is also evident from the derivation that if we break this two-way coupling by leaving out the displacement current *or* omitting the magnetic induction term electromagnetic waves are not predicted.

Electromechanical interactions are usually not appreciably affected by the propagational character of electromagnetic fields because the velocity of propagation c is very large. Suppose that we are concerned with a system whose largest dimension is l. The time l/c required for the propagation of a wave between extremes of the system is usually short compared with characteristic dynamical times of interest; for example, in a device in which $l = 0.3$ m the time l/c equals 10^{-9} sec. If we were concerned with electromechanical motions with a time constant of a microsecond (which is extremely short for a device characterized by 30 cm), it would be reasonable to ignore the wave propagation. In the absence of other dynamic effects this could be done by assuming that the fields were established everywhere within the device instantaneously.

Even though it is clear that the propagation of electromagnetic waves has nothing to do with the dynamics of interest, it is not obvious how to go about simplifying Maxwell's equations to remove this feature of the dynamics. A pair of particular examples will help to clarify approximations made in the next section. These examples, which are considered simultaneously so that they can be placed in contrast, are shown in Fig. B.2.1.

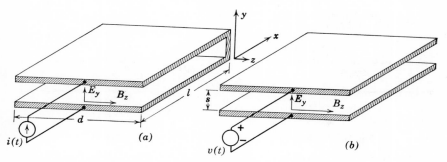

Fig. B.2.1 Perfectly conducting plane-parallel electrodes driven at $x = -l$: (a) $i(t) = i_o \cos \omega t$; (b) $v(t) = v_o \cos \omega t$.

A pair of perfectly conducting parallel plates has the spacing s which is much smaller than the x-z dimensions l and d. The plates are excited at $x = -l$ by

a current source	a voltage source
$i(t) = i_o \cos \omega t$ (amperes). (B.2.10a)	$v(t) = v_o \cos \omega t$ (volts). (B.2.10b)

At $x = 0$, the plates are terminated in

a perfectly conducting short circuit plate.	an open circuit.

If we assume that the spacing s is small enough to warrant ignoring the effects of fringing and that the driving sources at $x = -l$ are distributed along the z-axis, the one-dimensional fields B_z and E_y predicted by (B.2.6) and (B.2.7) represent the fields between the plates. Hence we can think of the current and voltage sources as exciting electromagnetic waves that propagate along the x-axis between the plates. The driving sources impose conditions on the fields at $x = -l$. They are obtained by

integrating (B.1.33) around the contour C (Fig. B.2.2a) which encloses the upper plate adjacent to the current source. (The surface S enclosed by C is very thin so that negligible displacement current links the loop).

integrating the electric field between (a) and (b) in Fig. B.2.2b to relate the potential difference of the voltage source to the electric field intensity $E_y(-l, t)$.

$$B_z(-l, t) = -\mu_0 K = -\frac{\mu_0 i(t)}{d}$$

$$\text{(B.2.11a)}$$

$$\int_s^0 E_y \, dy = -sE_y(-l, t) = v(t).$$

$$\text{(B.2.11b)}$$

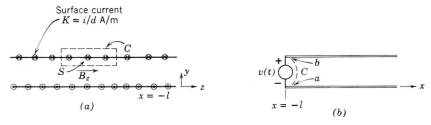

Fig. B.2.2 Boundary conditions for the systems in Fig. B.2.1

Similar conditions used at $x = 0$ give the boundary conditions

$$E_y(0, t) = 0 \qquad \text{(B.2.12a)} \qquad B_z(0, t) = 0 \qquad \text{(B.2.12b)}$$

It is not our purpose in this chapter to become involved with the formalism of solving the wave equation [or (B.2.6) and (B.2.7)] subject to the boundary conditions given by (B.2.11) and (B.2.12). There is ample opportunity to solve boundary value problems for electromechanical systems in the text, and the particular problem at hand forms a topic within the context of transmission lines and waveguides. For our present purposes, it suffices to guess solutions to these equations that will satisfy the appropriate boundary conditions. Then direct substitution into the differential equations will show that we have made the right choice.

$$E_y = -i_o \frac{\sin \omega t \sin (\omega x/c)}{d\epsilon_0 c \cos (\omega l/c)}, \qquad \text{(B.2.13a)}$$

$$E_y = -\frac{v_o \cos \omega t \cos (\omega x/c)}{s \cos (\omega l/c)}, \qquad \text{(B.2.13b)}$$

$$B_z = -\frac{\mu_0 i_o \cos \omega t \cos(\omega x/c)}{d \cos (\omega l/c)}, \qquad \text{(B.2.14a)}$$

$$B_z = -\frac{v_o \sin \omega t \sin (\omega x/c)}{cs \cos (\omega l/c)}, \qquad \text{(B.2.14b)}$$

Note that at $x = -l$ the boundary conditions B.2.11 are satisfied, whereas at $x = 0$ the conditions of (B.2.12) are met. One way to show that Maxwell's equations are satisfied also (aside from direct substitution) is to use trigometric identities* to rewrite these standing wave solutions as the superposition of two traveling waves in the form of (B.2.9). Our solutions are sinusoidal, steady-state solutions, so that with the understanding that the amplitude of the field at any point along the x-axis is varying sinusoidally with time we can obtain an impression of the dynamics by plotting the instantaneous amplitudes, as shown in Fig. B.2.3. In general, the fields have the sinusoidal distribution along the x-axis of a standing wave. From (B.2.13 to B.2.14) it

* For example in (B.2.13a) $\sin \omega t \sin (\omega x/c) \equiv \frac{1}{2}\{\cos [\omega(t - x/c)] - \cos [\omega(t + x/c)]\}$.

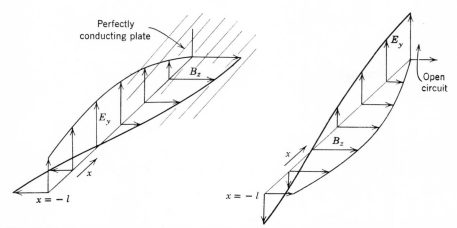

Fig. B.2.3 Amplitude of the electric field intensity and magnetic flux density along the x-axis of the parallel-plate structures shown in Fig. B.2.1 For these plots $\omega l/c = 3\pi/4$.

is clear that as a function of time the electric field reaches its maximum amplitude when $B_z = 0$ and vice versa. Hence the amplitudes of E_y and B_z shown in Fig. B.2.3 are for different instants of time. The fields near $x = 0$ do not in general have the same phase as those excited at $x = -l$. If, however, we can make the approximation that times of interest (which in this case are $1/\omega$) are much longer than the propagation time l/c,

$$\frac{l/c}{1/\omega} = \frac{\omega l}{c} \ll 1. \tag{B.2.15}$$

The sine functions can then be approximated by their arguments (which are small compared with unity) and the cosine functions are essentially equal to unity. Hence, when (B.2.15) is satisfied, the field distributions (B.2.13) and (B.2.14) become

$$E_y \simeq - \frac{i_o \sin \omega t}{d\epsilon_0 c}\left(\frac{\omega x}{c}\right), \qquad \text{(B.2.16a)} \qquad E_y \simeq -\frac{v_o}{s}\cos \omega t, \qquad \text{(B.2.16b)}$$

$$B_z \simeq -\frac{\mu_0 i_o \cos \omega t}{d}, \qquad \text{(B.2.17a)} \qquad B_z \simeq -\frac{v_o}{cs}\sin \omega t\left(\frac{\omega x}{c}\right). \qquad \text{(B.2.17b)}$$

The distribution of field amplitudes in this limit is shown in Fig. B.2.4. The most significant feature of the limiting solutions is that

the magnetic field between the short-circuited plates has the same distribution as if the excitation current were static.	the electric field between the open-circuited plates has the same distribution as if the excitation voltage were constant.

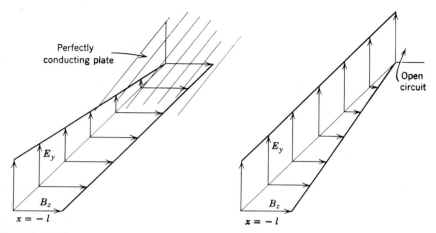

Fig. B.2.4 The distribution of field amplitudes between the parallel plates of Fig. B.2.1 in the limit in which $(\omega l/c) \ll 1$.

Note that the fields as they are excited at $x = -l$ retain the same phase everywhere between the plates. This simply reflects the fact that according to the approximate equations there is no time lag between an excitation at $x = -l$ and the field response elsewhere along the x-axis. It is in this limit that the ideas of circuit theory are applicable, for if we now compute

the voltage $v(t)$ at $x = -l$	the current $i(t)$ at $x = -l$

$$v(t) = -sE_y(-l, t) \qquad (B.2.18a)$$

$$i(t) = -B_z(-l, t)\frac{d}{\mu_0} \qquad (B.2.18b)$$

we obtain the terminal equation for an inductance

we obtain the terminal equation for a capacitance

$$v = L\frac{d}{dt}(i_o \cos \omega t), \qquad (B.2.19a)$$

$$i(t) = C\frac{d}{dt}(v_o \cos \omega t), \qquad (B.2.19b)$$

where the inductance L is

where the capacitance C is

$$L = \frac{sl\mu_0}{d}.$$

$$C = \frac{\epsilon_0 dl}{s}.$$

A comparison of the examples will be useful for motivating many of the somewhat subtle ideas introduced in the main body of the book. One of the most important points that we can make here is that even though we have solved the same pair of Maxwell's equations (B.2.6) and (B.2.7) for both examples, subject to the same approximation that $\omega l/c \ll 1$ (B.2.15), we have been led to very different physical results. The difference between these two examples arises from the boundary condition at $x = 0$. In the case of

a short circuit a static excitation leads to a uniform magnetic field but no electric field. The electric field is generated by Faraday's law because the magnetic field is in fact *only quasi-static* and varies slowly with time.

an open circuit a static excitation results in a uniform electric field but no magnetic field. The magnetic field is induced by the displacement current in Ampère's law because the electric field is, in fact, *only quasi-static* and varies slowly with time.

B.2.2 Quasi-Static Electromagnetic Field Equations

As long as we are not interested in phenomena related to the propagation of electromagnetic waves, it is helpful to recognize that most electromechanical situations are in one of two classes, exemplified by the two cases shown in Fig. B.2.1. In the situation in which the plates are short-circuited together (Fig. B.2.1a) the limit $\omega l/c \ll 1$ means that the *displacement current* is of *negligible* importance. A characteristic of this system is that with a static excitation a large current results; hence there is a large static magnetic field. For this reason it exemplifies a *magnetic field system*. By contrast, in the case in which the plates are open-circuited, as shown in Fig. B.2.1b, a static excitation gives rise to a static electric field but no magnetic field. This example exemplifies an *electric field system*, in which the *magnetic induction* of Faraday's law is of *negligible* importance. To emphasize these points consider how we can use these approximations at the outset to obtain the approximate solutions of (B.2.19). Suppose that the excitations in Fig. B.2.1 were static. The fields between the plates are then independent of x and given by

$$E_y = 0, \qquad \text{(B.2.20a)}$$

$$E_y = -\frac{v}{s}, \qquad \text{(B.2.20b)}$$

$$B_z = -\frac{\mu_0 i}{d}, \qquad \text{(B.2.21a)}$$

$$B_z = 0. \qquad \text{(B.2.21b)}$$

Now suppose that the fields vary slowly with time [the systems are quasi-static in the sense of a condition like (B.2.15)]. Then i and v in these equations are time-varying, hence

B_z is a function of time.
From Faraday's law of induction as expressed by (B.2.7)

E_y is a function of time.
From Ampère's law, as expressed by (B.2.6)

$$\frac{\partial E_y}{\partial x} = \frac{\mu_0}{d}\frac{di}{dt}. \qquad \text{(B.2.22a)}$$

$$\frac{\partial B_z}{\partial x} = \frac{\mu_0 \epsilon_0}{s}\frac{dv}{dt}. \qquad \text{(B.2.22b)}$$

Now the right-hand side of each of these equations is independent of x; hence they can be integrated on x. At the same time, we recognize that

$$E_y(0, t) = 0, \qquad (B.2.23a) \qquad B_z(0, t) = 0, \qquad (B.2.23b)$$

so that integration gives

$$E_y = \frac{\mu_0 x}{d} \frac{di}{dt}. \qquad (B.2.24a) \qquad B_z = \frac{\mu_0 \epsilon_0 x}{s} \frac{dv}{dt}. \qquad (B.2.24b)$$

Recall how the terminal voltage and current are related to these field quantities (B.2.18) and these equations become

$$v(t) = L\frac{di}{dt}, \qquad (B.2.25a) \qquad i(t) = C\frac{dv}{dt}, \qquad (B.2.25b)$$

where again the inductance L and capacitance C are defined as following (B.2.19). Hence making these approximations at the outset has led to the same approximate results as those found in the preceding section by computing the exact solution and taking the limits appropriate to $\omega l/c \ll 1$.

The simple example in Fig. B.2.1 makes it plausible that Maxwell's equations can be written in two quasi-static limits appropriate to the analysis of two major classes of electromechanical interaction:

Magnetic Field Systems		**Electric Field Systems**	
$\nabla \times \mathbf{B} = \mu_0 \mathbf{J},$	(B.2.26a)	$\nabla \times \mathbf{B} = \mu_0 \mathbf{J} + \mu_0 \epsilon_0 \dfrac{\partial \mathbf{E}}{\partial t},$	(B.2.26b)
$\nabla \times \mathbf{E} = -\dfrac{\partial \mathbf{B}}{\partial t},$	(B.2.27a)	$\nabla \times \mathbf{E} = 0,$	(B.2.27b)
$\nabla \cdot \mathbf{B} = 0,$	(B.2.28a)	$\nabla \cdot \epsilon_0 \mathbf{E} = \rho_e,$	(B.2.28b)
$\nabla \cdot \mathbf{J} = 0,$	(B.2.29a)	$\nabla \cdot \mathbf{J} + \dfrac{\partial \rho_e}{\partial t} = 0.$	(B.2.29b)

Here the displacement current has been omitted from Ampère's law in the magnetic field system, whereas the magnetic induction has been dropped from Faraday's law in the electric field system. Note that if the displacement current is dropped from (B.2.26a) the charge density must be omitted from the conservation of charge equation (B.2.29a) because the latter expression is the divergence of (B.2.26a).

We have not included Guass's law for the charge density in the magnetic field system or the divergence equation for $\mathbf{B}$ in the electric field system because in the respective situations these expressions are of no interest. In fact, only the divergence of (B.2.26b) is of interest in determining the dynamics of most electric field systems and that is (B.2.29b).

It must be emphasized that the examples of Fig. B.2.1 serve only to motivate the approximations introduced by (B.2.26 to B.2.29). The two systems of equations have a wide range of application. The recognition that a given physical situation can be described as a magnetic field system, as opposed to an electric field system, requires judgment based on experience. A major intent of this book is to establish that kind of experience.

In the cases of Fig. B.2.1 we could establish the accuracy of the approximate equations by calculating effects induced by the omitted terms; for example, in the magnetic field system of Fig. B.2.1a we ignored the displacement current to obtain the quasi-static solution of (B.2.21a) and (B.2.24a). We could now compute the correction $B_z{}^c$ to the quasi-static magnetic field induced by the displacement current by using (B.2.6), with $\mathbf{E}$ given by (B.2.24a). This produces

$$\frac{\partial B_z{}^c}{\partial x} = -\frac{\mu_0{}^2 \epsilon_0 x}{d} \frac{d^2 i}{dt^2}. \tag{B.2.30}$$

Because the right-hand side of this expression is a known function of x, it can be integrated. The constant of integration is evaluated by recognizing that the quasi-static solution satisfies the driving condition at $x = -l$; hence the correction field $B_z{}^c$ must be zero there and

$$B_z{}^c = -\frac{\mu_0{}^2 \epsilon_0 (x^2 - l^2)}{2d} \frac{d^2 i}{dt^2}. \tag{B.2.31}$$

Now, to determine the error incurred in ignoring this field we take the ratio of its largest value (at $x = 0$) to the quasi-static field of (B.2.21a):

$$\frac{|B_z{}^c|}{|B_z|} = \frac{l^2}{2c^2} \frac{|d^2 i / dt^2|}{|i|}. \tag{B.2.32}$$

If this ratio is small compared with 1, the quasi-static solution is adequate. It is evident that in this case the ratio depends on the time rate of change of the excitation. In Section B.2.1, in which $i = i_o \cos \omega t$, (B.2.32) becomes

$$\frac{|B_z{}^c|}{|B_z|} = \frac{1}{2}\left(\frac{\omega l}{c}\right)^2 \ll 1, \tag{B.2.33}$$

which is essentially the same condition given by (B.2.15).

Once the fields have been determined by using either the magnetic field or the electric field representation it is possible to calculate the effects of the omitted terms. This procedure results in a condition characterized by (B.2.33). For this example, if the device were 30 cm long and driven at 1 MHz (this is an extremely high frequency for anything 30 cm long to respond to electro-mechanically) (B.2.33) becomes

$$\frac{1}{2}\left(\frac{\omega l}{c}\right)^2 = \frac{1}{2}\left(\frac{2 \cdot \pi \cdot 10^6 \cdot 0.3}{3 \times 10^8}\right)^2 = 2\pi^2 \times 10^{-6} \ll 1, \qquad (B.2.34)$$

and the quasi-static approximation is extremely good.

It is significant that the magnetic and electric field systems can be thought of in terms of their respective modes of electromagnetic energy storage. In the quasi-static systems the energy that can be attributed to the electromagnetic fields is stored either in the magnetic or electric field. This can be seen by using (B.2.26 to B.2.27) to derive Poynting's theorem for the conservation of electromagnetic energy. If the equations in (B.2.27) are multiplied by $\mathbf{B}/\mu_0$ and subtracted from the equations in (B.2.26) multiplied by $\mathbf{E}/\mu_0$, it follows that

$$\frac{\mathbf{E}}{\mu_0} \cdot \nabla \times \mathbf{B} - \frac{\mathbf{B}}{\mu_0} \cdot \nabla \times \mathbf{E} = \mathbf{E} \cdot \mathbf{J}$$

$$+ \frac{\mathbf{B}}{\mu_0} \cdot \frac{\partial \mathbf{B}}{\partial t}. \qquad (B.2.35a)$$

$$\frac{\mathbf{E}}{\mu_0} \cdot \nabla \times \mathbf{B} - \frac{\mathbf{B}}{\mu_0} \cdot \nabla \times \mathbf{E} = \mathbf{E} \cdot \mathbf{J}$$

$$+ \epsilon_0 \mathbf{E} \cdot \frac{\partial \mathbf{E}}{\partial t}. \qquad (B.2.35b)$$

Then, because of a vector identity,* these equations take the form

$$-\nabla \cdot \left(\mathbf{E} \times \frac{\mathbf{B}}{\mu_0}\right) = \mathbf{E} \cdot \mathbf{J}$$

$$+ \frac{\partial}{\partial t}\left(\frac{1}{2}\frac{\mathbf{B} \cdot \mathbf{B}}{\mu_0}\right). \qquad (B.2.36a)$$

$$-\nabla \cdot \left(\mathbf{E} \times \frac{\mathbf{B}}{\mu_0}\right) = \mathbf{E} \cdot \mathbf{J}$$

$$+ \frac{\partial}{\partial t}\left(\frac{1}{2}\epsilon_0 \mathbf{E} \cdot \mathbf{E}\right). \qquad (B.2.36b)$$

Now, if we integrate these equations over a volume V enclosed by a surface S, the divergence theorem (B.1.14) gives

$$-\oint_S \frac{\mathbf{E} \times \mathbf{B}}{\mu_0} \cdot \mathbf{n}\, da = \int_V \mathbf{E} \cdot \mathbf{J}\, dV + \frac{\partial}{\partial t}\int_V w\, dV, \qquad (B.2.37)$$

where

$$w = \frac{1}{2}\frac{\mathbf{B} \cdot \mathbf{B}}{\mu_0}. \qquad (B.2.38a)$$

$$w = \frac{1}{2}\epsilon_0 \mathbf{E} \cdot \mathbf{E}. \qquad (B.2.38b)$$

The term on the left in (B.2.37) (including the minus sign) can be interpreted as the flux of energy into the volume V through the surface S. This energy is either dissipated within the volume V, as expressed by the first term on the right, or stored in the volume V, as expressed by the second term. Hence

* $\nabla \cdot (\mathbf{A} \times \mathbf{C}) = \mathbf{C} \cdot \nabla \times \mathbf{A} - \mathbf{A} \cdot \nabla \times \mathbf{C}.$

(w) can be interpreted as an electromagnetic energy density. The electromagnetic energy of the magnetic field system is stored in the magnetic field alone. Similarly, an electric field system is one in which the electromagnetic energy is stored in the electric field.

The familiar elements of electrical circuit theory illustrate the division of interactions into those defined as magnetic field systems and those defined as electric field systems. From the discussion in this and the preceding section it is evident that the short-circuited plates in Fig. B.2.1 constitute an inductor, whereas the open-circuited plates can be represented as a capacitor. This fact is the basis for the development of electromechanical interactions undertaken in Chapter 2. From this specific example it is evident that the magnetic field system includes interactions in which we can define lumped-parameter variables like the inductance, but it is not so evident that this model also describes the magnetohydrodynamic interactions of a fluid and some plasmas with a magnetic field and the magnetoelastic interactions of solids in a magnetic field, even including electromechanical aspects of microwave magnetics.

Similarly, the electric field system includes not only the electromechanics of systems that can be modeled in terms of circuit concepts like the capacitance but ferroelectric interactions between solids and electric fields, the electrohydrodynamics of a variety of liquids and slightly ionized gases in an electric field, and even the most important oscillations of an electron beam. Of course, if we are interested in the propagation of an electromagnetic wave through an ionospheric plasma or through the slightly ionized wake of a space vehicle, the full set of Maxwell's equations must be used.

There are situations in which the propagational aspects of the electromagnetic fields are not of interest, yet neither of the quasi-static systems is appropriate. This is illustrated by short-circuiting the parallel plates of Fig. B.2.1 at $x = 0$ by a resistive sheet. A static current or voltage applied to the plates at $x = -l$ then leads to both electric and magnetic fields between the plates. If the resistance of the sheet is small, the electric field between the plates is also small, and use of the exact field equations would show that we are still justified in ignoring the displacement current. In this case the inductance of Fig. B.2.1a is in series with a resistance. In the opposite extreme, if the resistance of the resistive sheet were very high, we would still be justified in ignoring the magnetic induction of Faraday's law. The situation shown in Fig. B.2.1b would then be modeled by a capacitance shunted by a resistance. The obvious questions are, when do we make a transition from the first case to the second and why is not this intermediate case of more interest in electromechanics?

The purpose of practical electromechanical systems is either the conversion of an electromagnetic excitation into a force that can perform work on a mechanical system or the reciprocal generation of electromagnetic energy from a force of mechanical origin. From (B.1.10) and (B.1.40) there are two fundamental types of electromagnetic force. Suppose that we are interested in producing a force of electrical origin on the upper of the two plates in Fig. B.2.1. We have the option of imposing a large current to interact with its induced magnetic field or of using a large potential to create an electric field that would interact with induced charges on the upper plate. Clearly, we are not going to impose a large potential on the plates if they are terminated in a small resistance or attempt to drive a large current through the plates with an essentially open circuit at $x = 0$. The electrical dissipation in both cases would be prohibitively large. More likely, if we intended to use the force $\mathbf{J} \times \mathbf{B}$, we would make the resistance as small as possible to minimize the dissipation of electric power and approach the case of Fig. B.2.1a. The essentially open circuit shown in Fig. B.2.1b would make it possible to use a large potential to create a significant force of the type $\rho_e\mathbf{E}$ without undue power dissipation. In the intermediate case the terminating resistance could be adjusted to make the electric and magnetic forces about equal. As a practical matter, however, the resulting device would probably melt before it served any useful electromechanical function. The power dissipated in the termination resistance would be a significant fraction of any electric power converted to mechanical form.*

The energy densities of (B.2.38) provide one means of determining when the problem shown in Fig. B.2.1 (but with a resistive sheet terminating the plates at $x = 0$) is intermediate between a magnetic and an electric field system. In the intermediate case the energy densities are equal

$$\frac{1}{2}\epsilon_0\mathbf{E} \cdot \mathbf{E} = \frac{1}{2}\frac{\mathbf{B} \cdot \mathbf{B}}{\mu_0}. \tag{B.2.39}$$

Now, if the resistive sheet has a total resistance of R, then from (B.2.18a) applied at $x = 0$

$$E_y s = -iR. \tag{B.2.40}$$

The current can be evaluated in terms of the magnetic field at $x = 0$ by using (B.2.18b):

$$E_y s = B_z \frac{dR}{\mu_0}. \tag{B.2.41}$$

Substitution of the electric field, as found from this expression into (B.2.39), gives

$$\frac{\epsilon_0}{2}B_z{}^2\left(\frac{Rd}{s\mu_0}\right)^2 = \frac{1}{2}\frac{B_z{}^2}{\mu_0}. \tag{B.2.42}$$

---

* It is interesting that for this particular intermediate case the electric force tends to pull the plates together, whereas the magnetic force tends to push them apart. Hence, because the two forces are equal in magnitude, they just cancel.

Hence, if the energy densities are equal, we obtain the following relation among the physical parameters of the system:

$$\frac{dR}{s} = \left(\frac{\mu_0}{\epsilon_0}\right)^{1/2}. \tag{B.2.43}$$

It would be a digression to pursue this point here, but (B.2.43) is the condition that must be satisfied if an electromagnetic wave launched between the plates at $x = -l$ is to be absorbed, without reflection, by the resistive sheet*; that is, the intermediate case is one in which all the power fed into the system, regardless of the frequency or time constant, is dissipated by the resistive sheet.

B.3 MACROSCOPIC MODELS AND CONSTITUENT RELATIONS

When solids, liquids, and gases are placed in electromagnetic fields, they influence the field distribution. This is another way of saying that the force of interaction between charges or between currents is influenced by the presence of media. The effect is not surprising because the materials are comprised of charged particles.

Problems of physical significance can usually be decomposed into parts with widely differing scales. At the molecular or submolecular level we may be concerned with the dynamics of individual charges or of the atoms or molecules to which they are attached. These systems tend to have extremely small dimensions when compared with the size of a physical device. On the macroscopic scale we are not interested in the detailed behavior of the microscopic constituents of a material but rather only a knowledge of the average behavior of variables, since only these averages are observable on a macroscopic scale. The charge and current densities introduced in Section B.1 are examples of such variables, hence it is a macroscopic picture of fields and media that we require here.

There are three major ways in which media influence macroscopic electromagnetic fields. Hence the following sections undertake a review of magnetization, polarization, and conduction in common materials.

B.3.1 Magnetization

The macroscopic motions of electrons, even though associated with individual atoms or molecules, account for aggregates of charge and current

---

* The propagation of an electromagnetic wave on structures of this type is discussed in texts concerned with transmission lines or TEM wave guide modes. For a discussion of this matching problem see R. B. Adler, L. J. Chu, and R. M. Fano, *Electromagnetic Energy Transmission and Radiation*, Wiley, New York, 1960, p. 111, or S. Ramo, J. R. Whinnery, and T. Van Duzer, *Fields and Waves in Communication Electronics*, Wiley, New York, p. 27.

(when viewed at the macroscopic level) that induce electric and magnetic fields. These field sources are not directly accessible; for example, the equivalent currents within the material cannot be circulated through an external circuit. The most obvious sources of magnetic field that are inaccessible in this sense are those responsible for the field of a permanent magnet. The earliest observations on magnetic fields involved the lodestone, a primitive form of the permanent magnet. Early investigators such as Oersted found that magnetic fields produced by a permanent magnet are equivalent to those induced by a circulating current. In the formulation of electromagnetic theory we must distinguish between fields due to sources within the material and those from applied currents simply because it is only the latter sources that can be controlled directly. Hence we divide the source currents into *free currents* (with the density $\mathbf{J}_f$) and *magnetization currents* (with the density $\mathbf{J}_m$). Ampère's law then takes the form

$$\nabla \times \left(\frac{\mathbf{B}}{\mu_0}\right) = \mathbf{J}_m + \mathbf{J}_f. \tag{B.3.1}$$

By convention it is also helpful to attribute a fraction of the field induced by these currents to the magnetization currents in the material. Hence (B.3.1) is written as

$$\nabla \times \left(\frac{\mathbf{B}}{\mu_0} - \mathbf{M}\right) = \mathbf{J}_f, \tag{B.3.2}$$

where the *magnetization density* $\mathbf{M}$ is defined by

$$\nabla \times \mathbf{M} = \mathbf{J}_m. \tag{B.3.3}$$

Up to this point in this chapter it has been necessary to introduce only two field quantities to account for interactions between charges and between currents. To account for the macroscopic properties of media we have now introduced a new field quantity, the magnetization density $\mathbf{M}$, and in the next section similar considerations concerning electric polarization of media lead to the introduction of the polarization density $\mathbf{P}$. It is therefore apparent that macroscopic field theory is formulated in terms of four field variables. In our discussion these variables have been $\mathbf{E}$, $\mathbf{B}$, $\mathbf{M}$, and $\mathbf{P}$. An alternative representation of the fields introduces the *magnetic field intensity* $\mathbf{H}$, in our development *defined* as

$$\mathbf{H} = \left(\frac{\mathbf{B}}{\mu_0} - \mathbf{M}\right). \tag{B.3.4}$$

From our definition it is clear that we could just as well deal with $\mathbf{B}$ and $\mathbf{H}$ as the macroscopic magnetic field vectors rather than with $\mathbf{B}$ and $\mathbf{M}$. This is particularly appealing, for then (B.3.2) takes the simple form

$$\nabla \times \mathbf{H} = \mathbf{J}_f. \tag{B.3.5}$$

When the source quantities $\mathbf{J}_f$ and $\mathbf{M}$ are specified independently, the magnetic field intensity $\mathbf{H}$ (or magnetic flux density $\mathbf{B}$) can be found from the quasi-static magnetic field equations. A given constant magnetization density corresponds to the case of the permanent magnet. In most cases, however, the source quantities are functions of the field vectors, and these funtional relations, called *constituent relations*, must be known before the problems can be solved. The constituent relations represent the constraints placed on the fields by the internal physics of the media being considered. Hence it is these relations that make it possible to separate the microscopic problem from the macroscopic one of interest here.

The simplest form of constituent relation for a magnetic material arises when it can be considered *electrically linear* and *isotropic*. Then the *permeability* μ is constant in the relation

$$\mathbf{B} = \mu\mathbf{H}. \tag{B.3.6}$$

The material is isotropic because $\mathbf{B}$ is collinear with $\mathbf{H}$ and a particular constant (μ) times $\mathbf{H}$, regardless of the direction of $\mathbf{H}$. A material that is *homogeneous* and isotropic will in addition have a permeability μ that does not vary with position in the material. Another way of expressing (B.3.6) is to define a magnetic susceptibility χ_m (dimensionless) such that

$$\mathbf{M} = \chi_m\mathbf{H}, \tag{B.3.7}$$

where

$$\mu = \mu_0(1 + \chi_m). \tag{B.3.8}$$

Magnetic materials are commonly found with $\mathbf{B}$ not a linear function of $\mathbf{H}$ and the constitutive law takes the general form

$$\mathbf{B} = \mathbf{B}(\mathbf{H}). \tag{B.3.9}$$

We deal with some problems involving materials of this type, but with few exceptions confine our examples to situations in which $\mathbf{B}$ is a single-valued function of $\mathbf{H}$. In certain magnetic materials in some applications the $\mathbf{B}$-$\mathbf{H}$ curve must include hysteresis and (B.3.9) is not single-valued.*

The differential equations for a magnetic field system in the presence of moving magnetized media are summarized in Table 1.2.

B.3.2 Polarization

The force between a charge distribution and a test charge is observed to change if a dielectric material is brought near the region occupied by the test

---

* G. R. Slemon, *Magnetoelectric Devices*, Wiley, New York, 1966, p. 115.

charge. Like the test charge, the charged particles which compose the dielectric material experience forces due to the applied field. Although these charges remain identified with the molecules of the material, their positions can be distorted incrementally by the electric force and thus lead to a polarization of the molecules.

The basic sources of the electric field are charges. Hence it is natural to define a *polarization charge density* ρ_p as a source of a fraction of the electric field which can be attributed to the inaccessible sources within the media. Thus Gauss's law (B.1.16) is written

$$\nabla \cdot \epsilon_0 E = \rho_f + \rho_p, \tag{B.3.10}$$

where the *free charge density* ρ_f resides on conducting electrodes and other parts of the system capable of supporting conduction currents. The free charges do not remain attached to individual molecules but rather can be conducted from one point to another in the system.

In view of the form taken by Gauss's law, it is convenient to identify a field induced by the polarization charges by writing (B.3.10) as

$$\nabla \cdot (\epsilon_0 E + P) = \rho_f, \tag{B.3.11}$$

where the *polarization density* P is related to the polarization charge density by

$$\rho_p = -\nabla \cdot P. \tag{B.3.12}$$

As in Section B.3.1, it is convenient to define a new vector field that serves as an alternative to P in formulating the electrodynamics of polarized media. This is the *electric displacement* D, defined as

$$D = \epsilon_0 E + P \tag{B.3.13}$$

In terms of this field, Gauss's law for electric fields (B.3.11) becomes

$$\nabla \cdot D = \rho_f. \tag{B.3.14}$$

The simple form of this expression makes it desirable to use D rather than P in the formulation of problems.

If a polarization charge model is to be used to account for the effects of polarizable media on electric fields, we must recognize that the motion of these charges can lead to a current. In fact, now that two classes of charge density have been identified we must distinguish between two classes of current density. The free current density J_f accounts for the conservation of free charge so that (B.1.18) can be written as

$$\nabla \cdot J_f + \frac{\partial \rho_f}{\partial t} = 0. \tag{B.3.15}$$

In view of (B.3.11), this expression becomes

$$\mathbf{\nabla} \cdot \mathbf{J}_f + \frac{\partial}{\partial t} \mathbf{\nabla} \cdot (\epsilon_0 \mathbf{E} + \mathbf{P}) = 0. \tag{B.3.16}$$

Now, if we write Ampère's law (B.2.26b) as

$$\mathbf{\nabla} \times \left(\frac{\mathbf{B}}{\mu_0}\right) = \mathbf{J}_f + \mathbf{J}_p + \frac{\partial}{\partial t} \epsilon_0 \mathbf{E}, \tag{B.3.17}$$

where $\mathbf{J}_p$ is a current density due to the motion of polarization charges, the divergence of (B.3.17) must give (B.3.16). Therefore

$$\mathbf{\nabla} \cdot \mathbf{J}_p + \frac{\partial}{\partial t} (-\mathbf{\nabla} \cdot \mathbf{P}) = 0. \tag{B.3.18}$$

which from (B.3.12) is an expression for the conservation of polarization charge. This expression does not fully determine the polarization current density $\mathbf{J}_p$, because in general we could write

$$\mathbf{J}_p = \frac{\partial \mathbf{P}}{\partial t} + \mathbf{\nabla} \times \mathbf{A}, \tag{B.3.19}$$

where $\mathbf{A}$ is an arbitrary vector, and still satisfy (B.3.18). At this point we could derive the quantity $\mathbf{A}$ (which would turn out to be $\mathbf{P} \times \mathbf{v}$, where $\mathbf{v}$ is the velocity of the polarized medium). It is important, however, to recognize that this represents an unnecessary digression. In the electric field system the magnetic field appears in only one of the equations of motion—Ampère's law. It does not appear in (B.2.27b) to (B.2.29b), nor will it appear in any constitutive law used in this book. For this reason the magnetic field serves simply as a quantity to be calculated once the electromechanical problem has been solved. We might just as well lump the quantity $\mathbf{A}$ with the magnetic field in writing Ampère's law. In fact, if we are consistent, the magnetic field intensity $\mathbf{H}$ can be defined as given by

$$\mathbf{\nabla} \times \mathbf{H} = \mathbf{J}_f + \frac{\partial \mathbf{D}}{\partial t}, \tag{B.3.20}$$

with no loss of physical significance. In an electric field system the magnetic field is an alternative representation of the current density $\mathbf{J}_f$. A review of the quasi-static solutions for the system in Fig. B.2.1b illustrates this point.

In some materials (ferroelectrics) the polarization density $\mathbf{P}$ is constant. In most common dielectrics, however, the polarization density is a function of $\mathbf{E}$. The simplest constituent relation for a dielectric is that of linear and isotropic material,

$$\mathbf{P} = \epsilon_0 \chi_e \mathbf{E}, \tag{B.3.21}$$

where χ_e is the *dielectric susceptibility* (dimensionless) that may be a function of space but not of $\mathbf{E}$. For such a material we define the *permittivity* ϵ as

$$\epsilon = \epsilon_0(1 + \chi_e). \tag{B.3.22}$$

and then write the relation between $\mathbf{D}$ and $\mathbf{E}$ as [see (B.3.13)]

$$\mathbf{D} = \epsilon\mathbf{E}. \tag{B.3.23}$$

This mathematical model of polarizable material is used extensively in this book.

The differential equations for the electric field system, in the presence of moving polarized media, are summarized in Table 1.2.

B.3.3 Electrical Conduction

In both magnetic and electric field systems the conduction process accounts for the free current density $\mathbf{J}_f$ in a fixed conductor. The most common model for this process is appropriate in the case of an isotropic, linear, conducting medium which, when stationary, has the constituent relation (often called *Ohm's law*)

$$\mathbf{J}_f = \sigma\mathbf{E}. \tag{B.3.24}$$

Although (B.3.24) is the most widely used mathematical model of the conduction process, there are important electromechanical systems for which it is not adequate. This becomes apparent if we attempt to derive (B.3.24), an exercise that will contribute to our physical understanding of Ohm's law.

In many materials the conduction process involves two types of charge carrier (say, ions and electrons). As discussed in Section B.1.2, a macroscopic model for this case would recognize the existence of free charge densities ρ_+ and ρ_- with charge average velocities $\mathbf{v}_+$ and $\mathbf{v}_-$, respectively. Then

$$\mathbf{J}_f = \rho_+\mathbf{v}_+ + \rho_-\mathbf{v}_-. \tag{B.3.25}$$

The problem of relating the free current density to the electric field intensity is thus a problem in electromechanics in which the velocities of the particles carrying the free charge must be related to the electric fields that apply forces to the charges.

The charge carriers have finite mass and thus accelerate when subjected to a force. In this case there are forces on the positive and negative carriers, respectively, given by (B.1.10) (here we assume that effects from a magnetic field are ignorable):

$$\mathbf{F}_+ = \rho_+\mathbf{E}, \tag{B.3.26}$$

$$\mathbf{F}_- = \rho_-\mathbf{E}. \tag{B.3.27}$$

As the charge carriers move, their motion is retarded by collisions with other particles. On a macroscopic basis the retarding force of collisions can be thought of as a viscous damping force that is proportional to velocity. Hence we can picture the conduction process in two extremes. With no collisions between particles the electric force densities of (B.3.26 and B.3.27) continually accelerate the charges, for the only retarding forces are due to acceleration expressed by Newton's law. In the opposite extreme a charge carrier suffers collisions with other particles so frequently that its average velocity quickly reaches a limiting value, which in view of (B.3.26 and B.3.27) is proportional to the applied electric field. It is in this second limiting case that Ohm's law assumes physical significance. By convention *mobilities* μ_+ and μ_- which relate these limiting velocities to the field $\mathbf{E}$ are defined

$$\mathbf{v}_+ = \mu_+\mathbf{E}, \tag{B.3.28}$$

$$\mathbf{v}_- = \mu_-\mathbf{E}. \tag{B.3.29}$$

In terms of these quantities, (B.3.25) becomes

$$\mathbf{J}_f = (\rho_+\mu_+ + \rho_-\mu_-)\mathbf{E}. \tag{B.3.30}$$

It is important to recognize that it is only when the collisions between carriers and other particles dominate the accelerating effect of the electric field that the conduction current takes on a form in which it is dependent on the instantaneous value of $\mathbf{E}$. Fortunately, (B.3.30) is valid in a wide range of physical situations. In fact, in a metallic conductor the number of charge carriers is extremely high and very nearly independent of the applied electric field. The current carriers in most metals are the electrons, which are detached from atoms held in the lattice structure of the solid. Therefore the negatively charged electrons move in a background field of positive charge and, to a good approximation, $\rho_+ = -\rho_-$. Then (B.3.30) becomes

$$\mathbf{J} = \sigma\mathbf{E}, \tag{B.3.31}$$

where the conductivity is defined as

$$\rho_+(\mu_+ - \mu_-). \tag{B.3.32}$$

The usefulness of the conductivity as a parameter stems from the fact that both the number of charges available for conduction and the net mobility (essentially that of the electrons) are constant. This makes the conductivity essentially independent of the electric field, as assumed in (B.3.24).*

---

* We assume here that the temperature remains constant. A worthwhile qualitative description of conduction processes in solids is given in J. M. Ham and G. R. Slemon, *Scientific Basis of Electrical Engineering*, Wiley, New York, 1961, p. 453.

In some types of material (notably slightly ionized gases) which behave like insulators, the conduction process cannot be described simply by Ohm's law. In such materials the densities of charge carriers and even the mobilities may vary strongly with electric field intensity.

B.4 INTEGRAL LAWS

The extensive use of circuit theory bears testimony to the usefulness of the laws of electricity and magnetism in integral form. Physical situations that would be far too involved to describe profitably in terms of field theory have a lucid and convenient representation in terms of circuits. Conventional circuit elements are deduced from the integral forms of the field equations. The description of lumped-parameter electromechanical systems, as undertaken in Chapter 2, requires that we generalize the integral laws to include time-varying surfaces and contours of integration. Hence it is natural that we conclude this appendix with a discussion of the integral laws.

B.4.1 Magnetic Field Systems

Faraday's law of induction, as given by (B.1.42), has the differential form

$$\nabla \times \mathbf{E} = - \frac{\partial \mathbf{B}}{\partial t}. \qquad (B.4.1)$$

This expression can be integrated over a surface S enclosed by the contour C. Then, according to Stokes's theorem,

$$\oint_C \mathbf{E} \cdot d\mathbf{l} = - \int_S \frac{\partial \mathbf{B}}{\partial t} \cdot \mathbf{n} \, da. \qquad (B.4.2)$$

Now, if S and C are fixed in space, the time derivative on the right can be taken either before or after the surface integral of $\mathbf{B} \cdot \mathbf{n}$ is evaluated. Note that $\int_S \mathbf{B} \cdot \mathbf{n} \, da$ is only a function of time. For this reason (B.1.41) could be written with the total derivative outside the surface integral. It is implied in the integral equation (B.1.41) that S is fixed in space.

Figure B.4.1 shows an example in which it is desirable to be able to use (B.4.2), with S and C varying in position as a function of time. The contour C is a rectangular loop that encloses a surface S which makes an angle $\theta(t)$ with the horizontal. Although the induction law is not limited to this case, the loop could comprise a one-turn coil, in which case it is desirable to be able to use (B.4.2) with C fixed to the coil. The integral law of induction would be much more useful if it could be written in the form

$$\oint_C \mathbf{E}' \cdot d\mathbf{l} = - \frac{d}{dt} \int_S \mathbf{B} \cdot \mathbf{n} \, da. \qquad (B.4.3)$$

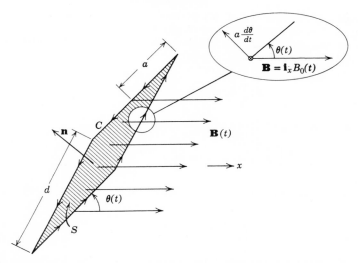

Fig. B.4.1 Contour C enclosing a surface S which varies as a function of time. The rectangular loop links no magnetic flux when $\theta = 0, \pi, \ldots$.

In this form the quantity on the right is the negative time rate of change of the flux linked by the contour C, whereas $\mathbf{E}'$ is interpreted as the electric field measured in the moving frame of the loop. An integral law of induction in the form of (B.4.3) is essential to the lumped-parameter description of magnetic field systems. At this point we have two choices. We can accept (B.4.3) as an empirical result of Faraday's original investigations or we can show mathematically that (B.4.2) takes the form of (B.4.3) if

$$\mathbf{E}' = \mathbf{E} + \mathbf{v} \times \mathbf{B}, \tag{B.4.4}$$

where $\mathbf{v}$ is the velocity of $d\mathbf{l}$ at the point of integration. In any case this topic is pursued in Chapter 6 to clarify the significance of electric and magnetic fields measured in different frames of reference.

The mathematical connection between (B.4.2) and (B.4.3) is made by using the integral theorem

$$\frac{d}{dt} \int_S \mathbf{A} \cdot \mathbf{n} \, da = \int_S \left[\frac{\partial \mathbf{A}}{\partial t} + (\nabla \cdot \mathbf{A})\mathbf{v} \right] \cdot \mathbf{n} \, da + \oint_C (\mathbf{A} \times \mathbf{v}) \cdot d\mathbf{l}, \tag{B.4.5}$$

where $\mathbf{v}$ is the velocity of S and C and in the case of (B.4.3), $\mathbf{A} \to \mathbf{B}$. Before we embark on a proof of this theorem, an example will clarify its significance.

Example B.4.1. The coil shown in Fig. B.4.1 rotates with the angular deflection $\theta(t)$ in a uniform magnetic flux density $\mathbf{B}(t)$, directed as shown. We wish to compute the rate of change of the flux linked by the coil in two ways: first by computing $\displaystyle\int_S \mathbf{B} \cdot \mathbf{n} \, da$ and taking its derivative [the left-hand side of (B.4.5)], then by using the surface and contour integrations indicated on the right-hand side of (B.4.5). This illustrates how the identity allows us to carry out the surface integration before rather than after the time derivative is taken. From Fig. B.4.1 we observe that

$$\int_S \mathbf{B} \cdot \mathbf{n} \, da = -B_0(t)2ad \sin \theta, \tag{a}$$

so that the first calculation gives

$$\frac{d}{dt} \int_S \mathbf{B} \cdot \mathbf{n} \, da = -2ad \sin \theta \, \frac{dB_0}{dt} - B_0 2ad \cos\theta \, \frac{d\theta}{dt}. \tag{b}$$

To evaluate the right-hand side of (B.4.5) observe that $\nabla \cdot \mathbf{B} = 0$ and [from (a)]

$$\int_S \frac{\partial \mathbf{B}}{\partial t} \cdot \mathbf{n} \, da = -2ad \sin \theta \, \frac{dB_0}{dt}. \tag{c}$$

The quantity $\mathbf{B} \times \mathbf{v}$ is collinear with the axis of rotation in Fig. B.4.1; hence there is no contribution to the line integral along the pivoted ends of the loop. Because both the velocity $\mathbf{v} = \mathbf{i}_\theta a \, (d\theta/dt)$ and line elements $d\mathbf{l}$ are reversed in going from the upper to the lower horizontal contours, the line integral reduces to twice the value from the upper contour.

$$\oint_C \mathbf{B} \times \mathbf{v} \cdot d\mathbf{l} = -2B_0 ad \cos \theta \, \frac{d\theta}{dt} \tag{d}$$

From (c) and (d) it follows that the right-hand side of (B.4.5) also gives (b). Thus, at least for this example, (B.4.5) provides alternative ways of evaluating the time rate of change of the flux linked by the contour C.

The integral theorem of (B.4.5) can be derived by considering the deforming surface S shown at two instants of time in Fig. B.4.2. In the incremental time interval Δt the surface S moves from S_1 to S_2, and therefore by

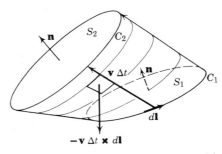

Fig. B.4.2 When $t = t$, the surface S enclosed by the contour C is as indicated by S_1 and C_1. By the time $t = t + \Delta t$ this surface has moved to S_2, where it is enclosed by the contour C_2.

definition

$$\frac{d}{dt}\int_S \mathbf{A}\cdot\mathbf{n}\,da = \lim_{\Delta t\to 0}\frac{1}{\Delta t}\left(\int_{S_2}\mathbf{A}\Big|_{t+\Delta t}\cdot\mathbf{n}\,da - \int_{S_1}\mathbf{A}\Big|_t\cdot\mathbf{n}\,da\right). \quad (B.4.6)$$

Here we have been careful to show that when the integral on S_2 is evaluated $t = t + \Delta t$, in contrast to the integration on S_1, which is carried out when $t = t$.

The expression on the right in (B.4.6) can be evaluated at a given instant in time by using the divergence theorem (B.1.14) to write

$$\int_V \boldsymbol{\nabla}\cdot\mathbf{A}\,dV \cong \int_{S_2}\mathbf{A}\Big|_t\cdot\mathbf{n}\,da - \int_{S_1}\mathbf{A}\Big|_t\cdot\mathbf{n}\,da - \Delta t\oint_{C_1}\mathbf{A}\cdot\mathbf{v}\times d\mathbf{l} \quad (B.4.7)$$

for the volume V traced out by the surface S in the time Δt. Here we have used the fact that $-\mathbf{v}\,\Delta t\times d\mathbf{l}$ is equivalent to a surface element $\mathbf{n}\,da$ on the surface traced out by the contour C in going from C_1 to C_2 in Fig. B.4.2. To use (B.4.7) we make three observations. First, as $\Delta t\to 0$,

$$\int_{S_2}\mathbf{A}\Big|_{t+\Delta t}\cdot\mathbf{n}\,da \cong \int_{S_2}\mathbf{A}\Big|_t\cdot\mathbf{n}\,da + \int_{S_1}\frac{\partial\mathbf{A}}{\partial t}\Big|_t\Delta t\cdot\mathbf{n}\,da + \cdots. \quad (B.4.8)$$

Second, it is a vector identity that

$$\mathbf{A}\cdot\mathbf{v}\times d\mathbf{l} = \mathbf{A}\times\mathbf{v}\cdot d\mathbf{l}. \quad (B.4.9)$$

Third, an incremental volume dV swept out by the surface da is essentially the base times the perpendicular height or

$$dV = \Delta t\mathbf{v}\cdot\mathbf{n}\,da. \quad (B.4.10)$$

From these observations (B.4.7) becomes

$$\Delta t\int_{S_1}(\boldsymbol{\nabla}\cdot\mathbf{A})\mathbf{v}\cdot\mathbf{n}\,da \cong \int_{S_2}\mathbf{A}\Big|_{t+\Delta t}\cdot\mathbf{n}\,da - \int_{S_1}\Delta t\frac{\partial\mathbf{A}}{\partial t}\Big|_t\cdot\mathbf{n}\,da$$
$$- \int_{S_1}\mathbf{A}\Big|_t\cdot\mathbf{n}\,da - \Delta t\oint_{C_1}\mathbf{A}\times\mathbf{v}\cdot d\mathbf{l}. \quad (B.4.11)$$

This expression can be solved for the quantity on the right in (B.4.6) to give

$$\frac{d}{dt}\int_S\mathbf{A}\cdot\mathbf{n}\,da = \lim_{\Delta t\to 0}\left\{\int_{S_1}\left[(\boldsymbol{\nabla}\cdot\mathbf{A})\mathbf{v} + \frac{\partial\mathbf{A}}{\partial t}\right]\cdot\mathbf{n}\,da + \oint_{C_1}\mathbf{A}\times\mathbf{v}\cdot d\mathbf{l}\right\}.$$
$$(B.4.12)$$

The limit of this expression produces the required relation (B.4.5).

Use of (B.4.5) to express the right-hand side of (B.4.2) results in

$$\int_S \frac{\partial \mathbf{B}}{\partial t} \cdot \mathbf{n}\, da = \frac{d}{dt}\int_S \mathbf{B} \cdot \mathbf{n}\, da - \int_S (\nabla \cdot \mathbf{B})\mathbf{v} \cdot \mathbf{n}\, da - \oint_C (\mathbf{B} \times \mathbf{v}) \cdot d\mathbf{l}.$$

(B.4.13)

Because $\nabla \cdot \mathbf{B} = 0$, (B.4.2) then reduces to (B.4.3), with $\mathbf{E}'$ given by (B.4.4).

The integral laws for the magnetic field system are summarized in Table 1.2 at the end of Chapter 1. In these equations surfaces and contours of integration can, in general, be time-varying.

B.4.2 Electric Field System

Although the integral form of Faraday's law can be taken as an empirical fact, we require (B.4.5) to write Ampère's law in integral form for an electric field system. If we integrate (B.3.20) over a surface S enclosed by a contour C, by Stokes's theorem it becomes

$$\oint_C \mathbf{H} \cdot d\mathbf{l} = \int_S \mathbf{J}_f \cdot \mathbf{n}\, da + \int_S \frac{\partial \mathbf{D}}{\partial t} \cdot \mathbf{n}\, da.$$

(B.4.14)

As with the induction law for the magnetic field system, this expression can be generalized to include the possibility of a deforming surface S by using (B.4.13) with $\mathbf{B} \rightarrow \mathbf{D}$ to rewrite the last term. If, in addition, we use (B.3.14) to replace $\nabla \cdot \mathbf{D}$ with ρ_f, (B.4.14) becomes

$$\oint_C \mathbf{H}' \cdot d\mathbf{l} = \int_S \mathbf{J}'_f \cdot \mathbf{n}\, da + \frac{d}{dt}\int_S \mathbf{D} \cdot \mathbf{n}\, da,$$

(B.4.15)

where

$$\mathbf{H}' = \mathbf{H} - \mathbf{v} \times \mathbf{D},$$

(B.4.16)

$$\mathbf{J}'_f = \mathbf{J}_f - \rho_f \mathbf{v}.$$

(B.4.17)

The fields $\mathbf{H}'$ and $\mathbf{J}'_f$ can be interpreted as the magnetic field intensity and free current density measured in the moving frame of the deforming contour. The significance of these field transformations is discussed in Chapter 6. Certainly the relationship between $\mathbf{J}'_f$ (the current density in a frame moving with a velocity $\mathbf{v}$) and the current density $\mathbf{J}_f$ (measured in a fixed frame), as given by (B.4.17), is physically reasonable. The free charge density appears as a current in the negative $\mathbf{v}$-direction when viewed from a frame moving at the velocity $\mathbf{v}$. If was reasoning of this kind that led to (B.1.25).

As we have emphasized, it is the divergence of Ampère's differential law that assumes the greatest importance in electric field systems, for it accounts for conservation of charge. The integral form of the conservation of charge

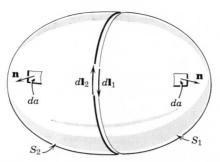

Fig. B.4.3 The sum of two surfaces S_1 and S_2 "spliced" together at the contour to enclose the volume V.

equation, including the possibility of a deforming surface of integration, is obtained by using (B.4.15). For this purpose integrations are considered over two deforming surfaces, S_1 and S_2, as shown in Fig. B.4.3. These surfaces are chosen so that they are enclosed by the same contour C. Hence, taken together, S_1 and S_2 enclose a volume V.

Integration of (B.4.15) over each surface gives

$$\oint_C \mathbf{H}' \cdot d\mathbf{l}_1 = \int_{S_1} \mathbf{J}'_f \cdot \mathbf{n}\, da + \frac{d}{dt} \int_{S_1} \mathbf{D} \cdot \mathbf{n}\, da. \qquad (B.4.18)$$

$$\oint_C \mathbf{H}' \cdot d\mathbf{l}_2 = \int_{S_2} \mathbf{J}'_f \cdot \mathbf{n}\, da + \frac{d}{dt} \int_{S_2} \mathbf{D} \cdot \mathbf{n}\, da. \qquad (B.4.19)$$

Now, if $\mathbf{n}$ is defined so that it is directed out of the volume V on each surface, the line integral enclosing S_1 will be the negative of that enclosing S_2. Then the sum of (B.4.18 and B.4.19) gives the desired integral form of the conservation of charge equation:

$$\oint_S \mathbf{J}'_f \cdot \mathbf{n}\, da + \frac{d}{dt} \int_V \rho_f \, dV = 0. \qquad (B.4.20)$$

In writing this expression we have used Gauss's theorem and (B.3.14) to show the explicit dependence of the current density through the deforming surface on the enclosed charge density.

The integral laws for electric field systems are summarized in Table 1.2 at the end of Chapter 1.

B.5 RECOMMENDED READING

The following texts treat the subject of electrodynamics and provide a comprehensive development of the fundamental laws of electricity and magnetism.

R. M. Fano, L. J. Chu, and R. B. Adler, *ElectromagneticFields, Energy, and Forces*, Wiley, New York, 1960; J. D. Jackson, *Classical Electrodynamics*, Wiley, New York, 1962: S. Ramo, J. R. Whinnery, and T. Van Duzer, *Fields and Waves in Communication Electronics*, Wiley, New York, 1965; W. K. H. Panofsky and M. Phillips, *Classical Electricity and Magnetism*, Addison-Wesley, Reading, Mass., 1956; J. A. Stratton, *Electromagnetic Theory*, McGraw-Hill, New York, 1941.

Many questions arise in the study of the effects of moving media on electric and magnetic fields concerning the macroscopic representation of polarized and magnetized media; for example, in this appendix we introduced the fields E and B as the quantities defined by the force law. Then P and M (or D and H) were introduced to account for the effects of polarization and magnetization. Hence the effect of the medium was accounted for by equivalent polarization charges ρ_p and magnetization currents J_m. Other representations can be used in which a different pair of fundamental vectors is taken, as defined by the force law (say, E and H), and in which the effects of media are accounted for by an equivalent magnetic charge instead of an equivalent current. If we are consistent in using the alternative formulations of the field equations, they predict the same physical results, including the force on magnetized and polarized media. For a complete discussion of these matters see P. Penfield, and H. Haus, *Electrodynamics of Moving Media*, M.I.T. Press, Cambridge, Mass., 1967.

Appendix C

SUMMARY OF PARTS I AND II AND USEFUL THEOREMS

IDENTITIES

$$\mathbf{A} \times \mathbf{B} \cdot \mathbf{C} = \mathbf{A} \cdot \mathbf{B} \times \mathbf{C},$$

$$\mathbf{A} \times (\mathbf{B} \times \mathbf{C}) = \mathbf{B}(\mathbf{A} \cdot \mathbf{C}) - \mathbf{C}(\mathbf{A} \cdot \mathbf{B})$$

$$\nabla(\phi + \psi) = \nabla\phi + \nabla\psi,$$

$$\nabla \cdot (\mathbf{A} + \mathbf{B}) = \nabla \cdot \mathbf{A} + \nabla \cdot \mathbf{B},$$

$$\nabla \times (\mathbf{A} + \mathbf{B}) = \nabla \times \mathbf{A} + \nabla \times \mathbf{B},$$

$$\nabla(\phi\psi) = \phi \nabla\psi + \psi \nabla\phi,$$

$$\nabla \cdot (\psi\mathbf{A}) = \mathbf{A} \cdot \nabla\psi + \psi\nabla \cdot \mathbf{A},$$

$$\nabla \cdot (\mathbf{A} \times \mathbf{B}) = \mathbf{B} \cdot \nabla \times \mathbf{A} - \mathbf{A} \cdot \nabla \times \mathbf{B},$$

$$\nabla \cdot \nabla\phi = \nabla^2\phi,$$

$$\nabla \cdot \nabla \times \mathbf{A} = 0,$$

$$\nabla \times \nabla\phi = 0,$$

$$\nabla \times (\nabla \times \mathbf{A}) = \nabla(\nabla \cdot \mathbf{A}) - \nabla^2\mathbf{A},$$

$$(\nabla \times \mathbf{A}) \times \mathbf{A} = (\mathbf{A} \cdot \nabla)\mathbf{A} - \tfrac{1}{2}\nabla(\mathbf{A} \cdot \mathbf{A}),$$

$$\nabla(\mathbf{A} \cdot \mathbf{B}) = (\mathbf{A} \cdot \nabla)\mathbf{B} + (\mathbf{B} \cdot \nabla)\mathbf{A} + \mathbf{A} \times (\nabla \times \mathbf{B}) + \mathbf{B} \times (\nabla \times \mathbf{A})$$

$$\nabla \times (\phi\mathbf{A}) = \nabla\phi \times \mathbf{A} + \phi\nabla \times \mathbf{A},$$

$$\nabla \times (\mathbf{A} \times \mathbf{B}) = \mathbf{A}(\nabla \cdot \mathbf{B}) - \mathbf{B}(\nabla \cdot \mathbf{A}) + (\mathbf{B} \cdot \nabla)\mathbf{A} - (\mathbf{A} \cdot \nabla)\mathbf{B}.$$

THEOREMS

$$\int_a^b \mathbf{\nabla}\phi \cdot d\mathbf{l} = \phi_b - \phi_a.$$

Divergence theorem $\qquad \oint_S \mathbf{A} \cdot \mathbf{n}\, da = \int_V \mathbf{\nabla} \cdot \mathbf{A}\, dV$

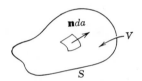

Stokes's theorem $\qquad \oint_C \mathbf{A} \cdot d\mathbf{l} = \int_S (\mathbf{\nabla} \times \mathbf{A}) \cdot \mathbf{n}\, da$

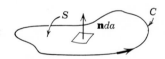

INDEX

Numbers preceded by letters are Appendix references. Appendices A, B, and C are in Part One; Appendices D and E, Part Two; and Appendices F and G, Part Three.

1